Major Problems in
Developmental Biology

Current Status of
Some Major Problems in Developmental Biology

The Twenty-Fifth Symposium

The Society for

Developmental Biology

(Formerly The Society for the Study of Development and Growth)

Haverford, Pennsylvania, June 1966

EXECUTIVE COMMITTEE
1965–1966

Major Problems in Developmental Biology

Edited by

Michael Locke

Developmental Biology Center
Western Reserve University
Cleveland, Ohio

1966

ACADEMIC PRESS, New York and London

ACADEMIC PRESS INC.
111 Fifth Avenue, New York, New York 10003

United Kingdom Edition published by
ACADEMIC PRESS INC. (LONDON) LTD.
Berkeley Square House, London W.1

LIBRARY OF CONGRESS CATALOG CARD NUMBER: 55-10678

PRINTED IN THE UNITED STATES OF AMERICA

Contributors and Presiding Chairmen

Numbers in parentheses indicate the pages on which the authors' contributions begin.

JANE M. OPPENHEIMER, Department of Biology, Bryn Mawr College, Bryn Mawr, Pennsylvania (1).

JAMES D. EBERT AND M. EDWARD KAIGHN, Department of Embryology, Carnegie Institution of Washington, Baltimore, Maryland (29).

ERNST HADORN, Zoologisch-vergleichend anatomisches Institut der Universität Zürich, Zürich, Switzerland (85).

Chairman: PAUL WEISS, Rockefeller University, New York, New York.

C. H. WADDINGTON, Institute of Animal Genetics, Edinburgh, Scotland (105).

J. P. TRINKAUS, Yale University, New Haven, Connecticut (125).

Chairman: DIETRICH BODENSTEIN, University of Virginia, Charlottesville, Virginia.

HEINRICH URSPRUNG, Department of Biology, The Johns Hopkins University, Baltimore, Maryland (177).

D. E. KOSHLAND, JR., AND M. E. KIRTLEY, Department of Biochemistry, University of California, Berkeley, California (217).

Chairman: CLEMENT MARKERT, Yale University, New Haven, Connecticut.

ANTON LANG, MSU/AEC Plant Research Laboratory, Michigan State University, East Lansing, Michigan (251).

JOHN W. SAUNDERS, JR. AND JOHN F. FALLON, Department of Biology, Marquette University, Milwaukee, Wisconsin (289).

Chairman: F. C. STEWARD, Cornell University, Ithaca, New York.

H. RUBIN, Department of Molecular Biology and Virus Laboratory, University of California, Berkeley, California (315).

MARCUS JACOBSON, Department of Biological Sciences, Purdue University, Lafayette, Indiana (339).

Chairman: VIKTOR HAMBURGER, Washington University, St. Louis, Missouri.

Contents

The Growth and Development of Developmental Biology

JANE M. OPPENHEIMER

The Keys to Change: Factors Regulating Differentiation

JAMES D. EBERT AND M. EDWARD KAIGHN

Dynamics of Determination

ERNST HADORN

Fields and Gradients

C. H. WADDINGTON

Morphogenetic Cell Movements

J. P. TRINKAUS

The Formation of Patterns in Development

HEINRICH URSPRUNG

Protein Structure in Relation to Cell Dynamics and Differentiation

D. E. KOSHLAND, JR. AND M. E. KIRTLEY

Intercellular Regulation in Plants

ANTON LANG

Cell Death in Morphogenesis

JOHN W. SAUNDERS, JR. AND JOHN F. FALLON

Fact and Theory about the Cell Surface in Carcinogenesis

H. RUBIN

Starting Points for Research in the Ontogeny of Behavior

MARCUS JACOBSON

Major Problems in
Developmental Biology

The Growth and Development of Developmental Biology

JANE M. OPPENHEIMER

Department of Biology, Bryn Mawr College, Bryn Mawr, Pennsylvania

Introduction

The first symposium on Development and Growth was held in August 1939 (Fig. 1). Six years before, in 1933, Thomas Hunt Morgan, in his earlier years an experimental embryologist, was awarded the Nobel Prize for his discoveries concerning the function of chromosomes in the transmission of heredity; four years before the first symposium, in 1935, Hans Spemann had received the prize for his discovery of the organizer effect in embryonic development. Yet Pontecorvo, in his introduction to "Trends in Genetic Analysis," has stated that: "It is no exaggeration to say that before about 1940 what was known on the nature and mode of genetic specificity—i.e., what was known about chromosomal heredity —was but a series of developments on the theory of the gene" (Pontecorvo, 1958, p. 2). Richard Goldschmidt wrote in the preface to his "Physiological Genetics" in 1938 that: "It is emphasized over and over again by writers of texts and by general speakers [that] we know next to nothing of the action of the hereditary material in controlling development" (Goldschmidt, 1938, p. v).

This introductory paper will shortly attempt to describe some of what Pontecorvo called "the historical landscape" (1958, p. 3) of over twenty-five years ago. Since genetics and the study of development have converged during the intervening quarter-century, together with the study of molecules and macromolecules: of proteins, enzymes, nucleoproteins, and others; of cells and organelles; of metabolic pathways and immune reactions; of microbes and protozoans and fungi; and since their convergence has transformed biology and has carried it to depths hardly dreamed of when this Society first met as a Society in 1940, it may be appropriate to inquire to what degree the Society, and in particular its symposia, may have reflected, or possibly have contributed to, the development of the new biology.

1

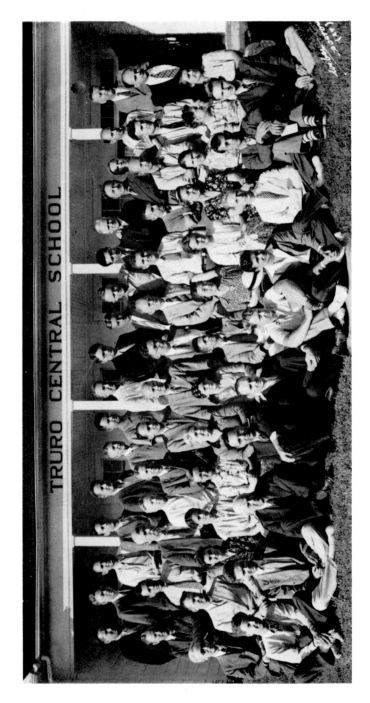

Fig. 1. First symposium for Growth and Development, North Truro, Massachusetts, August 7–11, 1939.

Front to back: *First Row, left to right:* Drs. L. C. Dunn, Columbia; V. Hamburger, Washington University; W. H. Lewis, Carnegie Institution; M. G. Brown, Washington University; R. L. Risley, State University of Iowa; L. Walp, Marietta College, Ohio; C. L. Schneider, Harvard; R. S. Childs, Columbia; E. Brill, Harvard; R. Gillette, Washington University.

Second Row: Drs. L. Loeb, Washington University; W. F. Dove, University of Maine; T. B. Steele, Lankenau Hospital Research Institute; Mrs. L. G. Barth; Mrs. J. Needham; Dr. Florence Peebles, Chapman College; Mrs. A. B. Dawson; Dr. F. S. Hammett, Lankenau Hospital Research Institute; Mrs. L. Loeb; K. Hyde, Lankenau Hospital Research Institute; Drs. Louise P. Wilson, Wellesley; Julia Outhouse, University of Illinois; Myrtle McGraw, Columbia; Mrs. Dammann, Columbia.

Third Row: Drs. P. W. Gregory, University of California, Davis; C. Deuber, Yale; H. Dorsey, University of Connecticut; P. White, Rockefeller Institute; E. W. Sinnott, Columbia; P. A. Weiss, University of Chicago; A. B. Dawson, Harvard; R. Grant, McGill University; O. Rahn, Cornell; R. Aronson, Lankenau Hospital Research Institute; H. S. Burr, Yale; C. H. Waddington, Cambridge University; N. J. Berrill and G. H. Sander, McGill University.

Fourth Row: Drs. J. W. Wilson, Brown University; L. B. Clark, Union College; L. G. Barth, Union College; K. V. Thimann, and L. Hoadley, Harvard; A. D. Mead, Brown University; N. Padis and S. P. Reimann, Lankenau Hospital Research Institute; J. Needham, Cambridge University; O. Glaser, Amherst; G. Toennies and B. Miller, Lankenau Hospital Research Institute; J. F. Daniel, University of California, Berkeley; O. Schotté, Amherst; J. H. Woodger, University of London; C. Stern, University of Rochester; G. Smith, Yale.

Photograph and key kindly supplied by Dr. Paul Weiss

The Greek word *symposium* means *drinking together,* and the equivalent Latin word *convivium,* the German *Gastmahl,* the French *banquet* that resembles our own, all imply that people get together and have a good time; that has been true for members of the Society for the Study of Development and Growth, now the Society for Developmental Biology, since its origin. At a Greek symposium the guests first dined, and then exchanged ideas over wine. In the symposium so vividly described by Plato, the ideas were about Eros; our symposia deal with his fruits. The meetings of what we are in the habit of calling the Growth Society have always been distinguished by a special conviviality. The first seventeen were held in New England, where *Homarus americanus* finds its most favorable environment, and lobster dinners, especially at the North Truro meetings, but often elsewhere too, were particularly felicitous occasions. There used to be music at a Greek symposium, after dining. We had our musician too, of sorts, though with a different tune; none of us who attended the early meetings can forget Walter Wilson's whistle—many decibels of it—when he called us to order. And those of us who were so fortunate as to attend those first meetings remember with pleasure their unhurried pace, now no longer possible in the days of subsidy by governmental agencies, and the generous opportunity for smaller as well as larger groups to exchange ideas in freedom and in leisure.

The pattern for the symposium meetings was set at the first one in North Truro, Massachusetts, where Frederick Hammett, then working in North Truro at the Marine Experimental Station of the Lankenau Hospital Research Institute, expended "tireless efforts for [the] comfort [of those who attended], for their entertainment and for their enjoyment of the sessions" (Hoadley, 1950, p. [261]). The establishment of the Society is bound up historically, in fact, with that of the Lankenau Hospital Research Institute, and also with that of the periodical *Growth,* and these relationships may be briefly examined.

The origins of the Institute, of the journal, and of the Society have been described in a volume of *Growth* dedicated to Hammett at the time of his retirement (Diller, 1950; Hoadley, 1950; Reimann, 1950; White, 1950). Reimann, in his remarks, gave the credit to Hammett for crystallizing the idea of the Institute. According to Reimann, Hammett asked him, "Why don't you try to gather together a few people, try to interest someone in building a laboratory at Lankenau Hospital, and start work on problems of growth and development?" "Growth and development—both normal and abnormal?" I asked, and he nodded his head vigorously" (Reimann, 1950, p. [255]). It was under the leader-ship of Hammett, who became scientific director of the Institute in 1927, that the journal *Growth* was established; its first issue appeared in 1937, and Hammett, "as originator of the plan and its mainspring, was to be Editor-in-Chief" (White, 1950, p. [259]) ; his poor health permitted him to retain this position for a short time only. With all due respect to and gratitude for the very considerable role that Hammett's interest and enthusiasm played in giving impetus to the establishment of the Institute, of the journal, and thus of the Society, we must also remember, with equal gratitude, the tremendous contribution made by Reimann himself, through his own energy and imagination, in designing the symposia and in the early implementation of the plans.

The first symposium on Development and Growth was sponsored by the editors of *Growth,* and it was held in August 1939, at North Truro, as we have said. The meetings were held in the small village school-house; at each session, morning and afternoon for five days, a single talk was the main intellectual sustenance, and the remainder of the time was spent on discussion—what happy days were those! The Society was organized as a result of the success of that first meeting, about whose content more will be said later, and symposia have been held annually since, except during the war years 1943 and 1944, and in 1950 when all members of the Society were invited to attend the Seventh Inter-national Congress of Cell Biology that met in New Haven in Septem-ber. The symposium held in North Truro in 1945 was the only one for which the papers were not published; their titles and authors are, how-ever, listed in a cumulative index included in the fifteenth symposium volume.

The papers delivered at the first ten symposia (minus those given in 1945) appeared, under the able editorship of Irene Corey Diller, in *Growth,* which was from 1941 to 1951 the official organ of the Society, or in supplements to it. The subsequent symposia were published as hardbound books, edited, in turn, by E. J. Boell, Elmer Butler, and for a number of years Dorothea Rudnick, who has found a worthy successor in Michael Locke.

So much, rather formalistic—except for the nostalgic memories of the little schoolhouse and the lobster dinners at North Truro—is factual data reassembled here as an introduction to the main theme of this essay, which is to assay how the content and the nature of the symposia have been related to progress in what we now call developmental biology.

Holding symposia on specialized scientific topics was not a new idea at the end of the 1930's; the Cold Spring Harbor Symposia on Quantitative Biology were in full swing; in fact, one of these, in 1934, had already been devoted to "Some Aspects of Growth," and in 1938 Barth had been the senior author of a paper on the organizer delivered at a Cold Spring Harbor Symposium on proteins (Barth and Graff, 1938). The American Association for the Advancement of Science began to publish symposia in 1938, and the Biological Symposia, edited by Jaques Cattell, began to appear in 1940. What seemed unique about the early Growth Symposia was that they were organized differently from others. When Hammett suggested to Reimann the establishment of an institute to study cancer from a biological point of view he was thinking of bringing to bear on one problem applicable evidence from studies on others; this has often been a successful maneuver in science. It was one of the distinguishing features of the early, as it has been of the later, Growth Symposia that their participants worked in widely divergent disciplines. Never has there been a Growth Symposium without a plant biologist as a speaker; never one without a geneticist, for instance. The diversity of fields covered in the symposia will be further exemplified in a later section of this essay.

The foreword of the first symposium specifies that at that meeting "representatives of the fields of agriculture, bacteriology, biochemistry, biophysics, botany, cytology, embryology, endocrinology, genetics, histology, mathematics, pathology, philosophy, physiology, and zoology concentrated on a single issue, and considerable correlation and conceptual integration was accomplished" (Berrill, 1939, p. [i]). Berrill might have added that representatives from at least two continents presented papers, a situation that was to prevail at an overwhelming majority of the meetings.

The "single issue" Berrill referred to was "Development and Growth," which we should now consider a fairly multiple one. In fact, the papers presented at the first symposium exemplified multiplicity. Warren Lewis, invited to discuss cell division, narrowed his topic to "Some Contributions of Tissue Culture to Development and Growth." Curt Stern and C. H. Waddington separately discussed genes in development, Needham the biochemical aspects of organizer phenomena, Schotté the origin and morphogenetic potencies of regenerates. Sinnott spoke on cell-organ relationships in plants. Two papers on size relationships in growth were delivered by P. W. Gregory and Otto Glaser, respectively. The first symposium, as the second was to do also, concluded with a paper by a real philosopher.

The papers in the first symposium were all rather closely related to what in the old days might have been called embryology. This was not to be true for long. As early as 1940, in the second symposium, every paper dealt with an aspect of what we would call molecular biology (a phrase which, by the way, was already in use in 1939, as we shall see). Although most of the speakers (including the philosopher) addressed themselves to the examination of chemical or physical factors in specific relationship to growth and development, O. L. Sponsler in his talk on proteins, and Rudolph Schoenheimer in his on the synthesis of protoplasmic constituents, made no direct reference to development (at least according to the printed record; only a 3½-page abstract of Schoenheimer's paper was published). Schoenheimer? What was he doing there? His book was not published until the following year. He was surprised himself, I have it on good authority, to have been invited. The reason for his invitation is a clue to the success of the Society: the officers who asked him to come could see the applicability of his work to developmental biology.

The State of Embryology in 1938 and 1939

In order to appreciate the changes in developmental biology that have come about since the Society was founded, and to relate the activities of the Society to these changes, we need to remind ourselves of what investigators of growth and development were thinking about in the late 1930's. It is impossible either to choose or to classify their studies except on a subjective basis, and the investigations to be listed in this and in the following section of this essay have been selected because they seem to me either to look backward or to look forward in an interesting way. Another writer would no doubt choose other examples.

Let us begin with some giants. In 1938 Holtfreter (1938a,b) published the results of the long and exhaustive studies in which he mapped in detail the potentialities of isolated portions of urodele and anuran gastrulae, and the following year (Holtfreter, 1939) his first major discussion of tissue affinity. Harrison published, in 1938, a lecture given the previous year on the multifold accomplishments of the neural crest. Harrison's own method of tissue culture had been useful in the acquisition of some of the results he reported. This technique, in the late 1930's, was beginning to be increasingly exploited by embryologists for the study of embryonic organization. Rudnick in 1938 (1938a,b) studied the differentiation in tissue culture of pieces of the early chick blastoderm at the head process and primitive streak stages; Nicholas (1938) cultured 9-day rat embryos in a circulating medium, and Pincus (Pincus and Werthessen, 1938; Pincus, 1939) attempted to study the development of fertilized and artificially activated rabbit eggs *in vitro*. In 1938 Törö reported the homeogenetic induction of neural folds in rat embryos maintained *in vitro;* this was, I believe, the first direct demonstration of neural induction in mammals; lampreys, teleosts, and birds had previously been shown to develop their central nervous tissue in response to inductive stimuli.

Even if all the vertebrates studied resembled each other in developing their nervous systems by induction, the mechanisms of induction were, in 1938 and 1939, as they had previously been and as they still remain, major enigmas.

Chuang, in 1938 and 1939, adduced the first conclusive evidence in favor of inductive specificity on the part of heterogeneous inductors; Toivonen (1938) independently came to similar conclusions. Shen (1939) quantitatively studied a polycyclic hydrocarbon (sodium endosuccinate salt of 1:2:5:6 dibenzanthracene) as an inductive factor, following up work by Waddington (1938) who had demonstrated inductive effects exerted by 1:2:5:6 dibenzanthracene itself. In 1938 Jean Brachet reported on the location of sulfhydrated proteins in developing amphibians; he had studied for four years the respiratory rate of various portions of the amphibian gastrula. In 1939, he discussed the relation of protein and carbohydrate metabolism to the problem of the amphibian organizer (Brachet, 1939).

Boell *et al.* reported in 1939 on anaerobic glycolysis in regions of the amphibian gastrula, and Boell and Poulson (1939) on the respiratory metabolism of normal and genet'cally deficient *Drosophila* eggs; in 1938 Boell had published a collaborative paper with Bodine on the effect of DNP's on respiratory metabolism during the development of grasshopper embryos (Bodine and Boell, 1938).

Bodenstein (1939) investigated metamorphosis in *Drosophila* by means of interspecific organ transplants; Hadorn and Neel (1938) reported on the hormonal influence of the corpus allatum on pupation in *Drosophila*. In 1939 Hamburger demonstrated sensory and motor hyperplasia in the chick following limb bud transplantation; the previous year (1938), Youngstrom published the first report of the correlation between the appearance of cholinesterase in the embryo and the development of behavior patterns.

Hörstadius, having completed a large number of his isolation and recombination experiments, reported in 1938 the results of constriction experiments on sea urchin eggs; Lindahl and Öhmann (1938) tried to account for gradients in echinoderm development in metabolic terms. Ries, in 1939, reported the result of pioneering histochemical studies on ooplasmic segregation in a number of invertebrates.

In 1939 White described the growth of excised plant callus *in vitro* in artificial nutrients; the same year Gautheret and Nobécourt in France performed successful culture of undifferentiated plant tissues for potentially unlimited periods. Went, in 1939, reported on the effects of auxin on root formation. English *et al.* (1939) isolated from beans a crystalline substance that showed wound hormone activity. J. R. Raper published in 1939 the first of a series of papers on sexual hormones in *Achlya,* and the same year K. B. Raper (1939; Raper and Smith, 1939) published two papers on conditions favorable for the growth of *Dictyostelium.*

Developmental biologists tend to believe that they are well-supplied with books in the mid-1960's, since new ones appear in frequent succession. A considerable number of books on developmental biology appeared, or were being prepared, during 1938 and 1939, too. The English translation of Spemann's Silliman Lectures on embryonic induction was published in 1938. Dalcq published in English, in 1938, a book on "Form and Causality," and in French, in 1941, a longer one on "L'Oeuf et son Dynamisme Organisateur." In 1939 Paul Weiss published a fine book on "Principles of Development," and his ideas, as expressed in that book, in later talks to the Growth Society, and in papers published elsewhere, were to exert strong influence on the new embryology. The year 1940 saw the appearance of Waddington's "Organisers & Genes" and Windle's "Physiology of the Fetus." Child published in 1941 an 811-page monograph on "Patterns and Problems of Development" in which he considered experimental data to show, as he put it, "that various sorts of gradients which appear in development are manifestations or expressions of underlying physiological differentials of some sort, which are organismic in order of magnitude" (Child, 1941, p. 7). Its length might suggest that its writing had been under way in 1938 and 1939. Gerontology in the later 1960's is supposed to be a modern science; in 1939 Cowdry published the first edition of a 758-page compendium on "Problems of Ageing. Biological and Medical Aspects."

If all these were major interests of embryologists during the late 1930's, what was the state of the sciences then seemingly apart from

them, and now so closely allied to them? Let us examine now the landscape of the areas surrounding embryology upon which it had not
yet encroached.

The State of Some Nonembryological Areas of Biology from 1938 to 1940

Let us begin with some comments about genetics to try to document
the remarks made for us above by Goldschmidt and Pontecorvo. In 1937
and 1938 Poulson published brief résumés of the effects of X-chromosome deficiencies on the embryonic development of *Drosophila;* this
work, described in full in 1940, was extremely important in that it was
the first attempt, and a successful one at that, to examine the deviations
from normal early development caused by genetic aberrations that
could be pinpointed in an organism with a known genetic constitution.
Nonetheless it could be encompassed by Pontecorvo's generalization that
knowledge prior to 1940 was but a series of developments of the theory
of the gene. So too perhaps could the studies being carried out at the
time on the chemistry of eye color hormones; at least, at that time no
one could be sure to what they might lead. Tatum and Beadle (1938),
following earlier work by Ephrussi and co-workers (Khouvine and
Ephrussi, 1937) studied some of the chemical and physical properties
of the v⁺ hormone, and Tatum (1939) reported its synthesis by bacteria.

In 1938 Caspersson and Schultz postulated that the nucleic acid
metabolism of chromosomes could be related to gene reproduction,
but when Sturtevant and Beadle published their magnificent "Introduction to Genetics" in 1939, the most they could say about the chemistry of gene action (or the nature of genes, as they called it) was the
following: "A reasonable supposition is that genes either are proteins
or are associated with proteins. In size they are of the order of large
protein molecules and it is therefore conceivable that they are single
large molecules. On the other hand, they may be aggregates of smaller
molecules. Since genes are small in size and appear to be permanent
(*i.e.,* not used up in development), it has several times been suggested
that they might act directly as enzymes in catalyzing reactions, or might
produce enzymes as immediate products" (Sturtevant and Beadle, 1939,
pp. 335–336). In the next paragraph, on the methods of direct study
of genes, they did add that "Caspersson has shown, among other things,
that nucleic acids are an important constituent of chromosomes (as was
already known) and that these are concentrated in the dark bands of

the salivary gland chromosomes of Drosophila. One of the difficulties here is that there is reason to suspect from size considerations that a band of a salivary chromosome contains a high proportion of extragenic material and a low proportion of actual genes" (Sturtevant and Beadle, 1939, p. 336). The topics they covered all related to multicellular forms; bacteria and viruses were not mentioned, nor were protozoa. Sonneborn had in 1938 and 1939 published briefly on mating types, but killers were not yet then alive in the literature.

In 1938, as we have said, Caspersson and Schultz had begun to relate nucleic acids to gene reproduction; but in 1938 Levene's tetranucleotide theory of nucleic acid structure still prevailed, and was to do so for some time. I have made no special effort to track down a statement published in 1938 or 1939 as to how many amino acids there were then supposed to be, but the introduction to the first paper in the first volume of *Advances in Enzymology,* published in 1941, begins by saying that "it hardly seems necessary to enter into the chemistry of the amino acids in any completeness of detail" (Bull, 1941, p. 1) and continues by pointing out that H. V. Vickery listed 25 amino acids "as having undoubted occurrence in proteins" at a symposium held in early February of 1940. Bull added that in addition to Vickery's 25 "there are 22 amino acids whose status is doubtful." In 1939 Pauling published the first edition of "The Nature of the Chemical Bond"; neither proteins nor helices were mentioned in it. In 1938, Jim Watson was 10 years old.

Harrow published in 1938 a textbook entitled "Biochemistry for Medical, Dental and College Students." When he sent its second edition to press in 1940 (under the title "Textbook of Biochemistry") he added to the new edition: "Stanley's work on mosaic-diseased tobacco plants; Northrop's purification of bacteriophage; the multiple nature of vitamin A; the chemistry of pantothenic acid, vitamin B_6, and vitamin E; the story of vitamin K and blood coagulation; sulfanilamide and sulfa-pyridine; the use of the nitrogen isotope by Schoenheimer in the study of protein metabolism; the much-discussed Kögl's work on d-glutamic acid and tumor tissue; and newer conceptions of coenzymes and carriers in biological oxidation" (Harrow, 1940, p. iii). The chapter on nucleo-proteins was identical in the 1938 and 1940 editions, as were the references accompanying it.

Yet in 1939 Astbury could say that "the problem of protein synthesis is not one of proteins alone, but of proteins plus other molecules—saccharides, nucleic acids, etc. The ghost of a generalization that is looming up, that different amino acid constitutions may be associated with similar structures, hints at a world behind it, and activities of which we are unaware. When proteins are born, other molecules assist at their birth; and perhaps chief among them are the nucleic acids. The earliest reproductive processes that we know, those of the viruses and the chromosomes, always involve protein and nucleic acid" (Astbury, 1939, p. 123). And two pages further on he stated that "to the molecular biologist [yes, that is what he called himself then, and that is what he was] the most thrilling discovery of the century is that of the nature of the tobacco mosaic virus; . . . it is but a nucleoprotein" (Astbury, 1939, p. 125).

What was the state of viruses in 1938? Three years before (1935) Stanley had made his first public announcement of the isolation of a crystalline protein possessing the properties of tobacco mosaic virus. Northrop in 1938 reported the concentration and purification of bacteriophage, and the year after said that "viruses, like the enzymes, may eventually be found to be proteins" (1939, p. 105). Rivers, however, in the abstract of a paper delivered at the August, 1938 general meetings of the Society of American Bacteriologists, could still write: "The outstanding work of Stanley, in which a nucleoprotein composed of extremely large molecules and possessed of all the characteristics of the causative agent of tobacco mosaic was obtained in crystalline form from the sap of diseased plants, has struck the imagination of a host of workers. . . . Stanley's findings have been abundantly confirmed, but the origin of the macromolecules and the mode of their reproduction are not known. . . . There is already sufficient evidence that some of the viruses . . . are entities of a much greater complexity than are Stanley's macromolecules. Consequently, it is not wise at present to make too many generalizations regarding the nature or mode of reproduction of the agents placed in the virus group, because no evidence has been brought to show that all of them must be identical or similar in nature" (Rivers, 1938, p. 284).

Virology as we think of it was a science emerging in those years; bacteriology was older. What were the concerns of bacteriologists in 1938 and 1939?

Dubos, in early 1940, published a review on "The Adaptive Production of Enzymes by Bacteria"; he concluded that in some cases in microorganisms "the production of a given enzyme is greatly stimulated when the substrate which it attacks is a constituent of the culture medium. . . . Adaptive enzmyes do in fact exhibit a remarkable specificity toward the substrates which have stimulated their production and they bid fair, therefore, to serve as useful tools in the analysis of many biological and biochemical problems" (Dubos, 1940, p. 11).

Nonetheless, bacteriology was still a partially agricultural and predominantly medical science, and in 1938–1939 its greatest excitement was in response to the recent epoch-making discoveries that there were agents more harmful to bacteria than to patients infected with them. In 1939, Domagk was awarded a Nobel Prize for his discovery of the antibacterial effects of prontosil; in the same year, the important book on the sulfanilamides by Long and Bliss (1939) appeared. It is true that in 1939 Dubos (Dubos, 1939a,b) isolated and purified a cell-free extract from a soil bacillus that inhibited the growth of gram-positive microorganisms and exerted a bactericidal effect upon them *in vitro;* and he showed also that the agent protected mice against pneumococcal infection, and exerted a curative effect when administered several hours after infection with pneumococci. The antibiotics, however, including penicillin, were still unexplored as therapeutic agents in patients.

The word *antibiotic* had had a long history, but it was not until 1942 that Waksman and Woodruff used the term "to describe certain substances of microbial origin that exhibited the ability to inhibit the growth or the metabolic activities of other organisms" (Bryson, 1962, p. 346). Fleming's first paper on penicillin had appeared in 1929 but it was not until 1938 that Florey directed his attention to penicillin and was joined in his work by Chain; the first patient was not treated with it until February 12, 1941, and he died because although his initial response had been dramatic, the supply of penicillin ran out (Fulton, 1944). There were no prophets in 1938 or 1939 to predict that within a quarter of a century antibiotic substances would be indispensable agents in the study of differentiation on a molecular level.

To return to the biology of bacteria, let us quote from Topley and Wilson's textbook: "One of the most controversial questions in regard to the structure of the bacterial cell [in 1938 was] the presence or absence of the nucleus, and its nature if present" (Topley and Wilson, 1938, p. 18). After devoting several pages of fine print to the evidence pro and con, Topley and Wilson concluded that "taking the evidence as a whole the most probable conclusion would appear to be that bacteria are nucleated cells, but that their nuclear apparatus differs in important aspects from that of other unicellular or multicellular organisms" (Topley and Wilson, 1938, p. 21).

As far as bacterial reproduction is concerned, Topley and Wilson reported that "a question still at issue is the . . . existence or non-existence of a complex life-cycle in which sexual processes may or may not play a part" (Topley and Wilson, 1938, p. 26). Even in 1946, at the Cold Spring Harbor Symposium on "Heredity and Variation in Microorganisms," Tatum said there was no "apparent" sexual mechanism in bacteria, and Dubos, Lwoff and Luria "deplored the fact that there is [none]" (Lindegren, 1946, p. 283). As for genes, the most that Tatum would say at the same symposium was that "it seems probable . . . that the simpler microorganisms have genes" (Tatum, 1946, p. 282). In 1939, *Escherichia coli* was still often called *Bacterium coli* (see for instance, Zinsser and Bayne-Jones, 1939) and interest in it was largely clinical. Few if any experimental embryologists in 1938 or 1939 would have guessed that within a quarter century it would be utilized to answer their questions about the genetic control of morphogenesis.

As for immunology, Landsteiner, who received a Nobel Prize in 1930 for his discovery of the human blood groups, in 1938 summarized its state of affairs as follows: "An immune serum may exhibit cross reactions by virtue of an antibody able to combine with substances more or less closely related to the homologous antigen in chemical structure, or it may contain multiple antibodies, differing in specificity, some of which cross react with certain heterologous antigens. The appearance of several antibodies after immunization with a particular antigenic material may depend upon the presence in the latter of different antigenic molecules, or upon the existence, in a single molecule, of more than one determinant group; moreover, as has been shown in our studies on azoproteins . . . , multiple antibodies varying somewhat in specificity may be produced in response to one determinant structure in cases where the antigen does not contain divers chemical groupings that in part are shared by the reacting homologous antigens" (Landsteiner and van der Scheer, 1938, p. 709). Topley and Wilson concluded their chapter on antigen-antibody reactions with the remark that "so far as the antigen-antibody reactions are concerned, immunology has become a branch of chemistry" (Topley and Wilson, 1938, p. 184). Evidence was not yet at hand that it would in due time become a branch of developmental biology.

The progress of immunochemistry was furthered in 1938 and 1939 by the fact that Tiselius and Kabat were continuing work first reported in 1937 on the use of electrophoretic techniques for the separation of antibodies (Tiselius and Kabat, 1938, 1939). Progress in a number of areas was accelerated during the next quarter-century by the elaboration of old and the invention of new techniques, and the state of development of a few of them may be mentioned.

Svedberg and Pederson's book on the ultracentrifuge was published in 1940. While, as we have said, Tiselius was separating antibodies by electrophoresis in 1938 and 1939, chromatography was not yet a biochemical tool. In 1938 and 1939 there was no phase microscopy: Zernicke first developed in 1935 the vector analysis necessary for its invention, but the equipment was not produced and marketed commercially abroad until 1941 and until 1944 in the United States (Richards, 1946). As for electron microscopy, by 1938 progress was such that an instrument suitable for laboratory use had been designed for the Siemens and Halske Company in Germany; its resolving power was 100 Å. In 1939 a microscope with electrostatic lenses was produced abroad, and the same year RCA produced the first instrument using magnetic lenses with electronically controlled regulation of the power supply. It was only in 1940 that RCA and Siemens announced their first commercial models; the resolutions were 24 Å and 22 Å, respectively (Lane, 1961). I find it more interesting to contemplate the fact that the first English translation of Oparin's "The Origin of Life" appeared in 1938.

Some Society Earlies

These then, were some trends of thought and action which within a quarter of a century were to define the lines of the new developmental biology. It would require, I believe, a longer perspective than we yet have acquired to evaluate the sources and the strengths of the interactions of the various disciplines that have brought us to where we now stand. None of us would doubt, however, the importance of the new twentieth century concept of unity of biochemistry, which, as I have said elsewhere (Oppenheimer, 1957), supplants the eighteenth century's concept of unity of type and the nineteenth century's of unity of descent as a synthesizing scheme.

It would be pretentious to the extreme for this, or for any other single professional society, to see itself as a unique prime mover in an evolution as complicated as that in which all biology has recently participated. Nonetheless, in its own way, this Society has rendered exceptional service to its members and to the readers of its symposium volumes by apprising them of current ideas newly relatable to developmental biology, and, in what seems to me an extraordinary number of cases, by informing them early of work that was later to prove of extreme importance.

Look into the contents of the symposium volumes. How many selections of speakers made by the officers of the Society have been other than obvious ones? How many of the speakers would, like Schoenheimer, have been surprised to be invited to address themselves to investigators of growth and development? We have already briefly described the first and second symposia. Twenty-two paragraphs describing twenty-two additional symposia would hardly make rewarding reading. Accordingly, instead, some of what seem to have been particularly perspicacious choices of speakers will be enumerated; and here again, as in the two previous sections, the singling out of particular investigators can only be arbitrary.

At a Growth Symposium, the word *macromolecule* seems to have had its first hearing in 1942: "The molecules which shall interest us here are not of the 'ordinary' variety which form the bulk and substance of our texts on inorganic and organic chemistry. They belong to a class which during recent years have been tagged 'macromolecule,' or, still more impressively, 'megamolecules.' If their only claim to prominence were their large size, we might well dismiss them as the products of an age which tries to make 'bigger and better' things. But they are indeed of special interest to the student of living matter. . . . Those who study growth in the narrow and biological sense of the word, i.e., the increase in mass and number of cells of living organisms, are prone to take the cell and protoplasm for granted and to restrict their attention to an analysis of the factors which will affect . . . the further fate of these biological units. But there is reason to believe that an extension of this interest to the factors which govern the chemical growth of the macro-molecules, which in turn are the substrates of biological growth, may pay dividends in the form of a better understanding of many biological phenomena which are too complex to lend themselves to a more direct approach" (K. Stern, 1942, pp. 1–2). "Any consideration," Stern wrote later in the paper, "of the problems involved in the synthesis of protein and other macromolecules must, perforce, bring up the question of the *reproduction* of such large units. This problem, while it includes the problem of synthesis, is even more perplexing and certainly more complex, since it involves the almost human attributes of 'memory,' 'copying from models,' or 'manufacture to specifications.' " (K. Stern, 1942, p. 11). This is what we would have heard if we had gone to the fourth Growth Symposium at North Truro in 1942, and what we read in the symposium volume.

But if macromolecules were not called by that name at a Growth Symposium before 1942, they had been much spoken of by other names.

Protein structure was discussed by Sponsler in 1940, as we have already mentioned, at the second symposium, the first to be sponsored by the Society itself rather than by the editors of *Growth*. Sponsler discussed, among other things, the molecular weight of proteins as determined by Svedberg with the ultracentrifuge in 1937 and 1939. Svedberg's book itself, as we have also said, appeared in 1940. Members of the Growth Society would have been prepared to read it.

In 1941 Schmitt first reported to the Society on the binding action of histones. Schmitt was thinking then in terms of cells, but I am sure that many of us who heard or read that exposition remembered it when recently we read the Proceedings of the First World Conference on Histone Biology and Chemistry in 1964 (Bonner and Ts'o, 1964). Schmitt's paper was delivered and published the year before Mirsky and Pollister (1942) pointed out that what we now call DNA is associated with histones in the nucleus; Brachet remembered Schmitt's remarks when he presented a review of nucleic acids in development at the first symposium of the Society for Experimental Biology in 1946, although he then discussed them in terms of embryonic, not genetic, induction (Brachet, 1947).

The electron microscope was first put on the market in 1940, as we have said. Members of the Growth Society did not hear a paper devoted solely to the techniques of electron microscopy until 1947, but in 1941 Schmitt told them about electron microscope studies of virus structure made in 1939 on a Siemens instrument in the Siemens research laboratories (Kausche *et al.,* 1939).

Li, who first isolated the growth hormone of the anterior pituitary body of the ox in 1944 (Li and Evans, 1944) spoke to the Society about the hormone in 1948; we remembered him when in 1956 he isolated and partially characterized the human growth hormone (Li and Papkoff, 1956) and again just last May when he announced that he had completed the more difficult task of fully describing its amino acid sequence (Li *et al.,* 1966).

Shall we ascend temporarily from molecules to organisms? White, as we have said, was one of three who in 1939 began culturing undifferentiated plant tissues successfully; he addressed the Society on plant growth as a phenomenon of response to formative agents in 1942; Gautheret did not cross the Atlantic Ocean to come to the meetings to talk until 1946, but a major World War had intervened. Papers on reproductive patterns in the Acrasiae began to appear in 1939; Raper's first discussion of them before the Society was made in 1941; he was to return in 1953. Tartar in 1941 discussed facts and principles concerning patterns of morphogenesis and regeneration in the ciliates before the Society. By then he had himself published (Tartar, 1938) only slightly more than two pages on regeneration in *Condylostoma*. It was in his 1941 lecture to the Society that he first reported the feasibility of performing grafts on *Stentor*. Fourteen years later he told the Society the results of the experiments. Williams published the first of his papers on metamorphosis in *Cecropia* in 1946; he spoke to the Society in 1948. Gerontology is still considered by many to be a science of the future, or at least of the present; the Society heard its first paper specifically devoted to problems of growth and aging, in this case in relation to agriculture, exactly twenty years ago at the sixth symposium meeting.

Let us return to the molecules again. Cooper first reported the presence of adult antigens in frog eggs and embryos in 1946. It was in 1946 that Tyler addressed the Society on an auto-antibody concept of cell structure, growth, and differentiation. Weiss, five years before, had postulated to the Society, in connection with specificity of nerve connections, that selective adhesions between two organic systems might be accounted for by assuming specific protein configurations that resulted in selective interlocking "according to the hypothetical analogy of antigen-antibody union" (Weiss, 1941, p. 189). He had discussed "immunological models" as applied to growth and differentiation before the Society in 1945 (Weiss, 1947).

Woolley reported on structural analogs as antimetabolites in 1948. Tatum and Beadle spoke on the relation of genetics to growth factors and hormones in 1942; this was only ten months after the appearance of their first published report on *Neurospora* (Beadle and Tatum, 1941). Monod in 1947 gave an address on the phenomenon of enzymic adaptation and its bearings on problems of genetics and cellular differentiation. "It is generally recognized," he told us, "that one of the main problems of modern biology is the understanding of the physical basis of specificity, and of the mechanisms by which specific molecular configurations (or multimolecular patterns) are developed, maintained, and differentiated. The means, the experimental tools for this study, are found in those experiments which result in inducing the formation, or suppressing the synthesis, or modifying the distribution of a specific substance or substances. Most, if not all of these, may be considered as belonging to one (or several) of the following types of experiment: (A) Inducing mutations, segregating genes. (B) Inducing the formation of specific substances, or the differentiation of certain tissues, under the influence of other specific substances, or tissues (hormones, organizers). (C) Inducing the formation of antibodies to specific antigens. (D) Last, and so far, least, inducing the formation of a specific enzyme through the action of its specific substrate" (Monod, 1947, p. 224). That, in 1947, from our prospective Nobel laureate of 1965. (Lwoff, incidentally, addressed the Society in 1949, on kinetosomes.)

Monod and Lwoff (and Jacob, who in 1962 was senior author of a Growth Symposium paper on genetic repression, allosteric inhibition, and cellular differentiation) were not the only future Nobel laureates to win their prizes after speaking to the Society. Tatum and Beadle, we have said, were coauthors of a paper delivered to the Society in 1942; they were to share the prize in 1958. Lederberg, who also received part of the prize in 1958, spoke to our Society in 1955. The year 1955 was a banner one: not only the Lederbergs were on the program, with a paper on infection and heredity, but so was Billingham who reviewed the status of affairs with respect to acquired tolerance of foreign cells. When Medawar received his share of a Nobel Prize in 1960 for the discovery of acquired immunological tolerance he gave great credit to Billingham for his contribution to the work. Pauling, our only two-time laureate, I believe, talked to the Growth Society on the duplication of molecules in June, 1954; he won his award in chemistry in November of that year. Pauling won also a Nobel Peace Prize; and Szilard, coauthor of a paper delivered at a Growth Symposium in 1952, won an Atoms for Peace Prize, awards significant to developmental biologists as members of the human race.

The award of Nobel Prizes is one measure of the significance of scientific (and other) contributions. On a different level of magnitude, so is the simple hindsight of investigators working in a particular field. When we see now how developmental biology has changed since 1938 by merging with other disciplines, it is easy to point out some of the movements in research that have been important in effecting changes in lines of progress. Thus, we can dare to begin to evaluate the contributions to developmental biology of some of the earlier speakers. Intelligent judgments on the later ones are more difficult without the benefit of further perspective and I shall not attempt to make them. But I personally feel that our officers deserve thanks for permitting us to hear Horowitz in 1951; Kozloff in 1952; Taliaferro in 1953; both R. Y. Stanier and Seymour Cohen in 1954; Delbrück in 1955; Dulbecco in 1956 (as well as 1965); both Beermann and Lehninger in 1957; both

Herbert Stern and Novikoff in 1959; both Rich and Knox in 1960; both Granick and Yanofsky in 1962; all eight speakers on regeneration in 1961, and all ten on membranes in 1963.

The final paper in the twenty-fourth symposium volume of the Society had as its subject "Aging as a Consequence of Growth Cessation." Let us hope that our Society will not cease to grow, and that it will continue to spread its hyphae, like the wonderful slime molds that have deservedly been such popular subjects for symposium papers, into new areas; and then it cannot age.

Organizers of the Symposia and Officers of the Society from 1939 to 1965

1939

FIRST SYMPOSIUM

The Editors of *Growth*

John Berrill, S. Brody, H. S. Burr, S. A Courtis, C. H. Danforth, Charles B. Davenport, L. K. Frank, P. W. Gregory, F S. Hammett, Leigh Hoadley, Clyde Kluckhohn, Warren H Lewis, Leo Loeb, Carroll E. Palmer, Otto Rahn, H. S. Reed, S. P. Reimann, R. E. Scammon, E. W. Sinnott, K. V. Thimann, Paul Weiss, Philip R. White, D. M. Whitaker, B. H. Willier, Sewall Wright.

1940

SECOND SYMPOSIUM*

Warren H. Lewis, Chairman
Paul Weiss, Secretary
Leigh Hoadley, Treasurer
N. J. Berrill
Philip R. White
E. W. Sinnott

1941

THIRD SYMPOSIUM

E. W. Sinnott, President
P. Weiss, Secretary
L. Hoadley, Treasurer
O. L. Sponsler
B. H. Willier
P. White

1942

FOURTH SYMPOSIUM

P. Weiss, President
K. V. Thimann, Secretary
J. W. Wilson, Treasurer
O. L. Sponsler
B. H. Willier
E. W. Sinnott

1943–1944

NO SYMPOSIUM

B. H. Willier, President
J. W. Wilson, Secretary-Treasurer
O. L. Sponsler
G. S. Avery, Jr.
H. S. N. Greene
K. V. Thimann

* The members of this group served as an organizing committee for the Society for the Study of Development and Growth.

1945

FIFTH SYMPOSIUM

B H. Willier, President
J. W. Wilson, Secretary-Treasurer
O. L. Sponsler
G. S. Avery, Jr.
H. S. N. Greene
A. P. Blakeslee

1946

SIXTH SYMPOSIUM

A. V. Blakeslee, President
J. W. Wilson, Secretary
F. O. Schmitt, Treasurer
H. B. Tukey
G. S. Avery, Jr.
H. S. N. Greene

1947

SEVENTH SYMPOSIUM

Ross G. Harrison, President
G. S. Avery, Jr., Secretary
Francis O. Schmitt, Treasurer
James W. Marvin
Harry S. N. Greene

1948

EIGHTH SYMPOSIUM

Francis O. Schmitt, President
E. W. Shrigley, Secretary
Lindsay M. Black, Treasurer
James W. Marvin
Ross G. Harrison

1949

NINTH SYMPOSIUM

Ralph H. Wetmore, President
E. W. Shrigley, Secretary
Lindsay M. Black, Treasurer
James W. Marvin
Ross G. Harrison
Viktor Hamburger

1951

TENTH SYMPOSIUM

Viktor Hamburger, President
R. H. Goodwin, Secretary
Lindsay M. Black, Treasurer
Elmer G. Butler
Edward W. Shrigley
Ralph H. Wetmore

1952

ELEVENTH SYMPOSIUM

E. G. Butler, President
R. H. Goodwin, Secretary
L. G. Nickell, Treasurer
E. J. Boell
V. Hamburger
R. H. Wetmore

1953

TWELFTH SYMPOSIUM

E. J. Boell, President
R. H. Goodwin, Secretary
L. G. Nickell, Treasurer
E. G. Butler
D. R. Goddard
V. C. Twitty

1954

THIRTEENTH SYMPOSIUM

D. R. Goddard, President
M. V. Edds, Jr., Secretary
L. G. Nickell, Treasurer
E. J. Boell
J. T. Bonner
V. C. Twitty

1955

FOURTEENTH SYMPOSIUM

V. C. Twitty, President
M. V. Edds, Jr., Secretary
R. W. Briggs, Treasurer
J. T. Bonner
Harriet B. Creighton
D. R. Goddard

1956

FIFTEENTH SYMPOSIUM

K. V. Thimann, President
M. V. Edds, Jr., Secretary
R. W. Briggs, Treasurer
J. T. Bonner
Harriet B. Creighton
J. D. Ebert

1957

SIXTEENTH SYMPOSIUM

Gerhard Fankhauser, President
R. O. Erickson, Secretary
R. W. Briggs, Treasurer
Dorothea Rudnick, Editor
Harriet B. Creighton
J. D. Ebert
K. V. Thimann

1958

SEVENTEENTH SYMPOSIUM

J. D. Ebert, President
R. O. Erickson, Secretary
Edgar Zwilling, Treasurer
Dorothea Rudnick, Editor
Gerhard Fankhauser
F. K. Skoog
K. V. Thimann

1959

EIGHTEENTH SYMPOSIUM

R. O. Erickson, President
William R. Jacobs, Secretary
Edgar Zwilling, Treasurer
Dorothea Rudnick, Editor
Dietrich Bodenstein
Gerhard Fankhauser
F. K. Skoog

1960

NINETEENTH SYMPOSIUM

Edgar Zwilling, President
William P. Jacobs, Secretary
Howard C. Dalton, Treasurer
Dorothea Rudnick, Editor
Dietrich Bodenstein
Arthur W. Galston
F. K. Skoog

1961

TWENTIETH SYMPOSIUM

William P. Jacobs, President
Armin C. Braun, Secretary
H. Clark Dalton, Treasurer
Dorothea Rudnick, Editor
Dietrich Bodenstein
Arthur W. Galston
Clifford Grobstein

1962

TWENTY-FIRST SYMPOSIUM

Officers: 1961–1962

Clifford Grobstein, President
Armin C. Braun, Secretary
H. Clark Dalton, Treasurer
Dorothea Rudnick, Retiring Editor
Michael Locke, Editor
Arthur W. Galston
Marcus Singer
John G. Torrey

1963

TWENTY-SECOND SYMPOSIUM

Officers: 1962–1963

John G. Torrey, President
Wm. A. Jensen, Secretary
Marcus Singer, Treasurer
Michael Locke, Editor
Clifford Grobstein
Armin C. Braun
Clement L. Markert

1964	1965
TWENTY-THIRD SYMPOSIUM	TWENTY-FOURTH SYMPOSIUM
Officers: 1963–1964	*Officers: 1964–1965*
Clement L. Markert, President	Herbert Stern, President
Wm. A. Jensen, Secretary	Jerome A. Schiff, Secretary
Robert Auerbach, Treasurer	Robert Auerbach, Treasurer
Michael Locke, Editor	Michael Locke, Editor
Marcus Singer	William A. Jensen
John G. Torrey	Clement L. Markert
Herbert Stern	Howard A. Schneiderman

ACKNOWLEDGMENTS

Several years ago Dr. Salome Waelsch invited me to talk informally at the Albert Einstein Medical College on "Lines Defining Developmental Biology." I tried, but did not succeed. I should like to thank the Officers of the Society for Developmental Biology for giving me another opportunity. I should also like to thank Dr. J. Walter Wilson, Dr. Paul Weiss, and Dr. Irene Corey Diller for helpful information. I am particularly grateful to Dr. Kenneth Thimann for providing lists of the Society Officers during the years 1939 to 1952.

REFERENCES

ASTBURY, W. T. (1939). X-ray studies of the structure of compounds of biological interest. *Ann. Rev. Biochem.* **8**, 113–132.

BARTH, L. G., AND GRAFF, S. (1938). The chemical nature of the amphibian organizer. *Cold Spring Harbor Symp. Quant. Biol.* **6**, 385–391.

BEADLE, G. W., AND TATUM, E. L. (1941). Genetic control of biochemical reactions in *Neurospora. Proc. Natl. Acad. Sci. U.S.* **27**, 499–506.

BERRILL, N. J. (1939). Foreword. *1st Symp. Develop. Growth* Suppl. [i.].

BODENSTEIN, D. (1939). Investigations on the problem of metamorphosis. IV. Developmental relations of interspecific organ transplants in *Drosophila. J. Exptl. Zool.* **82**, 1–30.

BODINE, J. H., AND BOELL, E. J. (1938). The influence of some dinitrophenols on respiratory metabolism during certain phases of active development. *J. Cellular Comp. Physiol.* **11**, 41–63.

BOELL, E. J., AND POULSON, D. F. (1939). The respiratory metabolism of normal and genetically deficient eggs of *Drosophila melanogaster. Anat. Record* **75**, Suppl., 65–66.

BOELL, E. J., NEEDHAM, J., AND ROGERS, V. (1939). Morphogenesis and metabolism: studies with the Cartesian diver ultramicromanometer. I. Anaerobic glycolysis of the regions of the amphibian gastrula. *Proc. Roy. Soc. (London)* **B127**, 322–356.

BONNER, J. F., AND Ts'o, P., eds. (1964). "The Nucleohistones." Holden-Day, San Francisco, California.

BRACHET, J. (1938). La localisation des protéines sulfhydrilées pendant le développement des amphibiens. *Bull. Acad. Roy. Belg. Classe Sci., Ser. 4* **24**, 499–509.

BRACHET, J. (1939). Étude du métabolisme de l'oeuf de grenouille (*Rana fusca*) au cours du développement. V. Le métabolisme protéique et hydrocarboné de l'oeuf en relation avec le problème de l'organisateur. *Arch. Biol. (Liège)* **50**, 233–267.

BRACHET, J. (1947). Nucleic acids in the cell and the embryo. *Symp. Soc. Exptl. Biol.* **1**, 207–224.

BRYSON, V. (1962). Antibiotics: practical and experimental aspects. *Surv. Biol. Progr.* **4**, 345–440.

BULL, H. B. (1941). Protein structure. *Advan. Enzymol.* **1**, 1–42.

CASPERSSON, T., AND SCHULTZ, J. (1938). Nucleic acid metabolism of the chromosomes in relation to gene reproduction. *Nature* **142**, 294–295.

CHILD, C. M. (1941). "Patterns and Problems of Development." Univ. of Chicago Press, Chicago, Illinois.

CHUANG, H. H. (1938). Spezifische Induktionsleistungen von Leber und Niere im Explantatversuch. *Biol. Zentr.* **58**, 472–480.

CHUANG, H. H. (1939). Induktionsleistungen von frischen und gekochten Organteilen (Niere, Leber) nach ihrer Verpflanzung in Explantate und verschiedene Wirtsregionen von Tritonkeimen. *Arch. Entwicklungsmech. Organ.* **139**, 556–638.

COOPER, R. S. (1946). Adult antigens (or specific combining groups) in the egg, embryo and larva of the frog. *J. Exptl. Zool.* **101**, 143–171.

COWDRY, E. V., ed. (1939). "Problems of Ageing. Biological and Medical Aspects." Williams & Wilkins. Baltimore, Maryland.

DALCQ, A. (1938). "Form and Causality in Development." Cambridge Univ. Press, London and New York.

DALCQ, A. (1941). "L'oeuf et son Dynamisme Organisateur." Michel, Paris.

DILLER, I. C. (1950). *Growth* **14**, [253].

DUBOS, R. J. (1939a). Studies on a bactericidal agent extracted from a soil bacillus. I. Preparation of the agent. Its activity *in vitro*. *J. Exptl. Med.* **70**, 1–10.

DUBOS, R. J. (1939b). Studies on a bactericidal agent extracted from a soil bacillus. II. Protective effect of the bactericidal agent against experimental pneumococcus infections in mice. *J. Exptl. Med.* **70**, 11–17.

DUBOS, R. J. (1940). The adaptive production of enzymes by bacteria. *Bacteriol. Rev.* **4**, 1–16.

ENGLISH, J., JR., BONNER, J., AND HAAGEN-SMIT, A. J. (1939). The wound hormones of plants II. The isolation of a crystalline active substance. *Proc. Natl. Acad. Sci. U.S.* **25**, 323–329.

[FULTON, J. F.] (1944). The history of penicillin. *J. Am. Med. Assoc.* **126**, 170–172.

GAUTHERET, R. J. (1939). Sur la possibilité de réaliser la culture indéfinie des tissus de tubercules de carotte. *Compt. Rend.* **208**, 118–121.

GOLDSCHMIDT, R. B. (1938). "Physiological Genetics." McGraw-Hill, New York.

HADORN, E., AND NEEL, J. (1938). Der hormonale Einfluss der Ringdrüse (Corpus allatum) auf die Pupariumbildung bei Fliegen. *Arch. Entwicklungsmech. Organ.* **138**, 281–304.

HAMBURGER, V. (1939). Motor and sensory hyperplasia following limb-bud transplantations in chick embryos. *Physiol. Zool.* **12**, 268–284.

HARRISON, R. G. (1938). Die Neuralleiste. *Anat. Anz.* **85** (Erg.-heft), 4–30.

HARROW, B. (1938). "Biochemistry for Medical, Dental and College Students." Saunders, Philadelphia, Pennsylvania.

HARROW, B. (1940). "Textbook of Biochemistry," 2d Ed. Saunders, Philadelphia, Pennsylvania.

HOADLEY, L. (1950). Founding of the Society for Study of Development and Growth. *Growth* **14** [261].

HÖRSTADIUS, S. (1938). Schnürungsversuche an Seeigelkeimen. *Arch. Entwicklungsmech. Organ.* **138**, 197–258.

HOLTFRETER, J. (1938a). Differenzierungspotenzen isolierter Teile der Urodelengastrula. *Arch. Entwicklungsmech. Organ.* **138**, 522–656.

HOLTFRETER, J. (1938b). Differenzierungspotenzen isolierter Teile der Anurengastrula. *Arch. Entwicklungsmech. Organ.* **138**, 657–738.

HOLTFRETER, J. (1939). Gewebeaffinität, ein Mittel der embryonalen Formbildung. *Arch. Exptl. Zellforsch. Gewebezücht.* **23**, 169–209.

KAUSCHE, G. A., PFANKUCH, E., AND RUSKA, H. (1939). Die Sichtbarmachung von pflanzlichem Virus im Uebermikroskop. *Naturwissenschaften* **27**, 292–299.

KHOUVINE, Y., AND EPHRUSSI, B. (1937). Fractionnement des substances qui enterviennent dans la pigmentation des yeux de *Drosophila melanogaster*. *Compt. Rend. Soc. Biol.* **124**, 885–887.

LANDSTEINER, K., AND VAN DER SCHEER, J. (1938). On cross reactions of immune sera to azoproteins. II. Antigens with azocompounds containing two determinant groups. *J. Exptl. Med.* **67**, 709–723.

LANE, S. (1961). Electron microscope. *In* "The Encyclopedia of the Biological Sciences" (P. Gray, ed.), pp. 332–336. Reinhold, New York.

LI, C. H., AND EVANS, H. M. (1944). The isolation of pituitary growth hormone. *Science* **99**, 183–184.

LI, C. H., AND PAPKOFF, H. (1956). Preparation and properties of growth hormone from human and monkey pituitary glands. *Science* **124**, 1293–1294.

LI, C. H., LIU, W.-K., AND DIXON, J. S. (1966). Human pituitary growth hormone. XII. The amino acid sequence of the hormone. *J. Am. Chem. Soc.* **88**, 2050–2051.

LINDAHL, P. E., AND ÖHMANN, L. O. (1938). Weitere Studien über Stoffwechsel und Determination im Seeigelkeim. *Biol. Zentr.* **58**, 179–218.

LINDEGREN, C. C. (1946). [Discussion of paper by Tatum, 1946.] *Cold Spring Harbor Symp. Quant. Biol.* **11**, 283–284.

LONG, P. H., AND BLISS, E. A. (1939). "Clinical Use of Sulfanilamide and Sulfapyridine and Related Compounds." Macmillan, New York.

MIRSKY, A. E., AND POLLISTER, A. W. (1942). Nucleoproteins of cell nuclei. *Proc. Natl. Acad. Sci. U.S.* **28**, 344–352.

MONOD, J. (1947). The phenomenon of enzymatic adaptation and its bearing on problems of cell physiology, genetics and differentiation. *Growth* **11**, 223–289.

NICHOLAS, J. S. (1938). The development of rat embryos in a circulating medium. *Anat. Record* **70**, 199–210.

NOBÉCOURT, P. (1939). Sur le pérennité et l'augmentation de volume des cultures de tissus végétaux. *Compt. Rend. Soc. Biol.* **130**, 1270–1271.

NORTHROP, J. H. (1938). Concentration and purification of bacteriophage. *J. Gen. Physiol.* **21**, 335–366.

NORTHROP, J. H. (1939). "Crystalline Enzymes. The Chemistry of Pepsin, Trypsin, and Bacteriophage." Columbia Univ. Press, New York.

OPARIN, A. I. (1938). "The Origin of Life." Macmillan, New York.

OPPENHEIMER, J. M. (1957). Embryological concepts in the twentieth century. *Surv. Biol. Progr.* **3**, 1–46.

PAULING, L. (1939). "The Nature of the Chemical Bond and the Structure of Molecules and Crystals; an Introduction to Modern Structural Chemistry." Cornell Univ. Press, Ithaca, New York.

PINCUS, G. (1939). The comparative behavior of mammalian eggs *in vivo* and *in vitro*. IV. The development of fertilized and artificially activated rabbit eggs. *J. Exptl. Zool.* **82**, 85–129.

PINCUS, G., AND WERTHESSEN, N. T. (1938). The comparative behavior of mammalian eggs *in vivo* and *in vitro*. III. Factors controlling the growth of the rabbit blastocyst. *J. Exptl. Zool.* **78**, 1–18.

PONTECORVO, G. (1958). "Trends in Genetic Analysis." Columbia Univ. Press, New York.

POULSON, D. F. (1937). Chromosomal deficiencies and the embryonic development of *Drosophila melanogaster*. *Proc. Natl. Acad. Sci. U.S.* **23**, 133–137.

POULSON, D. F. (1938). Chromosomal deficiencies and embryonic determination in eggs of *Drosophila melanogaster*. *Anat. Record* **72**, Suppl., 72.

POULSON, D. F. (1940). The effects of certain X-chromosome deficiencies on the embryonic development of *Drosophila melanogaster*. *J. Exptl. Zool.* **83**, 271–325.

RAPER, J. R. (1939). Sexual hormones in *Achlya*. I. Indicative evidence for a hormonal coordinating mechanism. *Am. J. Botany* **26**, 639–650.

RAPER, K. B. (1939). Influence of culture conditions upon the growth and development of *Dictyostelium discoideum*. *J. Agr. Res.* **58**, 157–198.

RAPER, K. B., AND SMITH, N. R. (1939). The growth of *Dictyostelium discoideum* upon pathogenic bacteria. *J. Bacteriol.* **38**, 431–445.

REIMANN, S. P. (1950). *Growth* **14** [255–258].

RICHARDS, O. W. (1946). Biological phase microscopy. *Cold Spring Harbor Symp. Quant. Biol.* **11**, 208–214.

RIES, E. (1939). Histochemische Sonderungsprozesse während der frühen Embryonalentwicklung verschiedener wirbelloser Tiere. *Arch. Exptl. Zellforsch. Gewebezücht.* **22**, 569–584.

RIVERS, T. (1938). Viruses and virus diseases. *J. Bacteriol.* **36**, 283–284.

RUDNICK, D. (1938a). Differentiation in culture of pieces of the early chick blastoderm. I. The definitive primitive streak and head-process stages. *Anat. Record* **70**, 351–368.

RUDNICK, D. (1938b). Differentiation in culture of pieces of the early chick blastoderm. II. Short primitive streak stages. *J. Exptl. Zool.* **79**, 399–427.

SCHOENHEIMER, R. (1942). "The Dynamic State of Body Constituents." Harvard Univ. Press, Cambridge, Massachusetts.

SHEN, S. C. (1939). A quantitative study of amphibian neural tube induction with a water-soluble hydrocarbon. *J. Exptl. Biol.* **16**, 143–149.

SONNEBORN, T. M. (1938). Mating types, toxic interactions and heredity in *Paramecium aurelia*. I. Mating types. *Science* **88**, 503.

SONNEBORN, T. (1939). *Paramecium aurelia:* mating types and groups; lethal interactions; determination and inheritance. *Am. Naturalist* **73**, 390–413.

SPEMANN, H. (1938). "Embryonic Development and Induction." Yale Univ. Press, New Haven, Connecticut.

STANLEY, W. M. (1935). Isolation of a crystalline protein possessing the properties of tobacco-mosaic virus. *Science* **81**, 644–645.

STERN, K. G. (1942). Growth as a problem of chemical catalysis. *Growth* **6**, Suppl., 1–25.

STURTEVANT, A. H., AND BEADLE, G. W. (1939). "An Introduction to Genetics." Saunders, Philadelphia, Pennsylvania.

SVEDBERG, T., AND PEDERSON, K. O. (1940). "The Ultracentrifuge." Oxford Univ. Press (Clarendon), London and New York.

TARTAR, V. (1938). Regeneration in the starfish *Linckia* and in the protozoan *Condylostoma*. *Carnegie Inst. Wash. Yearbook* **37**, 99–102.

TATUM, E. L. (1939). Development of eye-colors in *Drosophila:* bacterial synthesis of v⁺ hormone. *Proc. Natl. Acad. Sci. U.S.* **25**, 486–497.

TATUM, E. L. (1946). Induced biochemical mutations in bacteria. *Cold Spring Harbor Symp. Quant. Biol.* **11**, 278–283.

TATUM, E. L., AND BEADLE, G. W. (1938). Development of eye colors in *Drosophila:* some properties of the hormones concerned. *J. Gen. Physiol.* **22**, 239–253.

TISELIUS, A., AND KABAT, E. A. (1938). Electrophoresis of immune serum. *Science* **87**, 416–417.

TISELIUS, A., AND KABAT, E. A. (1939). An electrophoretic study of immune sera and purified antibody preparations. *J. Exptl. Med.* **69**, 119–131.

TOIVONEN, S. (1938). Spezifische Induktionsleistungen von abnormen Induktoren im Implantatversuch. *Ann. Soc. Zool. Botan. Fenn. Vanamo* **6**, 1–12.

TOPLEY, W. W. C., AND WILSON, G. S. (1938). "The Principles of Bacteriology and Immunity," 2d Ed. Wood, Baltimore, Maryland.

TÖRÖ, E. (1938). The homeogenetic induction of neural folds in rat embryos. *J. Exptl. Zool.* **79**, 213–236.

WADDINGTON, C. H. (1938). Studies on the nature of the amphibian organization centre. VII. Evocation by some further chemical compounds. *Proc. Roy. Soc. (London)* **B125**, 365–372.

WADDINGTON, C. H. (1940). "Organisers & Genes." Cambridge Univ. Press, London and New York.

WEISS, P. (1939). "Principles of Development. A Text in Experimental Embryology." Holt, New York.

WEISS, P. (1941). Nerve patterns: the mechanics of nerve growth. *Growth* **5**, Suppl., 163–203.

WEISS, P. (1947). The problem of specificity in growth and development. *Yale J. Biol. Med.* **19**, 235–278.

WENT, F. W. (1939). The dual effect of auxin on root formation. *Am. J. Botany* **26**, 24–29.

WHITE, P. R. (1939). Potentially unlimited growth of excised plant callus in an artificial nutrient. *Am. J. Botany* **26**, 59–64.

WHITE, P. R. (1950). The origins of the journal *Growth*. *Growth* **14** [258–260].

WINDLE, W. F. (1940). "Physiology of the fetus. Origin and extent of function in prenatal life." Saunders, Philadelphia, Pennsylvania.

YOUNGSTROM, K. A. (1938). On the relationship between choline esterase and the development of behavior in amphibia. *J. Neurophysiol.* **1**, 357–363.

ZINSSER, H., AND BAYNE-JONES, S. (1939). "A Textbook of Bacteriology." 8th Ed. Appleton, New York.

The Keys to Change: Factors Regulating Differentiation

JAMES D. EBERT AND M. EDWARD KAIGHN

Department of Embryology, Carnegie Institution of Washington, Baltimore, Maryland

Introduction

We take as our point of departure the provocative article, "Theoretical Mechanisms of Differentiation" by Bernard Davis (1964). To be explicit, we adopt as our own his definitions of differentiation and morphogenesis.

Traditionally, the term "differentiation" has meant the complex of changes involved in the progressive diversification and specialization of cell structure and function, whereas the term "morphogenesis" has included changes in form resulting not only from the aggregation of molecules, but also from differential cell death, differential growth, and from the displacements of cells and cell groups (DeHaan and Ebert, 1964; Ebert, 1965; Waddington, 1966). Although the mechanisms of induction, nature, and persistence of selective gene action within a cell differ fundamentally from the mechanisms of interaction of cell surfaces with each other and with their environment which lead to supracellular organization, they also differ strikingly from the mechanisms of the formation of three-dimensional structures *within* the cell (Davis, 1964).

Therefore, for the purposes of this discussion, we shall regard *differentiation* as the outward sign of selective gene action, the reflection of a change in a cell's biochemical repertoire as a consequence of the release of information encoded in one-dimensional sequences (Allen, 1965). *Morphogenesis*, then, encompasses the processes concerned with the shaping of three-dimensional structures by folding and aggregation of one-dimensional gene products, or by aggregation or redistribution of cells.

In this paper we shall focus attention on intra- and extracellular factors impinging upon the nucleus and regulating the release of information. We shall make use of what Schultz (1965) has called an increasingly plausible concept, the argument that superposed on the basic template principles—the transcription of a DNA code to RNA messages translated into one-dimensional arrays of amino acids—there are control mechanisms. These controls would operate in differential replication and in differential release of information.

Many tissues go through a period of rapid cell division prior to specialization (Wessells, 1965; Wessells and Roessner, 1965). Observations on myogenesis (Okazaki and Holtzer, 1965), chondrogenesis (Abbott and Holtzer, 1966), and fibrogenesis in the lens (Takata et al., 1965), all stress the "mutual exclusivity" of DNA synthesis and differentiation. It is during proliferation that actinomycin D inhibits the subsequent appearance of specialized products, e.g., in the exocrine pancreas (Wessells and Wilt, 1965), in blood-forming regions of the early chick embryo (Wilt, 1965), and in the retina (Kirk, 1965). Brown and Gurdon (1966a,b) have, in fact, suggested that the transition from labile to stable mRNA implied by the loss in sensitivity to actinomycin D as proliferation ceases may involve or require a change in its size from high molecular weight polygenic RNA to mRNA of the size required to code for individual protein subunits. This change would occur only in cells at terminal stages of cytodifferentiation and might result in a special ribosome–messenger complex which would be protected from degradation (Brown and Gurdon, 1966b).

We will re-examine this old question, this time in another light. Instead of emphasizing "mutual exclusivity," we will examine evidence pointing up the possibility that is some cells, at least, new transcription may *depend upon* an immediately preceding replication. Among the several lines of evidence that might be brought to bear on this problem, none is more pertinent than that being derived from studies of cell transformations induced by viruses. We will attempt to treat this question critically, in some depth, emphasizing ideas emerging from our current investigations of the viral susceptibility of differentiating cells in clonal cultures (Kaighn et al., 1966; Lee et al., 1966).

The Constancy Hypothesis

The maintenance of a full genome in differentiated cells still lacks direct proof. It is commonly argued that the total content of information per nucleus in all cells of a given species is equivalent. Yet despite

the use of molecular hybridization techniques, the stringent requirements for establishing differences in information content between nuclei
have not been met (McCarthy and Hoyer, 1964; Schultz, 1965). There
are classes of cells having properties that support the argument for
DNA constancy. The diploid progenitor of the haploid gamete must
have all the genes present in the antecedent zygote. Some cells in
specialized tissues of higher plants are capable, in appropriate environments, of giving rise to a whole organism (Braun, 1959; Steward et al.,
1964; Vasil and Hildebrandt, 1965). The plants are only slightly more
versatile than animals in some of the lower phyla in which the whole
organism regenerates from a small fragment. Even the regenerative
capacity of vertebrates supports the argument at least for incomplete
loss if not for full informational content. In these systems reversibility
is advantageous (Schultz, 1965).

By comparison, consider *Ascaris* (Boveri, 1887) and *Sciara* (Metz,
1938) in which differentiation is associated with a regular loss of parts
of chromosomes, and the studies of sex-linked characters in mammals
which indicate an irreversible change in one of the X chromosomes
which becomes genetically inactive and cytologically compact at about
the time of gastrulation (Lyon, 1961; Russell, 1964).

These striking examples of reversible and irreversible "repression"
leave unanswered questions concerning not only the capacities of many,
if not most, cell types, but also concerning the orderly expression of the
genome in early embryogenesis.

Differential Replication of DNA

Before beginning our discussion of the clonal stability and phenotypic
expression of differentiating cells, we must focus attention on the units
of information and on mechanisms that may be responsible for repres-
sions or errors in replication.

As Schultz (1965) remarked, the idea of differential replication, of a
change in information *content* in different nuclei, has been recognized
only slowly, whereas the idea of differential release of information has
already won general acceptance. There are, however, examples of disproportionate replication of DNA; thus far, these examples are largely
limited to insects and some amphibians, and for most of them the exact
mechanisms remain to be analyzed. Nevertheless, the evidence is compelling, and studies in depth should clearly be rewarding.

We can do no more than enumerate some of the key examples. In the
development of the salivary gland nuclei in *Drosophila,* the euchromatic

regions of the chromosomes replicate, but the heterochromatic regions around the kinetochores do not (Rudkin and Schultz, 1961; Schultz, 1965). There is, however, evidence for differential replication even within the heterochromatic regions: the nucleolar organizer is located in the heterochromatic regions of the X chromosome. Salivary gland nuclei do have nucleoli; thus, even within the heterochromatin, the nucleolar organizer region must have replicated.

Schultz suggests that this approach to the study of the behavior of the centric heterochromatin in *Drosophila* may be instructive in analyzing chromosome diminution in *Ascaris* in which the distal heterochromatic regions are lost at early mitoses in the somatic line, but are retained in the germ line. He raises the question whether or not a differential replication during early cleavage would provide a mechanism for this loss, arguing that such a differential replication must take place in a semiconservative fashion at each of the first four cleavages, with the chromosomes in the germ line replicating equally thereafter. The diminution might be accomplished by a single nonreplicating locus.

There are, of course, disproportionate replications of DNA in which the DNA in specific regions is *increased*. We may cite the well-known "DNA puffs" of the giant chromosomes of *Rhynchosciara* and *Sciara,* in which compacted chromosomal bands are extended into giant puffs in which there is a disproportionate synthesis of DNA. In these insect salivary gland nuclei, there is no organized nucleolus; possibly the puff DNA serves the same function as the nucleolus of other cells in the synthesis of ribosomal RNA. Schultz calls for a comparison of this DNA with that of nuclei in the Malpighian tubules of the same insects, tissues in which the nucleolar organizer is functioning. In the oocytes of some amphibians, there is no single large nucleolus; rather, as in *Triturus* and *Xenopus,* there are over 1000 and from 600 to 1200 nucleoli, respectively. These nucleolar bodies do contain DNA (Davidson and Mirsky, 1965; Miller, 1964), this DNA presumably functioning as template for the synthesis of ribosomal RNA (Brown and Gurdon, 1964; Ritossa and Spiegelman, 1965).

Differential Release of Information: Puffing and Compacted Regions

The evidence for differential change in information content is clear; however, it is frequently overlooked. In contrast, the evidence for differential release of information has captured the interest of all of us because it fits so readily into the messenger hypothesis. The classic examples, the lampbrush chromosomes and puffs in giant polytene chromosomes, have been reviewed so often that it would be redundant to retell the story (see Clever, 1965; Davidson and Mirsky, 1965; Gall, 1963; Laufer, 1965; Pavan, 1965; Schultz, 1965). It should be mentioned, however, that in contrast to *Rhynchosciara* and *Sciara,* in which there is an exceptional synthesis of DNA in puffs, there appears to be no exceptional DNA synthesis related to puffing in either *Chironomus* or *Drosophila.*

The evidence bearing on the complementary questions, whether or not there are compactions of specific regions of chromosomes and whether or not they are signs of inacitvity or restriction in the release of information, is also widely known. We have already referred to the inactive X in mammals, indicating an irreversible change in one of the X chromosomes early in embryogenesis. An excellent example of the stability of chromosome differentiation is provided by studies of the production of the enzyme glucose-6-phosphate dehydrogenase in human cells. Studying cell cultures of heterozygotes for the sex-linked locus controlling the enzyme, Beutler *et al.* (1962) and DeMars and Nance (1964) found that cultures were mosaics: cells were phenotypically of one character or another. The genetic evidence available is relatively limited; what is known is discussed critically by Schultz (1965). We will only emphasize the correlation between compaction of regions of the chromosome and the ability to synthesize RNA. The more compact the chromosome, the less its activity in synthesis (reviewed by Hsu *et al.,* 1964).

The distinction between the replicative and transcriptive functions of DNA may thus be amplified. Genes in different cells may be the same in structure and in replicative function and at the same time different in transcriptive function. There is evidence for regionally selective action along chromosomes. As we have said, there is widespread acceptance of the concept of differential release of information, an acceptance based on the plausibility of the hypothesis of regulation of gene activity in bacteria and on the few clear examples of chromosome puffing and compaction. The evidence for differential replication of DNA is just as convincing, but the "need" for differential replication in terms of our current hypothesis has been, until recently, less compelling. Thus, before considering possible control mechanisms, we must consider the relations between replicative and transcriptive functions.

DNA and RNA Synthesis during Oogenesis and Early Development

In oogenesis and early development, these functions tend to be compartmentalized in time. In a comprehensive account of RNA synthesis during early development. Brown (1965; see also Brown and Littna, 1964a,b, 1966a,b) has emphasized that ribosomal RNA (rRNA), 4 S RNA, and DNA-like RNA (dRNA) are synthesized at rates which are characteristic of the developmental stage of the embryo. We should recall first (Brown, 1965; Ebert, 1965) that there are no studies to date which have unequivocally demonstrated protein synthesis within the oocyte. As we have already observed, a major event in amphibian oogenesis is the synthesis of rRNA. In fact, the unfertilized egg is endowed with an excess of ribosomes. In *Xenopus,* these ribosomes are conserved and function during early development, interacting with the progressively increasing amounts of dRNA and 4 S RNA that are synthesized. New ribosomes are not formed in significant numbers (i.e., there is no net increase) until hatching, in *Xenopus.* Moreover, anucleolate embryos develop normally until the tail bud stage. These facts add weight to the argument that all protein synthesis in early embryogenesis is accomplished on ribosomes formed during oogenesis and stored for later use. Thus, 4 S RNA and dRNA synthesis following cleavage, during gastrulation and neurulation up to hatching (Brown, 1965; Brown and Gurdon, 1966b; Brown and Littna, 1966a,b; Denis, 1965) proceed in the absence of rRNA synthesis. During this time, the ribosomes are seen to aggregate increasingly (Hay, in Brown, 1965); thus, it is suggested that new ribosomal synthesis is initiated only after all or most ribosomes have been aggregated or "fixed" into polyribosomes by increasing amounts of dRNA.

Briggs and Cassens (1966) have studied the recessive gene (o) of the axolotl which offers interesting possibilities for revealing direct gene products. This gene, discovered by Humphrey (1966), exerts a maternal effect, modifying the cytoplasm during oogenesis and leading to a cessation of development during gastrulation. The injection of normal cytoplasm leads to improved developement. Prior to maturation, the corrective component is concentrated in the nuclear sap, later being dispersed in the cytoplasm. Briggs and Cassens (1966) offer as one possible interpretation the idea that the component may be one of the RNA's that is produced and stored during oogenesis.

In summary, during oogenesis DNA is replicated. Much of this DNA is highly specialized as nucleolar DNA which functions in the synthesis of rRNA. There is some 4 S RNA and dRNA formed. DNA replication is the principal synthesizing activity during cleavage. Interposed between maturation and cleavage is fertilization. Despite the synthesis of dRNA and proteins immediately after fertilization in some species, e.g., the sea urchin, the synthesis of dRNA and 4 S RNA is generally accomplished only after substantial DNA synthesis has occurred.

In oogenesis and early development, the transcriptive events, at least those in which bulk syntheses are involved, follow DNA replication.

Flickinger (1966) has reported that *Rana pipiens* gastrulas cultured in 0.05% cytosine arabinoside for 1 day and subsequently grown in saline experienced a delay of 1 to 2 days in the developmental time-table, specifically in the time at which tail bud flexure was observed. The inhibitor blocked DNA synthesis, but stimulated the incorporation of uridine-C^{14} into RNA. Flickinger suggests that the inhibition of DNA synthesis results in a prolongation of time during which "certain types of differentiation" can be expressed. The fact that these delayed embryos developed normally is surprising; it implies that by early gastrulation there are no stable messages which might continue to function despite the inhibition of DNA synthesis. It is of added interest that when the experiments were initiated at the neural plate stage defects were observed, especially in the eyes.

Having raised the question of the relations of replication and transcription in early embryogenesis, we must inquire whether or not any of the events thus far described are reversible. In doing so we naturally turn to the findings of recent experiments using the technique of nuclear transplantation. In *Xenopus,* normal embryos are produced in low frequency by the transplantation of nuclei from intestinal epithelium. Gurdon (1966a,b) concludes that all the events up to that stage must be reversible. We find it difficult to argue with this conclusion, which is based on positive findings. The work has been questioned from time to time. It has been said that adequate criteria have not been provided to assure that the transplanted nuclei were, in fact, from specialized cells. On the one hand, it has been suggested that primordial germ cells may have been inadvertently chosen to provide nuclei, and on the other, that the ciliary brush borders on intestinal epithelial cells, taken as a criterion of differentiation, derive from basal granules (now believed to contain DNA) , and are therefore not adequate criteria of "differentiated cells" having nuclei that can provide a test of the capacity of differentiated nuclei to give normal development. Neither of these arguments appear to be compelling. We agree, however, that these questions will not be resolved fully until it is possible to transplant nuclei from controlled clonal lines of specialized cells.

Gurdon and Brown (1965) have initiated studies of the biochemical changes induced by nuclear transplantation. They have demonstrated that the kind of RNA synthesized by the progeny of a transplanted nucleus from an older donor differs from that produced by the nucleus before its transplantation. It will be recalled that after oogenesis rRNA is not synthesized again until early gastrulation, but is made in large quantities by differentiated endoderm cells. When nuclei from such cells were transplanted to enucleated eggs, and the resulting embryos collected at the late blastula stage, it was found that they had made no detectable rRNA. Thus, these nuclei had reverted to the functional status of cleavage nuclei. When such embryos were allowed to develop further, the synthesis of rRNA began at the "appointed time."

Graham *et al.* (1966; see also Gurdon, 1966a,b) have provided further evidence that the transplantation of a nucleus induces a reversible change, this time in DNA synthesis. When thymidine-H^3 was injected into the endoderm of swimming *Xenopus* tadpoles, 20 to 40% of the endoderm nuclei incorporated the label, as revealed by autoradiography. The number of labeled cells varied according to stage. When embryonic or larval nuclei were injected along with the same labeled compound into enucleated eggs, however, and the number of nuclei incorporating the label was again recorded autoradiographically, 50 to 75% of them (depending on stage) synthesized DNA before the first nuclear division at 1½ hours. With adult nuclei (such as frog brain, liver, or blood nuclei, several of which were injected), less than 1% synthesized DNA *in vivo,* but between 70 and 95% did so within the same time after injection into enucleated eggs. These authors consider, but have not proved, that the only nuclei which did *not* synthesize DNA after injection into eggs were those which were damaged or were in G$_2$ in the cell cycle (Gurdon, 1966c). Gurdon (1966a) cites the similar result obtained by Harris and Watkins (1965) who showed that mouse Ehrlich ascites cells can be induced to make DNA prematurely after they have been fused with HeLa nuclei lying adjacent to each other. In the 2-hour period following fusion, a higher percentage of ascites nuclei incorporated thymidine-H^3 than would have done so had they not been fused.

Briggs *et al.* (1961) and their associates have stressed the irreversibility of changes in *Rana pipiens.* The syndrome of defects in the "endoderm embryos," i.e., those produced by the transplantation of endoderm nuclei, are what might be expected if during the differentiation of the endoderm the activities of loci important for synthesis of materials specific to ectoderm and mesoderm are repressed. Smith (1965) has shown that the nuclei of primordial germ cells, similar in size to endoderm cells, nevertheless give a high frequency of normal development. Schultz (1965) believes that Smith's findings increase the probability that the interpretation that nuclei in *Rana* have undergone irreversible changes is correct.

Thus far, we have contrasted two of the three principal consequences of transplantation of nuclei of differentiated cells: normal development, in *Xenopus,* and the "endoderm embryo," in *Rana.* Yet perhaps the most frequent observation in such experiments is the decrease in ability, with increasing age of the donor, to support normal development at all, abnormal development being associated with chromosome aberrations. Presumably these aberrations occur during early cleavage; thus attention is again focused on replicative events. In the axolotl, Briggs *et al.* (1964) compared the ability of nuclei taken from different regions of the notochord to support development when transplanted. They found a direct correlation between the time elapsed beyond the last differential division and the incidence of chromosome aberrations, in relation to the ability of the nucleus to permit normal development.

These findings again force one to inquire not only into the relations between replication and transcription, but also into the relations between the phases of the cell cycle and transcription. Gurdon (1966a) poses the question in the following way ". . . our search for mechanisms by which nucleic acid synthesis might be regulated during embryogenesis should include at an early stage an examination of the pattern of nucleic acid synthesis in relation to the cell cycle phases. If sRNA and rRNA were synthesized only during certain phases of the cell cycle, regulation of the relative length of these phases during embryogenesis could influence the amount of synthesis which takes place."

Graham and Morgan's (1966; Gurdon, 1966a,b,c) study of the duration of the phases of the cell cycle in cytologically undifferentiated endoderm cells of *Xenopus* revealed that the duration of each phase (G_1, S, G_2, and M) changes independently of that of the others during early development. Gurdon has looked for associations between the stage at which a given phase appears and that at which a given synthesis begins, and also between the relative duration of cell cycle phases and relative amounts of DNA or RNA synthesis. He suggests that the absence of G_1 and most of G_2 during cleavage may be connected with the absence of sRNA and rRNA synthesis during cleavage. This type of investigation clearly is just beginning, but enough has been learned to encourage one to look further.

What can we conclude from the nuclear transplantation experiments and the related studies on biosynthesis? Nuclear transfer gives definite evidence that in one species, at least, nuclei do not undergo irreversible loss or permanent inactivation during early development. In experiments with contrary findings, in which transferred nuclei of older embryos support development less often than those from younger donors, it has not been shown definitely that genes are permanently lost or inactivated. Only time will tell whether or not the point of view adopted by Schultz (1965), who considered chromosome aberrations in the context of specific replicative errors, will prove fruitful.

The Viral Susceptibility of Differentiating Cells

We now propose to examine the controls operating in differential replication and in differential release of information, next discussing the question whether or not DNA synthesis and cell division are *essential* for differentiation. We have elected to consider first the requirement of DNA synthesis for cell transformation by oncogenic viruses, and the relations between viral susceptibility and "state of differentiation."

We have just remarked that the question whether or not the nucleus of any given highly specialized cell is irreversibly or reversibly altered in the course of its development may be resolved by the transplantation of nuclei from clones of differentiated cells. However, clonal techniques are attractive in ways other than in providing nuclei for transplantation, since they provide an approach *par excellence* for the study of cell transformation.

The Problem of Defining "State of Differentiation"

The foregoing discussion raises a question considered effectively by Grobstein (1966): how many properties define a differentiated cell or "cell type"? In discussing "endoderm embryos" in *Rana* we implied that some irreversible changes in endoderm nuclei confined the activities of these nuclei to a "set" of properties, further implying of course, that other "sets" of properties for ectodermal and mesodermal derivatives were inactivated. In discussing the reversibility of nuclear change in

Xenopus, we used two kinds of criteria: normal embryos and reversible changes in the synthesis of nucleic acids. The validity of the former criteria cannot be questioned. We may ask, however, whether it is valid to consider the synthesis of a single molecular marker as evidence of reversibility. Our answer is *yes,* providing the marker is one as fundamental as, for example, newly synthesized rRNA. However, Grobstein's point is well taken: the differentiated cell is recognized by a set of properties, and it may be misleading to identify a cell type on the basis of the occurrence of only one differentiated property. Grobstein selected collagen synthesis as an example: this protein occurs in connective tissue fibroblasts and in cartilage, both of which also produce acid mucopolysaccharides. In contrast, it seems unlikely that one might err in identifying the differentiation of erythrocytes with hemoglobin synthesis (Wilt, 1965). When we consider possible control mechanisms, however, it will be essential to bear in mind the fundamental question whether the phenotypic expression of a differentiating cell must be "all-or-none" or whether some individual properties may be expressed and not others.

Bearing this limitation clearly in mind, we may next focus briefly on reproduction of cell type, a subject discussed more fully by Konigsberg and Hauschka (1965). These authors brought together and weighed critically the evidence bearing on the manner in which populations of differentiated cells are augmented. They stressed the requirement for two different processes: (1) the replication of a progenitor cell and (2) the specialization of these progenitors. Drawing heavily on the findings and interpretations of Leblond (1964) they ordered cell populations in three classes: (1) static, (2) expanding, and (3) renewing. Static populations are homogeneous groups of cells with a constant content of DNA; renewing populations are those in which a high rate of proliferation is balanced by cell attrition or emigration, i.e., in the epidermis and hematopoietic tissues, respectively. In those populations, mitotic activity is frequently restricted to an unspecialized stem line. The "intermediate" category, the expanding populations, are more difficult to define, for mitoses can be detected in differentiated parenchymal cells. Thus, the requirement for an unspecialized "progenitor cell" appears to be less than absolute.

We must always ask, therefore, to what extent the repertoire of developmental responses of any progenitor cell has been restricted (Konigsberg and Hauschka, 1965). The latter authors cite as an example the well-known transformation of progenitors of keratinizing epidermis into mucoid-secreting epithelium by vitamin A (Fell, 1961). We shall return to this question when we consider the relations between DNA replication and protein synthesis in antibody-forming cells.

Students of development are so accustomed to thinking about cell and tissue interactions that they tend to forget that differentiated cells appear to attain a stage in which they have intrinsic sources of stability and may not depend on extrinsic influences. They must live, side by side, as sharply demarcated tissue types. This intrinsic stability, however, needs to provide for preservation of differences only within a given range of environment. It does not require irreversibility in the face of a radical alteration in environment (Davis, 1964).

Studies of the Susceptibility of Embryonic Tissues and Cells to Oncogenic Viruses in Vitro

The fact that animals become increasingly resistant to many viruses during embryonic and postembryonic development poses interesting questions for the developmental biologist. This is particularly true in the case of the tumor viruses since it is thought that the cellular response to these agents is in some way related to the restriction of developmental capacities. Whether this increased viral resistance is a consequence of changes brought about by an inductive interaction, whether it involves changes in the cell surface, a decrease in the rate of cellular proliferation, or a general decline in metabolic activity, studies of cell-virus interaction during differentiation might be expected to throw light upon the regulation of specific cell functions (Dulbecco, 1963).

Investigations by animal virologists, understandably, have concentrated on the structure, composition, and replication of the virus itself, whereas, with the exception of its role in viral synthesis, the contribution of the cell has received less attention. On the other hand, workers in the tumor virus field have been aware for some time of the importance of physiological and developmental influences on the susceptibility of cells to viral oncogenesis. The idea has been expressed with increasing conviction of late that an understanding of the factors regulating differentiation of normal cells would aid in understanding the mechanism of viral oncogenesis and vice versa (Ebert, 1961; Ebert and Wilt, 1960). In the following discussion of cellular susceptibility to tumor virus we shall emphasize the relations between replication of cellular DNA, differentiative state, and cell transformation.

Evidence suggesting a correlation between embryonic induction and the acquisition of cellular resistance to polyoma virus in the mouse has been published in a series of recent papers (Jainchill *et al.,* 1964;

Rapola *et al.,* 1963; Saxen *et al.,* 1963; Vainio *et al.,* 1963a,b). These workers employed an organ culture method devised by Grobstein (1955, 1956). In this method, rudiments of metanephrogenic mesenchyme are separated from inducing tissue (spinal cord) by a membrane filter. At first, condensations appear in the mesenchyme. Then, epithelial cells, and finally well-defined tubules are formed. Mesenchyme explanted without inducer tissue which cannot form tubules retains the ability to synthesize viral antigen as demonstrated by the fluorescent antibody technique. In rudiments undergoing differentiation of tubules as a result of inductive tissue interaction, however, the tubules and the mesenchymal condensations from which they form become resistant to polyoma virus. This acquisition of viral resistance appears to coincide with the formation of the pretubule condensations and is restricted to the tubular epithelium, whereas the undifferentiated juxtatubular mesenchyme remains fully sensitive. The behavior of the differentiating submandibular salivary glands stands in sharp contrast to that of the kidney. The emergence of a polyoma neoplasm from the salivary epithelium appears to depend upon the epigenetic influence of mesenchyme (Dawe *et al.,* 1966).

Thus the epithelio-mesenchymal complex appears to behave differently in kidney and salivary gland; in the former, induction results in increasing resistance; in the latter, in increasing susceptibility.

In the foregoing discussion, susceptibility has been defined as the capacity to make viral antigen demonstrable by immunofluorescence. Previously, Dawe (1960) had examined the response of the submandibular gland of the mouse in organ culture to polyoma virus. He observed both a proliferative and cytolytic response in the same culture with a trend toward an increased proliferative, and a decreased cytolytic, response with age. These dynamic changes in response emphasize the importance of the use of a precise definition of susceptibility.

Transformation of Trypsin-Dispersed Embryonic Cell Cultures by Polyoma Virus

Although the organ culture techniques just discussed preserve some of the tissue relationships of the developing embryo, they do not permit study of the cell-virus interaction at the cell level. An important technological advance was made when it was discovered independently in two laboratories (Vogt and Dulbecco, 1960; Sachs and Medina, 1961) that the oncogenic effect of polyoma could be obtained in cultures of cells derived from mouse and hamster embryos. This made it possible to investigate the relationship between the cytolytic and the oncogenic or proliferative response to the virus.

The proportion of cells undergoing lysis or proliferation in response to polyoma virus varies greatly depending upon the nature of the cell population. For example, in cultures of mouse embryo cells, the lytic titer is a million times that of the transforming titer, while in hamster embryo cells the two responses are about the same (Dulbecco, 1963). These cells were obtained by trypsinizing whole embryos, so that the interpretation of the findings is difficult, especially at the single cell level.

It appeared from earlier studies that only a small fraction (of the order of 1%) of cells in cultures prepared from whole hamster or mouse embryos could be transformed by polyoma virus (Sachs et al., 1962). Did this mean that 99% of the cells were genetically resistant to viral transformation? Sachs and his colleagues reasoned that if this were true, homogeneous clonal populations should differ in their frequencies of transformation. Clones were isolated from primary cell suspensions and then subcloned. The rate of transformation of these homogeneous populations did not differ significantly from that of the original mixed population in the case of both mouse and hamster cells. It was concluded that the failure of the bulk of the population to be transformed was not due to genetic incompetence but must have another explanation. At about the same time studies by Stoker's group on hamster embryo cells gave similar results (Stoker and Macpherson, 1961). In subsequent studies employing an established cell line (BHK-21) derived from neonatal hamster kidney (Macpherson and Stoker, 1962; Stoker and Abel, 1962) the incidence of transformation remained low although these cells had an increased plating efficiency. Selection of random mutants by the virus seems unlikely because the virus-induced rate of transformation is about 1000 times the spontaneous rate. Physiological variation might account for this inefficient transformation.

Further clonal studies revealed marked morphological dissimilarities between transformed clones (Vogt and Dulbecco, 1963; Stanners et al., 1963). A particularly significant investigation, especially from the developmental viewpoint, has been reported only recently (Medina and Sachs, 1965). A wide spectrum of morphologically distinct transformed clones were observed 7–9 days after infection of a mixed cell population of hamster embryo cells with polyoma virus. The authors suggested two possible reasons to account for this phenomenon: (1) different kinds of cells were transformed or (2) differences in the mode of interaction between the virus and a given type of cell.

The experimental results favor the first explanation. In comparison with the wide spectrum of transformed clonal types from mixed cell populations, a significant reduction in the number of clonal morphologies, both normal and transformed, was observed when clones were prepared from different organs. For example, in polyoma virus-infected clonal cultures originating from a heterogeneous mixture of cells derived from whole embryos, eight or more morphological types of transformed clones were observed. In contrast, clones from liver and heart yielded two types each and clones from the lung gave three morphological clonal types. Only one type of clone was obtained from the end of the limb while no transformed clones were found in infected kidney cultures. Each of these clonal types produced only that identical type when subcloned.

If the diverse transformed clonal morphologies were due to differences in the mode of interaction of the virus with a particular type of cell, then a homogeneous population of cells derived from a single cell should produce the same clonal spectrum as seen in mixed cell populations. When this experiment was done, however, only one type of transformed clone was obtained from each clonal line. Furthermore, morphologically similar transformed clones from homogeneous populations showed similar physiological properties, whereas those from mixed populations differed under these conditions. These observations led the authors to conclude that the different types of transformed clones were the result of infection of different kinds of cells by the same virus.

We should point out that aside from the ability to survive in an unfavorable environment (physiological properties), only morphological criteria were used to distinguish these clones. It is well established that cell morphology in culture is exquisitely sensitive to slight alterations in environmental conditions. For this reason, it would be of great interest to employ other markers to distinguish "cell types," e.g., cell-specific antigens.

The Influence of the State of Cytodifferentiation on Oncogenesis by Avian Myeloblastosis Virus

Avian myeloblastosis virus (AMV), along with a group of related viruses known collectively as the avian leukosis viruses, produces a variety of neoplastic diseases in the chicken (Beard, 1957), including myeloblastic leukemia, visceral lymphomatosis, kidney tumors, and osteopetrosis (Burmester et al., 1959). This pleiotropic oncogenic behavior of AMV could be due to the occurrence of viral mutants capable of producing different kinds of neoplasms or to the ability of a single kind of virus to infect different types of susceptible cells. Evidence has been adduced in support of the second of these alternatives. Baluda and Jamieson (1961) were able to show that a single infectious unit was sufficient to induce all forms of the disease on the basis of titration data obtained by intravenous injection of chick embryos. The proportion of birds which developed one or more forms of leukosis followed the dose-response curve predicted by the zero term of the Poisson distribution, indicating random distribution of infectious units. The concept of susceptible cells is also supported by the effect of the age of the host both on the fraction of birds affected, which decreases exponentially with age after hatching, and the comparative incidence of tumor varieties (which is restricted with age). The latter observation could be explained by a loss of sensitivity by some susceptible cells, by a decrease in the number of such cells, or by the selective inhibition of some kinds of tumors by a host response.

The Target Cell Hypothesis

In an effort to reduce uncontrollable variables, studies were instituted by Baluda and his co-workers to develop a system in which the interaction of host cell and virus could be evaluated *in vitro*. Cultures were prepared from trypsinized cell suspensions of various organs of the chick embryo (Baluda and Goetz, 1961). When these cultures were infected with serial dilutions of AMV it was found that foci of small, round, converted cells appeared in some of the cultures within 5 to 7 days. The number of these foci was proportional to the virus dose. Conversion was due to the virus because no conversion was ever seen in uninfected cultures and preincubation of virus with anti-AMV serum reduced the focus-forming ability of the viral suspension by more than 100-fold (Baluda, 1962). Although cultures from different organs differed quantitatively in their susceptibility to conversion by AMV, those cells that were converted appeared to have similar morphologies regardless of origin. Furthermore, cultures from spleen, lung, and liver of birds infected *in vivo* were practically indistinguishable from comparable cultures infected *in vitro*.

A striking correlation was drawn between the differences in susceptibility to conversion of cultures from different organs or cultures from the same type of organ at different developmental stages, and the intensity of granulocytopoiesis taking place in that organ at the time of explantation. These observations led to the formulation of the target cell hypothesis (Baluda and Goetz, 1961) which states that conversion depends on the presence of susceptible target cells. Thus, the relative sensitivity of a given tissue to conversion by AMV would depend on the number of these cells present at the time of infection. These target cells are thought to be mesenchymal precursors of myeloblasts or osteoblasts. Although this hypothesis appears to explain the observed facts quite well, the true nature of the "mesenchymal precursor" is obscure.

While the capacity for neoplastic conversion is restricted to a single or, at most, a very few cell types, this is not true of the ability of a cell to synthesize infectious virus. All AMV-infected cell types, whether converted or not, were shown to be virus producers. This again, as is the case of polyoma virus infection, emphasizes the importance of carefully defining susceptibility. Here again, we see two types of cellular response to an oncogenic virus: proliferative, and productive infection without conversion.

Characteristics of a System Suitable for Analysis of Cell-Virus Interaction during Differentiation

The studies just described emphasize the difficulties in, and the crucial importance of, studying the interactions of transforming viruses with animal cells of known origin and constitution at precise times during the course of differentiation. Until recently, such investigations have been hampered by the lack of a suitable system in which to carry them out. This state of affairs was recognized by Dawe who, in 1960, wrote ". . . so far it has proved that material entities concerned with morphogenesis and differentiation in higher animals have been more difficult to isolate, preserve, and analyze than have viruses." To a large extent, this situation has changed due to the recent advances in the technology of culturing differentiating cells.

What attributes should a system have in order to render it useful for this kind of study? While our experimental approaches must ultimately be directed toward an explanation of infective oncogenic processes operative in the intact organism, the primary event takes place at the level of the individual cell. Thus, a system in which the contribution of immune mechanisms and physical barriers such as extracellular matrices can be avoided is a prerequisite.

The population of cells under study should be (1) homogeneous with respect to cell type (2) capable of yielding single cell suspensions by appropriate dissociation methods with the ability to grow and then undergo specific, easily detected characteristic differentiable changes *in vitro*, ideally in clonal culture.

The first such system was described just three years ago (Konigsberg, 1963). By empirical modification of the elegant methods of Puck and his associates (Puck *et al.*, 1956), Konigsberg was able to demonstrate the growth and histiotypic differentiation of single myoblasts isolated from embryonic chick skeletal muscle. The success of this method depended initially upon the use of a properly "conditioned" medium which had been in contact for a time with a nongrowing population of fibroblasts (Konigsberg and Hauschka, 1965).

Other workers, encouraged by the successful cloning of skeletal muscle were able to extend this approach to several other differentiated cell types of the chick embryo. To date, cardiac muscle (Cahn, 1964), retinal pigment cells (Cahn and Cahn, 1966), and cartilage cells (Coon, 1966) have also been cloned and subcloned, showing that these differentiated phenotypes are stably inherited through many generations. Each of these cell types has clearly recognizable features which permit ready identification of differentiated clonal type. Furthermore, these workers by a careful cooperative study of their culture media were able to eliminate the cumbersome requirement for "conditioned" medium. They found that high concentrations of chick embryo extract reduced both plating efficiency and the fraction of differentiated colonies. A very simple method was employed to separate the deleterious factors from those which stimulated growth and differentiation (Coon and Cahn, 1966). When the embryo extract was fractionated by gel-filtration, it was found that the low molecular weight fraction (L) promoted higher plating efficiencies and expression of differentiation in clones of cartilage and pigmented retina, whereas the high molecular weight fraction (H) while stimulating growth in low concentrations, inhibited phenotypic expression.

The results of, and conclusions to be derived from, these pioneering clonal analyses of differentiating cells are basic to an understanding of cell-virus interactions during differentiation. They suggest an explanation of the apparent paradox of "dedifferentiation" in mass cell cultures and the proven heritability of the differentiated state. Evidence was presented (Coon, 1966) that these earlier observations could have been due to the sensitivity of log phase cells to crowded conditions and to the inhibitory factors present in embryo extract.

Retinal pigment cells have been grown as clones from single cells while retaining their pigmentation and epithelial morphology (Cahn and Cahn, 1966). Pigmented cells have been subcloned four times, amounting to over 50 cell divisions, and have remained pigmented. Cartilage cells have been shown to retain their differentiated phenotype through at least 35 cell generations (Coon, 1966). On the other hand, myogenesis appears to require a progenitor cell. Is the fusion of myoblasts to form multinucleate myotubes an irrevocable event? If so, through how many cell generations can the descendants of a myoblast remain myoblasts? What is the life expectancy of such a cell line?

Infection of Differentiating Skeletal Muscle in Clonal Culture by Rous Sarcoma Virus

At the time this investigation was begun, the only embryonic cell type which had been shown to undergo an unambiguous histiotypic differentiation in clonal culture was the skeletal myoblast of the chick embryo (Konigsberg, 1963). Rous sarcoma virus (RSV) seemed a logical choice for three reasons. First, Mellors and Munroe (1960) had reported that RSV antigens might be localized on or near the sarcolemma of chick wing muscle 3 days after inoculation *in vivo*. Second, the virus was known to produce connective tissue tumors in chickens; and finally, it has the ability of transforming chick embryo "fibroblasts" *in vitro* into round virus-producing cells. This latter property formed the basis for a convenient quantitative tissue culture focus assay (Temin and Rubin, 1958).

Susceptibility was operationally defined as the ability of a cell to produce infectious virus measurable by the standard focus assay system, and to be morphologically transformed. Thus, the initial experimental goal was to determine whether or not the isolated myoblast fulfilled these criteria.

Transformation of Muscle and Fibroblast Clones by RSV

The morphological conversion or transformation of the "chick embryo fibroblast" has been investigated extensively. In reality, this is the morphological "cell type" obtained when eviscerated, decapitated whole chick embryos are disaggregated and the resulting cells are cultivated under conditions that promote proliferation but not differentiation. Such "fibroblasts" have originated from skin, muscle, and other unspecified tissues. For this reason we should describe them as cells of fibroblastic morphology. For convenience, however, we shall simply refer to them as "fibroblasts." Similarly, "fibroblasts" as well as myoblasts appear in cultures of skeletal muscle.

Our first problem was to find whether or not the skeletal myoblast could be transformed by RSV. The techniques and media employed generally followed those of Konigsberg (1963) as modified by Kaighn *et al.* (1966).

The investigation of the transformation of muscle was facilitated by the development of a method which yielded both a higher plating efficiency and a higher muscle frequency than usually obtained from primary cell suspensions. The procedure was based on the observation that bipolar myoblasts were less firmly attached to the culture dish than were fibroblasts. Accordingly mass cultures were prepared from primary muscle cells (2×10^6 cells in 5 ml conditioned medium in 50 mm Falcon plastic tissue culture dishes). The next day medium and loose cells were removed and a dilute solution of trypsin (0.001 to 0.0025%) was added. After about 5 minutes at room temperature, the bipolar processes of the myoblasts began to retract whereas the fibroblasts appeared unaffected. Digestion was allowed to proceed until the fibroblasts had just begun to contract. The plates were then swirled and the loose cells were collected. These cells had a plating efficiency of about 25% in conditioned medium, 50 to 80% of the clones being muscle. Using these cells, clonal cultures were prepared. Cultures were infected with concentrated or diluted virus stock at various times after plating.

It is possible to predict with better than 90% accuracy the clonal type (muscle or fibroblast) from the morphology of the isolated single cells after attachment to the surface. Thus, by marking the area of a plate containing isolated cells of a given type we could assure that any observed changes were due to the interaction of the virus with a single type of cell. The two representative muscle clones shown in Fig. 1 contain five and fifteen cells, respectively. Virus was added and allowed to remain in contact with the cells overnight in order to maximize the chance of infection. Figure 2 shows a normal and a transformed muscle colony which had been infected on the third day of culture and fixed and stained 5 days later.

About 4 days after infection, cells in both muscle and fibroblast clones begin to round up and form grapelike clusters. In fibroblast clones (Fig. 3) these clusters resemble foci observed in routine assay plates while in muscle clones they are usually bunched in close associa-

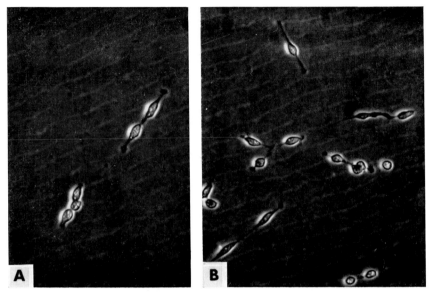

FIG. 1. Isolated colonies of dividing myoblasts 2 days after plating. A: 5-cells; B: 15-cells; unfixed; phase contrast. 230 ×.

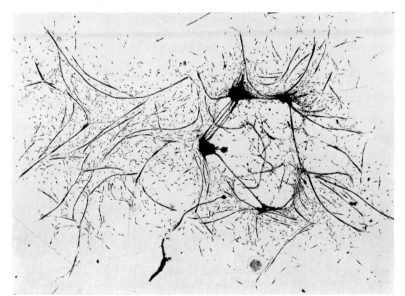

FIG. 2. Two overlapping muscle clones from a culture infected 3 days after plating, and fixed and stained 5 days later. The clone on the right is transformed. 20 ×.

tion with muscle fibers (Figs. 4 and 5). Centers of transformed cells appear with approximately equal frequency in both types of colony. No transformed clones were observed on uninfected plates or on plates to which anti-RSV serum had been added with the virus.

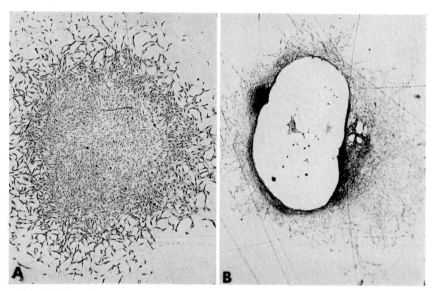

Fig. 3. Normal (A) and transformed (B) fibroblast clones. Details same as Fig. 2. 18 ×.

A further attempt was made to detect any quantitative difference between myoblasts and fibroblasts in their susceptibility to transformation. The rate of transformation of each type of colony as a function of virus concentration was determined. Cultures were infected with serial half-log dilutions as indicated in Table I.

Clones infected on day 2 contained a maximum of 15 single cells (Fig. 1), while at 5 days fusion of myoblasts to form myotubes had begun (Fig. 4). Neither the time of infection nor the nature of the colony appeared to influence the rate of transformation. At virus concentrations of 6×10^5 focus-forming units (ffu)/plate and higher, a maximum of about 50% of the clones was transformed. Below 6×10^5 ffu/plate the fraction of each clonal type transformed decreased with decreasing virus concentration. Thus, a quantitative difference could not be detected by the transformation assay.

The maximum of about 50% of the rate of transformation could have several possible causes. The first and most probable is viral interference. The Bryan strain of RSV is known to contain one or more closely related Rous-associated viruses (RAV) (Rubin and Vogt, 1962). Preinfection of a fibroblast with RAV or other similar avian leukosis viruses makes the cell resistant to superinfection by RSV. At the clonal

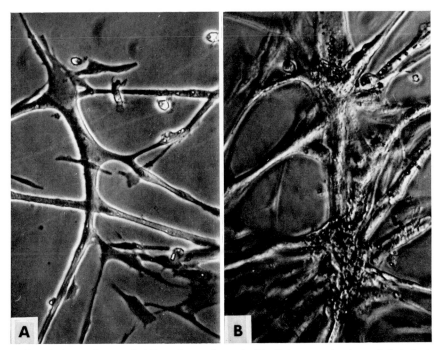

FIG. 4. Area of normal (A) and transformed (B) living muscle clones infected at the time of plating and photographed 5 days later by phase contrast. Note distended myotubes and heavy clusters. 230 ×.

level, this effect has been reported by Trager and Rubin (1964). Other possible explanations include genetic or epigenetic resistance of particular clones or simply lack of infection.

Virus Production in Isolated Muscle and Fibroblast Clones

To determine whether or not infected muscle colonies could make infectious virus as well as be transformed, well-separated muscle clones were isolated in porcelain cylinders. The medium in the cylinders was

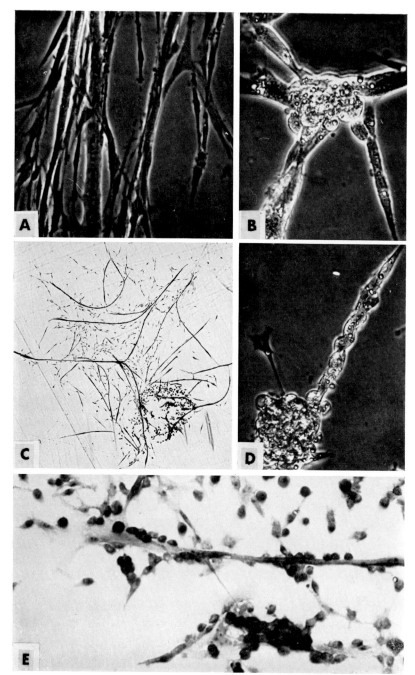

TABLE I
Effect of Virus Concentration on Rate of Transformation[a]

Virus conc. (ffu per plate)	Expt. I[b,c,e]		Expt. II[b,c,e]		Expt. II[b,d,e]	
	TM	TF	TM	TF	TM	TF
2×10^6	54	71	59	48	48	23
6×10^5	—	—	54	55	35	41
2×10^5	23	37	40	49	27	26
6×10^4	—	—	14	25	16	10
2×10^4	4.3	6.9	—	—	—	—
Uninfected	0	0	0	0	0	0

[a] Secondary cells (300) were plated in 5 ml CM in 100 mm petri dishes; 2 and 5 days after plating 0.2 ml of diluted virus was added; the medium was replaced every 2 days; after 10 days, the plates were fixed and stained with Delafield's hematoxylin.

[b] Plating efficiency in Expt. I was 21%; in Expt. II, 28%. Fraction of muscle was 53% in both experiments.

[c] Time of infection: 2 days.

[d] Time of infection: 5 days.

[e] TM: Percent transformed muscle colonies per total muscle colonies. TF: Percent transformed fibroblast colonies per total fibroblast colonies.

TABLE II
Transformation and Virus Production in Isolated Muscle Colonies[a]

	Morphology of clones					
Expt. No.	Trans-formed	Normal	Abortive	Total	Number[b] assayed	Virus producers
I	13	4	9	26	7	6
II	21	12	34	67	39	23
Total	34	16	43	93	46	29

[a] Clonal cultures were prepared. After 3 days 0.2 ml undiluted virus stock was added (Expt. II) and muscle colonies were ringed the next day. In Expt. I the colonies were ringed on day 4 and the virus added to the ring on day 5.

[b] Very small or unhealthy appearing colonies were not assayed.

Fig. 5. Transformation of muscle clones. A, B, and D: Detail of living colonies 11 days after plating; phase contrast. 230 $\times$. A: Uninfected control. B and D: Areas of infected muscle colony; note myotubes and grapelike clusters of transformed myoblasts. C: Muscle clone showing transformed area of rounded cells; fixed and stained 5 days after infection. 20 $\times$. E: Enlargement of a portion of transformed area in C showing rounded myoblasts associated with myotubes. 230 $\times$.

changed daily. Six days after infection the medium was assayed for RSV. The results are summarized in Table II.

A total of 34 out of 93 muscle colonies (37%) was transformed. All of these transformed colonies were not assayed since some were so small that the amount of virus they could produce would be below the sensitivity of the assay. Of the 46 colonies tested, 29 (63%) produced virus. Many of the colonies scored as abortive showed evidence of transformation. However, these were not used to calculate rate of transformation. The rather large fraction of abortive colonies observed in these experiments was probably due to unavoidable handling of the cultures during isolation of clones. Muscle cells are much more sensitive than fibroblasts to small changes in environmental conditions.

A definite correlation between transformation and virus production was observed (Table III).

TABLE III

RELATION BETWEEN TRANSFORMATION AND VIRUS PRODUCTION IN
MUSCLE COLONIES

Colony morphology	Producers	Nonproducers
Transformed	17	4
Nontransformed	1	11
Questionable transformation	5	1
Total	23	16

Cases of questionable transformation have not been considered in the following. Seventeen of the 23 virus-producing colonies were clearly transformed, whereas only one had normal morphology. On the other hand, only 4 of 16 nonproducers were transformed.

*Quantitative Comparison of Virus Production in Isolated
Muscle and Fibroblast Colonies*

The results of an experiment to determine the respective capacities of infected muscle and fibroblast colonies to produce virus are presented in Table IV.

Clonal cultures were infected at 2, 4, and 6 days after plating. Seven days after infection the medium from each cylinder was assayed. No significant differences between muscle and fibroblasts in the fraction of productive colonies were found. Furthermore, the time of infection did not significantly affect the proportion of productive colonies. Although

TABLE IV

RELEASE OF ROUS SARCOMA VIRUS BY MUSCLE AND FIBROBLAST COLONIES

Time of infection after plating	n	ffu per colony					Fraction of productive colonies
		0	$10-10^2$	10^2-10^3	10^3-10^4	$>10^4$	
				Muscle			
2 days	4	1	1	2	0	0	3/4
4 days	8	1	0	5	2	0	7/8
6 days	8	3	3	0	2	0	5/9
							15/20
				Fibroblast			
2 days	5	0	0	1	3	1	5/5
4 days	6	0	0	0	2	4	6/6
6 days	6	2	0	0	2	2	4/9
							15/17

the proportions of producers were the same in both cell types, fibroblast colonies produced more virus per colony, probably because fibroblast colonies contain more cells than muscle colonies. Because of cell fusion in muscle colonies, no estimate of virus yield per cell could be made.

The Presence of Viral Antigens in Muscle Colonies Infected with RSV

The preceding experiments have demonstrated that muscle clones are susceptible to RSV by our criteria of morphological transformation and virus production. At the time the isolated clones were sampled for the presence of RSV, however, intensive myotube formation had taken place; thus it was impossible to distinguish between virus production by infected myoblasts and myotubes. Although morphological changes were observed, e.g., distension of fibers, particularly in the perinuclear regions (Fig. 4), it was believed that virus production was the most reliable index of susceptibility. For this reason, the appearance of viral antigen in both elements of muscle clones was studied by the fluorescent antibody technique.

Standard immunofluorescence procedures for preparation, conjugation with fluorescein isothiocyanate, and removal of nonspecific fluorescent materials from anti-RSV serum globulin have been reported (Lee *et al.*, 1966). Nonfixed living cells were stained by both the direct and indirect

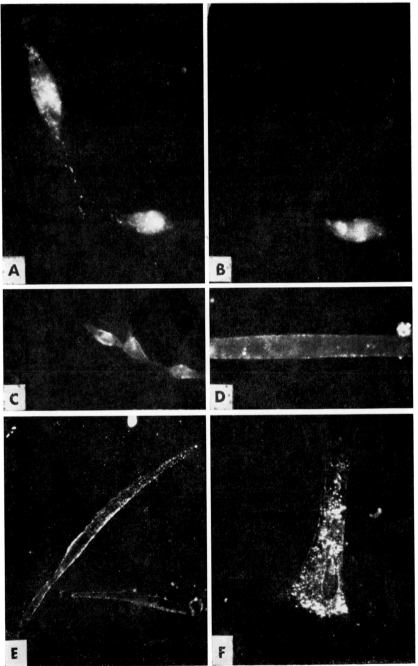

methods. Appropriate control experiments were done to ensure staining specificity.

Clonal cultures were prepared by plating 200–300 cells in a 100 mm petri dish containing 5 ml of conditioned medium and several collagen-coated cover slips (Hauschka and Konigsberg, 1966). Without collagen it was difficult not to lose the myotubes during the staining and rinsing procedure. When clones had reached the desired stage of development, they were infected with RSV and stained at intervals after infection.

Figure 6A shows two newly fused myoblasts photographed by dark-field microscopy. A corresponding photograph taken through the fluorescence microscope (Fig. 6B) shows intense fluorescence in the lower cell only. This antigen is localized at the cell surface in the form of heavy aggregates.

Three associated myoblasts which are probably beginning to fuse 48 hours after infection are shown in Fig. 6C. Intense fluorescence is again localized at the cell membrane. In Fig. 6E, two young myotubes, 48 hours postinfection, are seen. Fluorescent aggregates appear at the cell surface in this case as well. However, a larger more mature muscle fiber (Fig. 6D) has, at 56 hours after infection, a more diffuse fluorescent pattern. Figure 7 illustrates two muscle elements in the process of fusion at 20 hours after infection. The younger myotube has made lateral contact with the more mature fiber. Here, two distinct patterns of fluorescence are evident. In the older fiber, this pattern is diffuse; in the younger, the fluorescence is located in intense aggregates in those portions of the membrane contiguous to nuclei.

DNA Replication and Cell Transformation

Embryonic skeletal myoblasts and fibroblasts have been shown to be equally susceptible to Rous sarcoma virus both by their morphological transformation and by production of infectious virus. Fibroblasts change

---

Fig. 6. Viral antigen in muscle cells. A: Two newly fused myoblasts. 24 hours postinfection (p.i.) . 400 ×. Photographed by dark-field microscopy only. B: Fluorescence photomicrograph of Fig. A, the lower myoblast showing fluorescence. C: Three newly fused myoblasts; 48 hours p.i. 250 ×. Note fluorescence on the membrane. D. A mature myotube; 56 hours p.i. 250 ×. Note diffuse pattern of fluorescence and small fluorescent aggregates on membrane; the ellipsoid darker regions are nuclei. E: Two young myotubes; 48 hours p.i. 250 ×. Intense fluorescence associated with surface; stained by indirect method. F: An unidentified giant fibroblastic cell with fluorescent aggregates; 48 hours p.i. 400 ×.

from a flat, stellate cell firmly attached to the surface of the dish to a round, loosely attached, refractile sarcoma cell (Manaker and Groupé, 1956; Temin and Rubin, 1958) as a result of infection with RSV. Similarly, the myoblast loses its polar projections and rounds up. The minor differences between the transformation of fibroblast and myoblast colonies reflect the different growth pattern of the latter. A similar

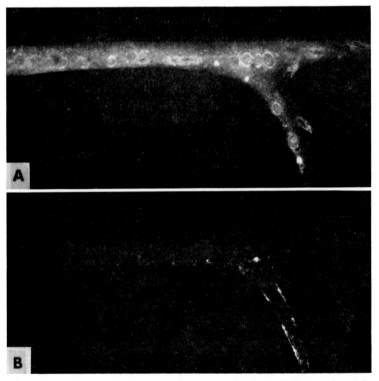

FIG. 7. Two myotubes fusing in an infected muscle clone 20 hours after infection. A: Dark-field optics. B: Stained with fluorescent antibody. 250 ×. (See text for further details.)

transformation has been observed in mass cultures of infected iris epithelium (Ephrussi and Temin, 1960; Temin, 1965). The results of the fluorescent antibody experiments supplement the transformation and virus production data by proving that myoblasts can synthesize viral antigen and by showing that infected cells can take part in myotube formation. The fact that antigen is localized either directly on the surface or closely associated with it is in accord with earlier studies *in vivo* showing RSV antigens to be localized on or near the sarcolemma of chick wing muscle 3 days after infection (Mellors and Munroe, 1960). Since myotubes form by fusion of myoblasts (Konigsberg *et al.,* 1960; Stockdale and Holtzer, 1961), viral particles could infect the myotubes in two ways. The first is by direct penetration of the myotube membrane. In the second possible mechanism, the virus could enter the myotube as a consequence of its subsequent fusion with an infected myoblast. At this writing, the weight of evidence favors the second explanation (Fig. 7). In view of the brief interval between infection and observation, however, direct penetration of the virus cannot be ruled out. Specific fluorescence has been detected in some mature myotubes as early as 20 hours postinfection. Furthermore, both modes of penetration could occur. Finally, although there is no precedent in the case or RSV infection, it is conceivable that the diffuse pattern of fluorescence might represent a noninfectious form of viral antigen. How sound is our evidence concerning the susceptibility of muscle cells? The possibility that transformation and viral synthesis in muscle clones really results from the presence of migrating susceptible fibroblasts must be taken into account (Medina and Sachs, 1965). We consider this improbable for a number of reasons. (1) The two cell types can be distinguished immediately following attachment. Cells were selected for isolation only if no nearby fibroblasts could be found. (2) The relatively high muscle frequency (50–80%) further reduces the chance of mixed colony formation. (3) Mixed colonies, which are easily identified by the two distinct cell types present, were never used in isolation experiments. (4) Direct observation confirmed that cells of typical bipolar shape were transforming. (5) Immunofluorescence studies revealed viral antigen in both single myoblasts and in myotubes. The pattern of fluorescence in fibroblasts was identical to that reported by Vogt and Rubin (1961).

The behavior of fibroblasts to RSV infection in our experiments was entirely consistent with the results reported by Trager and Rubin (1964). These authors, using the same virus strain (7B), obtained a maximum of about 40% transformed clones with about 40% of these releasing RSV. We observed about 50% transformed muscle and fibroblast clones. In both clonal types 50% or more of transformed clones produced virus. The rate of transformation of both muscle and fibroblast clones was proportional to virus concentration decreasing to around 5% at a 100-fold dilution of the virus.

Another cell-virus interaction previously reported in chick fibroblasts, the nonproducer phenomenon, may also be operative in myoblasts

(Temin, 1962; Hanafusa *et al.*, 1964). In Trager and Rubin's study, 62% of transformed clones did not produce virus. When these were superinfected with RAV all produced RSV and RAV. Of our transformed muscle clones, 20% failed to release virus. We have not determined whether or not they could be activated by RAV. The quantitative difference between our results with muscle, and Trager and Rubin's with fibroblasts, are easily explained by differences in conditions of infection.

The fact that the development of muscle involves the fusion of myoblasts into multinucleate fibers in which there is no further division or DNA synthesis raises an interesting question. Can a cell which, in the course of its differentiation, has lost the ability to divide, remain susceptible to infection by RSV? Neoplastic transformation by a DNA virus, polyoma, requires induction of cellular DNA synthesis (Dulbecco *et al.*, 1965; Gershon *et al.*, 1965; Hartwell *et al.*, 1965; Weil *et al.*, 1965; Winocour *et al.*, 1965; Vogt *et al.*, 1966).

In studies with another DNA virus, SV 40, two stages in the transformation process have been distinguished: (1) fixation of the transformed state in the infected cell; and (2) its expression as loss of sensitivity to contact inhibition of cell division. Both events require cell growth (presumably cellular DNA synthesis). One cell generation appears to be sufficient for fixation of the transformed state, while several generations are required for its full expression (Todaro and Green, 1966). On the basis of experiments employing inhibitors of both the function and synthesis of DNA, it has also been concluded that DNA synthesis is required for transformation of RSV-infected chicken embryo fibroblasts and for viral synthesis as well (Bader, 1965).

This evidence adds weight to our earlier argument that myotubes may be infected by the incorporation of infected myoblasts. The possibility remains that mature myotubes may contain immature virus particles or virus-associated antigens derived by a more direct route.

Thus, although the present investigation has shown that multinucleated myotubes contain virus-associated antigens, the question whether or not myoblasts and myotubes differ in their susceptibility to infection can only be resolved by experiments using isolated myotubes.

DNA Replication and Antibody Formation

The possibility that new synthesis may depend upon a preceding replication may also be explored in antibody-forming cells.

It is hardly necessary to document the thesis that knowledge of antibody formation will contribute significantly to our understanding of differentiation (Ebert, 1959; Ebert and DeLanney, 1960; Makinodan and Albright, 1962, 1963; Albright and Makinodan, 1964). Before examining the factors regulating antibody formation, however, it will be helpful to review briefly the structural basis of their specificity.

Antibody activity is present in three classes of serum proteins. The major component, γ_2 or 7 S γ, comprises about 85 to 90% of the total. A second component, γ_{1M} or β_{2M} (also known as 19 S γ), has a higher molecular weight and contains about five times as much carbohydrate as the major component. A third and less well understood, component is γ_{1A} or β_{2A}, with which the skin-sensitizing antibodies in human sera are associated. By analogy with the hemoglobin nomenclature, the 7 S, 19 S, and γ_{1A} immunoglobulin fractions are referred to as IgG, IgM, and IgA, respectively (Cohen and Porter, 1964).

We shall not consider the IgA fraction; we shall refer to IgM only briefly, centering most of our attention on the IgG fraction. Many different kinds of IgG molecules may be produced; however, as Dreyer and Bennett (1965) observe, although as many as 10,000 different kinds may be possible, they are remarkably similar, having a common molecular weight of 150,000.

These molecules consist of four subunit polypeptide chains: two identical light (L) chains (M. W. = 25,000) and two identical heavy (H) chains (M. W. = 50,000). The amino acid sequences are such that the molecules fold specifically, leading to molecular interactions, the complex structure being stabilized by interchain disulfide linkages (Cohen and Porter, 1964; Nisonoff and Inman, 1965). One part of the subunit structure serves the function of causing chain interaction, whereas other portions are capable of interacting with specific antigens. Moreover, peptide mapping of certain L chains (Bence–Jones proteins of different cell lines) reveal that while about half the amino acid sequences are always identical within this class of molecules (Bennett *et al.*, 1965), the remainder of each of these proteins contains strikingly different peptides (Putnam and Easley, 1965). There is no evidence that the two "halves" are in fact two subchains.

Thus, as Dreyer and Bennett put it (1965), ". . . one end of the light chain behaves as if it were made by the genetic code contained in any one of more than 1000 genes, while the other end of the L chains can be shown to be the product of a single gene." The latter portion may undergo mutation and Mendelian segregation, as revealed by studies of *allotypic* antigenic differences. In the rabbit, for example, the allotypic differences are controlled by at least three allelic genes at each of two genetic loci, *a* and *b* (Dray *et al.*, 1962). The allotypic specificities of the *b* locus are found on the light chains, while those of the *a* locus are associated with the heavy chains (reviewed by Small *et al.*, 1966). Immune sera prepared in two heterologous species, the chicken and the goat, contain antibodies specific for the allotypic variations of rabbit light chains (Bornstein and Oudin, 1964). Not only is there a set of alleles at the *b* locus which determine the allotypes of the light chains in rabbits, there is also evidence of allotypes of light chains of the mouse and of man.

Thus, we may first raise the question whether or not a single immunologically competent cell taken from an animal heterozygous for IgG allotypes produces globulins specific for one or both parental phenotypes (Cebra and Goldstein, 1965). In the three species examined thus far, mouse, rabbit, and man, Weiler (1965), Weiler *et al.* (1965), Pernis *et al.* (1965), and Bernier and Cebra (1965), respectively, have shown that heterozygous cells contain one or the other parental-type immunoglobulin, but not both. On the other hand, it is clear that both the maternal and paternal alleles function in the same cell to produce beta chains of hemoglobin (Matioli and Niewisch, 1965).

In one sense, then, a given cell appears to be determined to produce IgG of one genetic specificity. Superimposed on the genetic specificity of the globulin is its *functional* specificity, however, namely its capacity to react to a specific antigen. Is the cell also determined to produce *specific* antibody?

It is clear that the competent cell can form antibodies to at least two antigens (Attardi *et al.*, 1964a,b,c,d,e). Individual cells of the lymph nodes of rabbits injected with the immunologically unrelated antigens T2, T5, and C respond by making antibodies to each antigen alone with about equal frequency and at a not much reduced frequency to pairs of antigens. Cells responding to three antigens have not been observed. Attardi *et al.* (1964a,b,c,d,e) have discussed the possible bearing of these observations on the genetic basis of antibody specificity. If, in fact, the origin of antibody specificity is held to be genetic, two extreme models must be considered: each diploid cell carried either (1) two highly mutable allelic genes (Burnet, 1959; Lederberg, 1959) or (2) as many stable genes as there are distinct antibodies which the animal is capable of producing (Szilard, 1960; Ebert and Wilt, 1960). The data now available do not permit a distinction between these two extremes.

Thus far we have described the cells involved only as "immunologically competent cells." We do not propose to attempt to discuss fully the cellular basis of the immune response; instead we call attention to the principal areas of investigation: (1) There is a sequence of changes in some members of the lymphocytic series, e.g., within lymph nodes and spleen, progressing from "blast" cells, which have a poorly defined endoplasmic reticulum and a cytoplasm filled with many clusters of ribosomes, to highly organized plasma cells. Antibodies are first found in blast cells, and subsequently in increasing quantities in mature plasma cells (DePetris and Karlsbad, 1965; Mach and Vassalli, 1965). (2) It is uncertain whether the antibody-producing cells respond directly to antigenic stimulus or whether antigen must first be processed by macrophages. There are repeated references to interactions between lymphocytes and macrophages (e.g., Marks and Reinecke, 1964). Evidence is accumulating for the initial processing of antigen in macrophages but the nature of the stimulus transferred, whether it be a "superantigen," i.e., a modified antigen (one coupled with RNA), or information embodied in RNA is unclear [compare Askonas and Rhodes (1965) and Friedman *et al.* (1965) with Fishman and Adler (1963), Cohen and Parks (1964), Cohen *et al.* (1965), and Friedman (1964)].

We will not discuss the ontogeny of antibody-forming cells, this subject having been reviewed extensively (Ebert and DeLanney, 1960; Ebert, 1965; Good and Papermaster, 1964; Smith *et al.*, 1966). Antibodies to different antigens can first be detected at different times within a given species, and that there is a wide range of variability in the onset of antibody formation between species (Silverstein, 1964). We do wish to emphasize, however, that knowing the time at which an antibody can first be detected does not provide crucial information concerning the time at which cells first become competent to produce antibody. The limiting factor may not be the competence of one cell type to make antibody, but the competence of another cell type to recognize and "process" antigen. Thus it becomes of importance to examine critically the factors regulating the development of granulocytes and macrophages (DeLanney *et al.*, 1962; Mun *et al.*, 1962; Kimmel, 1966).

Returning to our main theme, we pick up our story by observing that cells potentially competent to respond to antigen arise during development, their number increasing rapidly after birth, reaching a maximum in the young adult and declining gradually with age (Makinodan and Peterson, 1964). The number of such cells is never large; they constitute a self-replenishing pool of stem cells. Whether one and the same cell may be stimulated along different hematopoietic pathways is uncertain;

Albright and Makinodan (1964; see also Perkins and Makinodan, 1964) argue that the younger the animal the more multipotent cells its spleen contains. These cells may, they believe, undergo erythropoiesis or myelopoiesis as well as differentiation into antibody-forming cells. We know very little about the primary events triggered by the first exposure of these stem cells to an antigen.

We do not know the first steps in the commitment of a given stem cell toward immunopoiesis. It appears that such a cell may take one of at least two different courses, depending upon the nature and dosage of the antigen: (1) It may make IgM alone. It is not known whether IgM synthesis must be preceded by replication of the genome, in whole or in part. (2) It may make IgM followed by IgG. Despite attempts to assign specific functions to IgM to account for its frequently observed early "burst," followed by prolonged production of IgG, its role remains largely conjectural (Nossal *et al.*, 1965). (3) It is uncertain whether any given cell responding to antigen for the first time can make IgG alone, without first producing IgM. The bulk of the "early" antibody in the primary response is usually IgM, with IgG being produced later. During embryogenesis, IgM has been detected first (Silverstein, 1964). It is also true that some cells have been observed to contain both IgM and IgG. In view of the large differences observed in the kinetics of response depending on antigen dosage (Nossal *et al.*, 1965), however, the question must be left open until more evidence is available.

We have said that it is not yet known whether or not IgM synthesis is accompanied by or requires DNA replication. IgG synthesis appears to be associated closely with cell proliferation. However, this question has been studied more thoroughly in the secondary response. Before going on to consider it, we must point up two other key changes during the primary response: (1) Some members of the stem cell population are restricted in their capacities and now become capable of responding to only the one specific antigen. Whether the appearance of these "memory" cells is a direct result of immunoglobulin synthesis or a related but independent process is not clear. (2) Other stem cells regenerate the stem cell populations. As Albright and Makinodan (1964) emphasized, it is necessary that this population be highly resistant to complete exhaustion.

The reactions of a previously immunized animal are better understood. One of the first responses to a secondary antigenic stimulus clearly is cell proliferation. Urso and Makinodan (1963) have shown that rabbit spleen and lymph node cells undergo rapid cell division during the

latent and logarithmic phases of antibody formation. Cohen and Talmage (1965) found that within 5 hours after the intravenous injection
of particulate antigen into the previously immunized mouse, precursors
of antibody-forming cells began DNA synthesis as shown by the incorporation of tritium-labeled thymidine. This synthesis continued for 24
hours, and had essentially stopped by 48 hours. Presumably the antibody
produced in such an experiment is IgG, although it is now clear that
the earlier argument that IgM is produced as the initial response in
primary immunization, followed by IgG, and that immunological memory involves only synthesis of IgG may be too limited (Nossal et al.,
1965).

How many spleen cells take part in this proliferation? Which cells
respond, i.e., what is the nature of the interaction between genetic determination and antigenic determination? The information available is
too fragmentary to permit us to try to formulate answers to these questions. We can do no more than indicate some of the directions being
taken.

The number of cells responding in a given spleen or lymph node to
a given antigen is small. Makinodan and Albright (1962; see also
Makinodan and Peterson, 1964) estimate that there are ~50 units of
potential antibody-forming cells responsive to a given antigen in the
spleen of a nonimmunized 12-week-old mouse, a "unit" containing between 1 and 10 cells. Jerne et al. (1963) concluded that there are about
100 competent cells per antigen in the spleens of nonimmunized mice.
Sado and Makinodan (1964) concluded from a study of the cell cycle
in rabbit spleen cells from primed donors that the number of blast
cells at any given time is dependent on the difference between the rate
at which precursor (multipotent) cells are becoming blast cells and
the rate at which blast cells are transforming into more mature cells.

The relations between genetic determination and antigenic determination can be analyzed critically only using clonal techniques. To the
best of our knowledge, antibody-forming cells have not yet been cloned
in vitro. There have been, however, preliminary attempts to study antibody formation in randomly selected clones of lymphoid cells in vivo.

Playfair et al. (1965) injected lethally irradiated mice with small
numbers of spleen cells and then immunized with sheep and pig erythrocytes. Antibody against each was found in separate areas of the
spleen, suggesting to the authors that each area may consist of the
progeny of a single precursor cell, restricted to forming a single antibody.
According to Nakano and Braun (1966) the pattern of distribution of

"clones" within the spleen is nonrandom. They report that cells responding in mouse spleen to sheep red blood cells are nonrandomly distributed and that their pattern differs from that of cells responding to chicken erythrocytes.

Feldman and Mekori (1966) observed, however, that a single antigen can elicit antibody formation in randomly selected clones of lymphoid cells *in vivo*. The importance of devising techniques for cloning lymphocytes *in vitro* cannot be overemphasized. It is essential that we know whether or not clonally derived lines of cells can respond to different antigens.

Thus far we have discussed two principal factors regulating the "suicidal" course of a spleen cell toward the production of a specific protein: its genetic constitution and the antigen to which it is exposed. We must now add a third: its site of origin in the embryo. The evidence on which this statement is made is convincing, but it is difficult to fit these findings into the picture we have just drawn of a multipotent stem cell "compartment" gradually reduced in size as the number of "memory" compartments grows.

Let us consider the spleen of the young chicken. Within a few weeks after hatching, the organ is found to contain at least two major "lines" of cells which are, or will become, capable of immune reactions (reviewed by Good and Papermaster, 1964; Smith *et al.*, 1966). One line, derived from the thymus, is biased to respond to histocompatibility antigens (Palm, 1965) which evoke homograft reactions; the other line, derived immediately from the bursa of Fabricius (which appears to be only a way station for cells derived from an earlier, unknown starting point—the yolk sac?), is biased to produce immunoglobulins in response to other antigenic stimuli (Cooper *et al.*, 1965; Moore and Owen, 1965).

It could be argued, of course, that the "thymic line" is restricted from the outset to homograft reactions, whereas the "bursal line" and the multipotent stem cells are synonymous. It remains to be seen, however, whether or not spleen cells derived from the bursa are capable of taking directions other than toward immunopoiesis.

Factors Regulating Differentiation

Intrinsic Controls

We have emphasized the necessity of keeping an open mind on the question of the maintenance of a full genome in most differentiated cells. At the one extreme, evidence is available for irreversible differentiation at the chromosomal level; at the other, there are examples of differentiated cells whose ability to take part in organ regeneration, in fact even to form a new organism, appears to demand the continued presence of a full genome any part of which is capable of expression. Of the vast area between the extremes we are largely ignorant, but we must proceed—and are proceeding—on the assumption that selective gene regulation underlies much, if not most, of differentiation.

It would be redundant to discuss the operon hypothesis (Jacob and Monod, 1963, 1964; Monod et al., 1963) at length, the model having been reviewed in this context repeatedly (Davis, 1964; Atwood, 1965; Ebert, 1965).

Instead we shall center attention only briefly on possible sites of action of effectors of differentiation. According to the operon hypothesis, a cytoplasmic aporepressor can be bound to the characteristic base sequences of DNA in the operator locus, the result of such a binding being the prevention of RNA synthesis on that operon. Thus one set of regulatory mechanisms may involve the transcriptive level. We recognize several possible targets for study: first, to function, the aporepressor presumably must be present, and in a specific configuration; its presence and proper configuration probably depend on the presence of corresponding low molecular corepressors, or on the absence of an inducer. Thus far the aporepressor remains intangible: is the aporepressor of a given function protein? RNA?

Assuming the correctness of the model in calling for an aporepressor, how is it bound to the characteristic base sequences of DNA?

The interaction of DNA with RNA's and proteins remains obscure. Although histones are effective inhibitors of both DNA replication and the synthesis of DNA-dependent RNA in vitro, the bulk of the evidence now available suggests that histones may be a necessary, but not sufficient, mechanism for effecting the control of differential gene activity in vivo (reviewed by Bonner, 1965; Hnilica, 1965). Histones probably do play a role in regulation, but the evidence suggests that specific histones do not interact with specific parts of the DNA. Hnilica (1965) remarked that "It looks like histones are tools, but not the hand that is moving the tool." The amounts and types of histones within animal cells are relatively constant, even in cells varying widely in their tissue of origin, age, character, and physiological state. Dulbecco (see Bonner and Ts'o, 1964) points out, however, that subtle interaction of histones and DNA might not have been revealed by the kinds of structural investigations conducted thus far (cf. Akinrimisi et al., 1965). Are histones removed from DNA by nuclear polyanions (Frenster, 1965)? It may be true, as Atwood observed, that the presence of histones has diverted attention from highly specific regulatory molecules which have no nonspecific affinity for nucleic acids. These recent explorations of the possible role of histones should make the search for specific regulators more vigorous, and possibly more enlightened.

Davis (1964) and Atwood (1965) have discussed the fragmentary evidence for regulation of translation in microorganisms, some of which Stent (1964) used in developing his general hypothesis of gene control at that level. As Atwood concludes, however, although the hypothesis is possible in a formal sense, the available data point more strongly to control at the level of transcription.

Nevertheless the idea continues to have appeal, and since evidence on regulation in differentiating cells is negligible, every avenue must be left open.

We must now examine the bearing of the existence of regulatory circuits on the mechanism of stabilization of differentiating cells and on intrinsic sources of stability. One factor contributing to stability of differentiation is undoubtedly the stability of messenger RNA (reviewed by Davis, 1964; Ebert, 1965; Grobstein, 1966). As Davis has made clear, however, this factor alone cannot be sufficient. It seems necessary to postulate a self-perpetuating effect of gene products on their own further formation. In an enlightening discussion, Davis observed that "The regulatory mechanisms seen in bacteria do not furnish a direct model, since they are homeostatic in their overall effect: a rise in the level of a metabolite exerts a *negative* feedback action on its own formation, tending to reverse any difference starting to develop in the cell. Differentiation, however, is the opposite of homeostasis: it seeks to perpetuate differences. . . . Differentiation could in principle be accomplished by *positive* feedback loops, in which a difference in the level of a substance tends to perpetuate itself" (see also Jacob and Monod, 1963).

Extrinsic Controls: Cell and Tissue Interactions

Thus far, we have emphasized the cell's inner controls (Grobstein, 1964a,b; Ebert, 1965). Yet within the organism, the differentiation of a cell must depend, at least in large part, upon the extrinsic forces which impinge upon it, not the least of which are the influences exerted by neighboring cells. This extensive subject, whether under the heading, "cell and tissue interactions" or "embryonic induction," has been considered in many of the symposia of this Society, especially in three notable articles (Grobstein, 1954; Lash, 1963; Konigsberg and Hauschka, 1965). It is true that the differentiation of a given cell type often requires the action of an effector produced by another type. Nevertheless we remain ignorant of the nature of these effectors and of their initial site of action, especially whether they impinge directly upon the genetic and regulatory circuits we have been discussing, or operate through intermediaries within the cell or at its surface.

Evidence continues to mount suggesting that differentiating cells can influence each other by evchange not only of small molecules but also of direct gene products (reviewed by Ebert and Wilt, 1960; Davis, 1964; see also Niu, 1964a,b). Nevertheless there have been no crucial experiments and no generally applicable and verifiable findings (Holtzer, 1963; Ebert, 1965; Cohen, 1965). In attempting to single out the most convincing of the lines of evidence available for the role of an RNA as an intermediary, one turns at once to the interaction between macrophage and lymphocyte. Yet as we have seen, since this subject was last reviewed in this context (Ebert, 1965), the meaning of the evidence that RNA isolated from antigenically stimulated macrophages can evoke specific antibody formation in lymphocytes *in vitro* has been questioned (Askonas and Rhodes, 1965). We must now ask whether the RNA is informational, or whether it combines with traces of antigen to form a "superantigen."

There is also evidence that the course of differentiation may be influenced by effectors acting at the cell's periphery. It now appears that collagen or materials associated with it may play a role in regulating many diverse differentiative events (Konigsberg and Hauschka, 1965; Grobstein and Cohen, 1965). The mechanism whereby the availability of such a molecule to an inductive interface may alter differentiation is completely obscure.

The mechanisms are obscure, but the phenomena are real. Grobstein (1966) pays special attention to the observation that in several inductive systems a "morphogenetic event," e.g., a change in shape in a cell collection, precedes the first recognizable differentiable changes within the cells. Similarly, an intriguing example is provided by the observation by Kocher-Becker *et al.* (1965) that one of the first effects of implanting a highly purified mesodermal factor into the blastocoel of the early *Triturus* gastrula is the spreading of endoderm over ectoderm, suggesting a change in cell affinities.

Is the importance of "morphogenesis" preceding differentiation real or illusory? If the analysis of morphogenesis is confined to the level of the cell group, it is hard to see how the approach can lead to meaningful distinctions, for an effector may have to activate a gene in order for the morphogenesis to be expressed. Thus a differentiation would inevitably precede morphogenesis and one should search for factors regulating, e.g., synthesis of a new surface protein. However, if it can be shown that an effector acts *directly* in altering the conformation—the folding and aggregation of a specific protein—then it will be meaningful to stress a primary role of morphogenesis in effector systems.

Conspectus

Clifford Grobstein entitled one of his recent articles, "What we do not know about differentiation" (1966). Our own article has been, to be sure, a mixture of old and new, of tried and untried ideas. Yet we would be remiss if we did not, in these concluding pages, again draw attention to crucial questions and to promising directions.

First we wish to reiterate the need for research in depth relating DNA structure to specific developmental events, especially in clonally derived cells. Too many of the key examples relating differentiable changes to chromosomal alterations, e.g., those in insects, although elegant, lend themselves to only a limited repertoire of experiments. In particular, it is important to perfect techniques of mapping specific regions of the genome. The molecular hybridization techniques, especially the hybridization of DNA and RNA, should permit a "molecular mapping" of the genome. It may be asked, for example, what are the linkage relations of the loci for the several classes of RNA? The independent continuing studies of Birnstiel and Brown and their colleagues of the sites controlling ribosomal RNA synthesis in *Xenopus* (Weber and Brown, 1966) exemplify what should be a rewarding approach.

Proceeding from the level of the genome itself to regulatory circuits, we would call attention to the possibilities, as yet largely unrealized, in somatic cell hybridization (reviewed by Ephrussi, 1965). As Ephrussi has remarked, we need pure lines of somatic cells which maintain *in vitro* the properties that characterize them *in situ;* and we need techniques for recombining their genes. As discussed earlier in these pages, the first requirement is at last being realized. It is not our intent to catalogue the evidence that hybrids can be obtained between genetically different cells. Ephrussi has provided evidence of the hybridization of cells and has summarized some of the evidence justifying his expressed optimism that somatic hybridization will provide evidence bearing on the genetic physiology of somatic cells.

No doubt each of the investigators now practicing this art has his own idea of the ultimate target of his research. Thus, Green *et al.* (1966) sought to explore the factors regulating synthesis of collagen and hyaluronic acid in fibroblasts. Hybrids were developed combining in a single cell the genomes of two fibroblasts differing in their rates of production of these substances. Cells of one line made considerable amounts of both collagen and hyaluronic acid; cells of the other produced little collagen and no detectable hyaluronic acid. The findings were clear: all hybrids synthesized measurable amounts of both substances, the values for the hybrids being intermediate between those in the two original lines. In this one example, the two parental genomes appear to be acting independently in the hybrid, without interaction. It will be necessary, of course, to explore many synthetic pathways before generalizations can be made about the suitability of the hybridization techniques for studying control mechanisms. An examination of the mechanisms controlling the synthesis of immunoglobulins might be especially rewarding (see p. 62).

We would like to emphasize, however, that it seems of the first order of importance to elucidate the molecular processes controlling the pathways involved in nuclear replication. We find the arguments of Mueller and Kajiwara (1965) compelling, viewed in the light of the increasing evidence for the requirement of replication preceding transcription in many differentiating systems. The progression of a cell through the division cycle seems to reflect the orderly expression of specific genes. Moreover, the replication of DNA in the nucleus of the mammalian cell may occur during two periods, the molecules made during one period being replicated in the same period in subsequent cycles of daughter cells. Mueller and Kajiwara discuss the hypothesis that the early-replicating DNA may constitute the DNA that is active in mRNA synthesis, while the late-replicating DNA may represent the repressed fraction. It might then be expected that differentiation in a cell line would be attended by a shift of DNA from one fraction to the other. Thus an understanding of the factors regulating replication should prove to be crucial to an understanding of factors regulating transcription. The possibilities are intriguing. Consider the observation (Mekori *et al.*, 1965) that identifiable lymphocytes did not appear in clones derived from injected suspensions of cells from mouse lymph nodes unless the cells were first treated with the mitogenic principle phytohemagglutinin. This factor causes peripheral lymphocytes to engage in DNA synthesis and nuclear replication. This example illustrates once again the principle that animal cells have mechanisms for regulating replication that depend on information coming from the environment. As Dulbecco (1965) put it, the cell surface has the role of a "sensor" which receives information from the environment and presumably transmits to a regulatory site.

Thus we come to the question we wish to put in the spotlight, inasmuch as it points up the relations between differentiation and morphogenesis: How do specific modifications of a cell surface influence genetic and regulatory mechanisms? Again the phenomenon is a real one (Abercrombie, 1962, 1965; Dulbecco, 1965; Rubin, 1956, 1961; Stoker and Macpherson, 1961; Abbott and Holtzer, 1966; Todaro and Green, 1966). The precise relations between contact inhibition and position in the mitotic cycle (Roizman, 1961; Roizman and Schluederberg, 1961; Basilico and Marin, 1966) must be elucidated.

From this consideration of the reception and transmission of signals by the cell surface membrane, it is but a short step to our last question, which we can take by recalling the title of one of Sonneborn's articles, "Does preformed cell structure play an essential role in cell heredity?" (1963; see also 1960, 1964).

There is extensive evidence from Sonneborn's studies in *Paramecium*, and in other systems, including the amphibian egg (Curtis, 1963; reviewed by Ebert, 1965), that the cell cortex contains informational material. The replication and development of other cytoplasmic structures, e.g., chloroplasts and mitochondria, which contain DNA, appears to involve the reading of an autonomous code (reviewed by Schiff and Epstein, 1965; Srb, 1965), but the manner in which this information is regulated, especially in relation to the circuitry regulating chromosomal heredity, is completely obscure.

Although we badly need enough information from diverse animal species to begin to assess the general significance of mitochondrial DNA, there is special merit in describing its occurrence and role in detail in one or a few species. It was a detailed description of the pattern of ribosomal RNA formation in *Xenopus laevis* that resulted in a series of fundamental observations on RNA synthesis and interactions in that species (reviewed by Brown, 1965). Thus it is of interest to report that the bulk of the cytoplasmic DNA of both *Xenopus laevis* and *Rana pipiens* is mitochondrial. In an elegant study, after confirming that the eggs of these species contain 300 to 500 times more DNA than their somatic cells, Dawid (1965) demonstrated that the cytoplasmic DNA is high molecular weight, double-stranded material, complementary in sequence to only a small proportion of liver DNA of the same species.

He has now presented direct evidence that the bulk of this egg DNA is mitochondrial (Dawid, 1966).

Dawid's earlier findings had excluded the well-known hypothesis that the cytoplasmic DNA might function as a reservoir of stored material for the rapid assembly of chromosomes during early development. The question must now be asked whether or not the patterns of mitochondrial and ribosomal synthesis during oogenesis and early development are similar. Is mitochondrial synthesis, like that of ribosomes, intense during oogenesis, only to cease until much later in development? Can mitochondrial replication be observed during cleavage and early development?

Do these self-perpetuating structures provide a key to the central problem of differentiation? An unequivocal answer is not yet possible; too many pieces of the puzzle are missing, especially those dealing with their control mechanisms. It would appear, however, that the role of autonomously replicating organelles may be to conserve patterns, rather than create new patterns during differentiation (Davis, 1964).

DEDICATION

This article is dedicated to Dr. Mary E. Rawles. Usually there is some "occasion" for a dedication: an anniversary or birthday; but Dr. Rawles has never recognized Time. Happily, Time, thus scorned, has chosen to ignore her. She remains an inspiration to all students of development. Lacking a suitable "occasion," we simply dedicate this article to her as a small token of our affection.

ACKNOWLEDGMENTS

For the past year the authors have been privileged to work in cooperation with Dr. Harold H. Lee whose contributions to the original work reported here have been invaluable. The authors also wish to express their indebtedness to Mrs. Delores Somerville, Mrs. Bessie Smith, and Mr. Richard Grill for their highly competent technical services. Dr. John B. Gurdon kindly made available a number of unpublished observations from his laboratory. During the preparation of the manuscript, we have profited from discussions with Dr. Lee and with Drs. D. D. Brown, C. B. Kimmel, I. R. Konigsberg, and Dorothea Rudnick.

REFERENCES

ABBOTT, J., AND HOLTZER, H. (1966). The loss of phenotypic traits by differentiated cells. III. The reversible behavior of chondrocytes in primary cultures. *J. Cell. Biol.* **28,** 473–487.

ABERCROMBIE, M. (1962). Contact-dependent behavior of normal cells and the possible significance of surface changes in virus-induced transformation. *Cold Spring Harbor Symp. Quant. Biol.* **27,** 427–431.

ABERCROMBIE, M. (1965) . Cellular interactions in development. *In* "Ideas in Modern Biology" (J. A. Moore, ed.) , pp. 261–280. Nat. Hist. Press, Garden City, New York.

AKINRIMISI, E. O., BONNER, J., AND Ts'o, P. O. P. (1965) . Binding of basic proteins to DNA. *J. Mol. Biol.* **11**, 128–136.

ALBRIGHT, J. F., AND MAKINODAN, T. (1964) . Dynamics of expression of competence of antibody producing cells. *In* "Molecular and Cellular Basis of Antibody Formation," pp. 427–446. Acad. Sci., Prague.

ALLEN, S. L. (1965) . Genetic control of enzymes in *Tetrahymena*. *In* "Genetic Control of Differentiation," pp. 27–54. Brookhaven Nat. Lab., Upton, New York.

ASKONAS, B. A., AND RHODES, J. M. (1965) . Immunogenicity of antigen-containing ribonucleic acid preparations from macrophages. *Nature* **205**, 470–474.

ATTARDI, G., COHN, M., HORIBATA, K., AND LENNOX, E. S. (1964a) . Antibody formation by rabbit lymph node cells. I. Single cell responses to several antigens. *J. Immunol.* **92**, 335–345.

ATTARDI, G., COHN, M., HORIBATA, K., AND LENNOX, E. S. (1964b) . Antibody formation by rabbit lymph node cells. II. Further observations on the behavior of single antibody-producing cells with respect to their synthetic capacity and morphology. *J. Immunol.* **92**, 346–355.

ATTARDI, G., COHN, M., HORIBATA, K., AND LENNOX, E. S. (1964c) . Antibody formation by rabbit lymph node cells. III. The controls for microdrop and micropipet experiments. *J. Immunol.* **92**, 356–371.

ATTARDI, G., COHN, M., HORIBATA, K., AND LENNOX, E. S. (1964d) . Antibody formation by rabbit lymph node cells. IV. The detailed methods for measuring antibody synthesis by individual cells, the kinetics of antibody formation by rabbits and the properties of cell suspensions. *J. Immunol.* **92**, 372–390.

ATTARDI, G., COHN, M., HORIBATA, K., AND LENNOX, E. S. (1964e) . Antibody formation by rabbit lymph node cells. V. Cellular heterogeneity in the production of antibody to T5′. *J. Immunol.* **93**, 94–95.

ATWOOD, K. C. (1965) . Transcription and translation of genes. *In* "Reproduction: Molecular, Subcellular, and Cellular" (M. Locke, ed.) , pp. 17–38. Academic Press, New York.

BADER, J. P. (1965) . Transformation by Rous sarcoma virus: a requirement for DNA synthesis. *Science* **149**, 757–758.

BALUDA, M. A. (1962) . Properties of cells infected with avian myeloblastosis virus. *Cold Spring Harbor Symp. Quant. Biol.* **27**, 415–425.

BALUDA, M. A., AND GOETZ, I. E. (1961) . Morphological conversion of cell cultures by avian myeloblastosis virus. *Virology* **15**, 185–199.

BALUDA, M. A., AND JAMIESON, P. P. (1961) . *In vivo* infectivity studies with avian myeloblastosis virus. *Virology* **14**, 33–45.

BASILICO, C., AND MARIN, G. (1966) . Susceptibility of cells in different stages of the mitotic cycle to transformation by polyoma virus. *Virology* **28**, 429–437.

BEARD, J. W. (1957) . Etiology of avian leukosis. *Ann. N. Y. Acad. Sci.* **68**, 473–486.

BENNETT, J. C., HOOD, L., DREYER, W. J., AND POTTER, M. (1965) . Evidence for amino acid sequence differences among proteins resembling the L-chain subunits of immunoglobulins. *J. Mol. Biol.* **12**, 81–87.

BERNIER, G. M., AND CEBRA, J. J. (1965). Frequency distribution of alpha, gamma, kappa and lambda polypeptide chains in human lymphoid tissues. *J. Immunol.* **95,** 246–253.

BEUTLER, E., YEH, M., AND FAIRBANKS, V. F. (1962). The normal human female as a mosaic of X-chromosome activity: studies using the gene for G-6-PD-deficiency as a marker. *Proc. Natl. Acad. Sci., U.S.* **48,** 9–19.

BONNER, J. (1965). "The Molecular Biology of Development." Oxford Univ. Press, London and New York.

BONNER, J., AND TS'O, P. (1964). "The Nucleohistones." Holden-Day, San Francisco, California.

BORNSTEIN, P., AND OUDIN, J. (1964). A study of rabbit γ-globulin allotypy by means of heteroimmunizations. *J. Exptl. Med.* **120,** 655–676.

BOVERI, T. (1887). Über Differenzierung der Zellkerne während der Furschung des Eies von *Ascaris megalocephala. Anat. Anz.* **2,** 688–693.

BRAUN, A. C. (1959). A demonstration of the recovery of the crown-gall tumor cell with the use of complex tumors of single-cell origin. *Proc. Natl. Acad. Sci. U.S.* **45,** 932–938.

BRIGGS, R., AND CASSENS, G. (1966). Accumulation in the oocyte nucleus of a gene product essential for embryonic development beyond gastrulation. *Proc. Natl. Acad. Sci. U.S.* **55,** 1103–1109.

BRIGGS, R., KING, T. J., AND DI BERARDINO, M. (1961). Development of nuclear-transplant embryos of known chromosome complement following parabiosis with known embryos. *In* "Symposium on the Germ Cells and Earliest Stages of Development," pp. 441–477. Baselli, Milan.

BRIGGS, R., SIGNORET, J., AND HUMPHREY, R. R. (1964). Transplantation of nuclei of various cell types from neurulae of the Mexican axolotl (*Ambystoma mexicanum*). *Develop. Biol.* **10,** 233–246.

BROWN, D. D. (1965). RNA synthesis during early development. *In* "Developmental and Metabolic Control Mechanisms and Neoplasia," pp. 219–236. Williams & Wilkins, Baltimore, Maryland.

BROWN, D. D., AND GURDON, J. (1964). Absence of ribosomal RNA synthesis in the anucleolate mutant *Xenopus laevis. Proc. Natl. Acad. Sci. U.S.* **51,** 139–146.

BROWN, D. D., AND GURDON, J. (1966a). The size distribution and stability of DNA-like RNA synthesized during development of anucleolate embryos of *Xenopus laevis. J. Mol. Biol.* **19,** 399–422.

BROWN, D. D., AND GURDON, J. (1966b). The synthesis of DNA-like RNA by the anucleolate mutant embryos of *X. laevis. Carnegie Inst. Wash., Yearbook* **65** (in press).

BROWN, D. D., AND LITTNA, E. (1964a). RNA synthesis during the development of *Xenopus laevis,* the South African clawed toad. *J. Mol. Biol.* **8,** 669–687.

BROWN, D. D., AND LITTNA, E. (1964b). Variations in the synthesis of stable RNA's during oogenesis and development of *Xenopus laevis. J. Mol. Biol.* **8,** 688–695.

BROWN, D. D., AND LITTNA, E. (1966a). The synthesis and accumulation of DNA-like RNA during embryogenesis of *Xenopus laevis. J. Mol. Biol.* **20,** 81–94.

BROWN, D. D., AND LITTNA, E. (1966b). The synthesis and accumulation of low molecular weight RNA during embryogenesis of *Xenopus laevis. J. Mol. Biol.* **20,** 95–112.

BURMESTER, B. R., WALTER, W. C., GROSS, M. A., AND FONTES, A. K. (1959). The oncogenic spectrum of two pure strains of avian leukosis. *J. Natl. Cancer Inst.* **23,** 277–291.

BURNET, F. M. (1959). "The Clonal Selection Theory of Acquired Immunity." Vanderbilt Univ. Press, Nashville, Tennessee.

CAHN, R. D. (1964). Maintenance of beating and dissociation of biochemical and functional differentiation in clones of chicken embryo heart cells. *J. Cell Biol.* **23,** 17A.

CAHN, R. D., AND CAHN, M. B. (1966). Heritability of cellular differentiation: Clonal growth and expression of differentiation in retinal pigment cells *in vitro*. *Proc. Natl. Acad. Sci. U.S.* **55,** 106–114.

CEBRA, J. J., AND GOLDSTEIN, G. (1965). Chromatographic purification of tetramethylrhodamine-immune globulin conjugates and their use in the cellular localization of rabbit γ-globulin polypeptide chains. *J. Immunol.* **95,** 230–245.

CLEVER, U. (1965). Chromosomal changes associated with differentiation. *In* "Genetic Control of Differentiation," pp. 242–253. Brookhaven Nat. Lab., Upton, New York.

COHEN, E. P., AND PARKS, J. J. (1964). Antibody production by nonimmune spleen cells incubated with RNA from immunized mice. *Science* **144,** 1012–1013.

COHEN, E. P., AND TALMAGE, D. W. (1965). Onset and duration of DNA synthesis in antibody forming cells after antigen. *J. Exptl. Med.* **121,** 125–132.

COHEN, E. P., NEWCOMB, R. W., AND CROSBY, L. K. (1965). Conversion of nonimmune spleen cells to antibody-forming cells by RNA: strain specificity of the response. *J. Immunol.* **95,** 583–590.

COHEN, S. (1965). Growth factors and morphogenic induction. *In* "Developmental and Metabolic Control Mechanisms and Neoplasia," pp. 251–272. Williams & Wilkins, Baltimore, Maryland.

COHEN, S., AND PORTER, R. R. (1964). Structure and biological activity of immunoglobulins. *Advan. Immunol.* **4,** 287–349.

COON, H. (1966). Clonal stability and phenotypic expression of chick cartilage cells *in vitro*. *Proc. Natl. Acad. Sci. U.S.* **55,** 66–73.

COON, H., AND CAHN, R. D. (1966). Differentiation *in vitro:* Effects of Sephadex fractions of chick embryo extract. *Science* **153,** 1116–1119.

COOPER, M. D., PETERSON, R. D. A., AND GOOD, R. A. (1965). Delineation of the thymic and bursal lymphoid systems in the chicken. *Nature* **205,** 143–146.

CURTIS, A. S. G. (1963). The cell cortex. *Endeavour* **22,** 134–137.

DAVIDSON, E. H., AND MIRSKY, A. E. (1965). Gene activity in oogenesis. *In* "Genetic Control of Differentiation," pp. 77–98. Brookhaven Natl. Lab., Upton, New York.

DAVIS, B. D. (1964). Theoretical mechanisms of differentiation. *Medicine* **43,** 639–649.

DAWE, C. J. (1960). Cell sensitivity and specificity of response to polyoma virus. *Natl. Cancer Inst. Monograph* **4,** 67–92.

DAWE, C. J., MORGAN, W. D., AND SLATICK, M. S. (1966). Influence of epitheliomesenchymal interactions on tumor induction by polyoma virus. *Int. J. Cancer* **1,** 419–450.

DAWID, I. B. (1965). Deoxyribonucleic acid in amphibian eggs. *J. Mol. Biol.* **12,** 581–599.

DAWID, I. B. (1966). Evidence for the mitochondrial origin of frog egg cytoplasmic DNA, *Proc. Natl. Acad. Sci. U.S.* **56**, 269–276.

DEHAAN, R. L., AND EBERT, J. D. (1964). Morphogenesis. *Ann. Rev. Physiol.* **26**, 15–46.

DELANNEY, L. E., EBERT, J. D., COFFMAN, C. M., AND MUN, A. M. (1962). On the chick spleen: Origin, patterns of normal development and their experimental modification. *Carnegie Inst. Wash., Contrib. Embryol.* **37**, 57–85.

DEMARS, R., AND NANCE, W. E. (1964). Electrophoretic variants of glucose-6-phosphate dehydrogenase and the single-action X in cultivated human cells. *Wistar Inst. Symp. Monograph* **1**, 35–48.

DENIS, H. (1965). Synthesis of messenger RNA studied by the agar-DNA technique. *Carnegie Inst. Wash., Yearbook* **64**, 452–465.

DEPETRIS, S., AND KARLSBAD, G. (1965). Localization of antibodies on electron microscopy in developing antibody-producing cells. *J. Cell. Biol.* **26**, 759–778.

DRAY, S., DUBISKI, S., KELUS, A., LENNOX, E. S., AND OUDIN, J. (1962). A notation for allotypy. *Nature* **195**, 785–786.

DREYER, W. J., AND BENNETT, J. C. (1965). The molecular basis of antibody formation: a paradox. *Proc. Natl. Acad. Sci. U.S.* **54**, 864–869.

DULBECCO, R. (1963). Transformation of cells *in vitro* by viruses. *Science* **142**, 932–936.

DULBECCO, R. (1965). Interaction of viruses with the genetic material of the host cells. *In* "Reproduction: Molecular, Subcellular, and Cellular" (M. Locke, ed.), pp. 95–106. Academic Press, New York.

DULBECCO, R., HARTWELL, L. H., AND VOGT, M. (1965). Induction of cellular DNA synthesis by polyoma virus. *Proc. Natl. Acad. Sci. U.S.* **53**, 403–410.

EBERT, J. D. (1959). The acquisition of biological specificity. *In* "The Cell" (J. Brachet and A. E. Mirsky, eds.), Vol. 1, pp. 619–693. Academic Press, New York.

EBERT, J. D. (1961). Antibodies, viruses and embryos. *In* "First International Conference on Congenital Malformations" (M. Fishbein, ed.), pp. 291–299. Lippincott, Philadelphia, Pennsylvania.

EBERT, J. D. (1965). "Interacting Systems in Development." Holt, New York.

EBERT, J. D., AND DELANNEY, L. E. (1960). Ontogenesis of the immune response. *Natl. Cancer Inst. Monograph* **2**, 73–111.

EBERT, J. D., AND WILT, F. H. (1960). Animal viruses and embryos. *Quart. Rev. Biol.* **35**, 261–312.

EPHRUSSI, B. (1965). Hybridization of somatic cells and phenotypic expression. *In* "Developmental and Metabolic Control Mechanisms and Neoplasia," pp. 486–503. Williams & Wilkins, Baltimore, Maryland.

EPHRUSSI, B., AND TEMIN, H. M. (1960). Infection of chick iris epithelium with the Rous sarcoma virus *in vitro*. *Virology* **11**, 547–552.

FELDMAN, M., AND MEKORI, T. (1966). Antibody production by "cloned" cell populations. *Immunology* **10**, 149–160.

FELL, H. B. (1961). Changes in synthesis induced in organ cultures. *In* "Molecular and Cellular Structure" (D. Rudnick, ed.), pp. 139–160. Ronald Press, New York.

FISHMAN, M., AND ADLER, F. L. (1963). Antibody formation initiated *in vitro*. II. Antibody synthesis in X-irradiated recipients of diffusion chambers containing nucleic acid derived from macrophages incubated with antigen. *J. Exptl. Med.* **117**, 595–602.

FLICKINGER, R. A. (1966). Reversible delay of normal development of frog embryos by inhibition of DNA synthesis. *J. Exptl. Zool.* **161,** 243–250.

FRENSTER, J. H. (1965). A model of specific de-repression within interphase chromatin. *Nature* **206,** 1269–1270.

FRIEDMAN, H. (1964). Antibody plaque formation by normal mouse spleen cell cultures exposed *in vitro* to RNA from immune mice. *Science* **146,** 934–936.

FRIEDMAN, H. P., STAVITSKY, A. B., AND SOLOMON, J. M. (1965). Induction *in vitro* of antibodies to phage T2: Antigens in the RNA extract employed. *Science* **149,** 1106–1107.

GALL, J. G. (1963). Chromosomes and cytodifferentiation. *In* "Cytodifferentiation and Macromolecular Synthesis" (M. Locke, ed.), pp. 119–143. Academic Press, New York.

GERSHON, D., HAUSEN, P., SACHS, L., AND WINOCOUR, E. (1965). On the mechanism of polyoma virus-induced synthesis of cellular DNA. *Proc. Natl. Acad. Sci. U.S.* **54,** 1584–1592.

GOOD, R. A., AND PAPERMASTER, B. W. (1964). Ontogeny and phylogeny of adaptive immunity. *Advan. Immunol.* **4,** 1–115.

GRAHAM, C. F., AND MORGAN, R. (1966). Changes in the cell cycle in early Amphibian development. *Develop. Biol.* (in press).

GRAHAM, C. F., ARMS, K., AND GURDON, J. B. (1966). The induction of DNA synthesis by frog egg cytoplasm. *Develop. Biol.* (in press).

GREEN, H., EPHRUSSI, B., YOSHIDA, M., AND HAMERMAN, D. (1966). Synthesis of collagen and hyaluronic acid by fibroblast hybrids. *Proc. Natl. Acad.. Sci. U.S.* **55,** 41–44.

GROBSTEIN, C. (1954). Tissue interactions in the morphogenesis of mouse embryonic rudiments *in vitro*. *In* "Aspects of Synthesis and Order in Growth" (D. Rudnick, ed.), pp. 233–256. Princeton Univ. Press, Princeton, New Jersey.

GROBSTEIN, C. (1955). Inductive interaction in the development of the mouse metanephros. *J. Exptl. Zool.* **130,** 319–340.

GROBSTEIN, C. (1956). Trans-filter induction in tubules in mouse metanephrogenic mesenchyme. *Exptl. Cell Res.* **10,** 424–440.

GROBSTEIN, C. (1964a). Cytodifferentiation and its controls. *Science* **143,** 643–650.

GROBSTEIN, C. (1964b). Interaction among cells in relation to cytodifferentiation. *J. Exptl. Zool.* **157,** 121–126.

GROBSTEIN, C. (1966). What we do not know about differentiation. *Am. Zoologist* **6,** 89–95.

GROBSTEIN, C., AND COHEN, J. (1965). Collagenase: effect of the morphogenesis of embryonic salivary epithelium *in vitro*. *Science* **150,** 626–628.

GURDON, J. B. (1966a). The control of gene activity during cell differentiation in higher organisms. *In* "Heritage from Mendel" (R. A. Brink, ed.), Univ. of Wisconsin Press, Madison, Wisconsin (In press).

GURDON, J. B. (1966b). The cytoplasmic control of gene activity. *Endeavour* **25,** 95–99.

GURDON, J. B. (1966c). Personal communication.

GURDON, J. B., AND BROWN, D. D. (1965). Cytoplasmic regulation of RNA synthesis and nucleolus formation in developing embryos of *Xenopus laevis J. Mol. Biol.* **12,** 27–35.

HANAFUSA, H., HANAFUSA, T., AND RUBIN, H. (1964). Analysis of the defectiveness of Rous sarcoma virus. I. Characterization of the helper virus. *Virology* **22**, 591–601.

HARRIS, H., AND WATKINS, J. F. (1965). Hybrid cells derived from mouse and man: artificial heterokaryons of mammalian cells from different species. *Nature* **205**, 640–646.

HARTWELL, L. H., VOGT, M., AND DULBECCO, R. (1965). Induction of cellular DNA synthesis by polyoma virus. II. Increase in the rate of enzyme synthesis after infection with polyoma virus in mouse kidney cells. *Virology* **27**, 262–272.

HAUSCHKA, S. D., AND KONIGSBERG, I. R. (1966). The influence of collagen on the development of muscle clones. *Proc. Natl. Acad. Sci. U.S.* **55**, 119–126.

HNILICA, L. S. (1965). The role of nuclear proteins in genetic regulations. *In* "Development and Metabolic Control Mechanisms and Neoplasia," pp. 273–295. Williams & Wilkins, Baltimore, Maryland.

HOLTZER, H. (1963). Comments on induction during cell differentiation. *Colloq. Ges. Physiol. Chem.* **13**, 128–143.

HSU, T. C., SCHMID, W., AND STUBBLEFIELD, E. (1964). DNA replication sequences in higher animals. *In* "The Role of Chromosomes in Development" (M. Locke, ed.), pp. 83–112. Academic Press, New York.

HUMPHREY, R. R. (1966). A recessive factor (o, for ova deficient) determining a complex of abnormalities in the Mexican axolotl. *Develop. Biol.* **13**, 57–76.

JACOB, F., AND MONOD, J. (1963). Genetic repression, allosteric inhibition, and cellular differentiation. *In* "Cytodifferentiation and Macromolecular Synthesis" (M. Locke, ed.), pp. 30–64. Academic Press, New York.

JACOB, F., AND MONOD, J. (1964). Mécanismes biochimiques et génetiques de la regulation dans la cellule bacterienne. *Bull. Soc. Chim. Biol.* **46**, 1499–1532.

JAINCHILL, J., SAXEN, L., AND VAINIO, T. (1964). Studies on kidney tubulogenesis. I. The effect of actinomycin D on tubulogenesis *in vitro*. *J. Embryol. Exptl. Morphol.* **12**, 597–608.

JERNE, K. K., NORDIN, A. A., AND HENRY, C. (1963). The agar plaque technique for recognizing antibody-producing cells. *In* "Cell-Bound Antibodies" (B. Amos and H. Koprowski, eds.), pp. 109–125. Wistar Inst. Press, Philadelphia, Pennsylvania.

KAIGHN, M. E., EBERT, J. D., AND STOTT, P M. (1966). The susceptibility of differentiating muscle clones to Rous sarcoma virus. *Proc. Natl. Acad. Sci. U.S.* **56**, 133–140.

KIMMEL, C. B. (1966). The response of lysosomes in the chick embryo spleen in the graft versus host reaction. *In* "Ontogeny of Immunity" (R. T. Smith, R. Good, and P. Miescher, eds.), Univ. of Florida Press, Gainesville, Florida. In press.

KIRK, D. L. (1965). The role of RNA synthesis in the production of glutamine synthetase by the developing chick neural retina. *Proc. Natl. Acad. Sci. U.S.* **54**, 1345–1353.

KOCHER-BECKER, U., TIEDEMANN, H., AND TIEDEMANN, H. (1965). Exovagination of newt ectoderm: Cell affinities altered by the mesodermal inducing factor. *Science* **147**, 167–169.

KONIGSBERG, I. R. (1963). Clonal analysis of myogenesis. *Science* **140**, 1273–1284.

KONIGSBERG, I. R., AND HAUSCHKA, S. D. (1965). Cell and tissue interactions in the reproduction of cell type. *In* "Reproduction: Molecular, Subcellular, and Cellular" (M. Locke, ed.), pp. 243–290. Academic Press, New York.

KONIGSBERG, I. R., McELVAIN, N., TOOTLE, M., AND HERRMANN, H. (1960). The dissociability of deoxyribonucleic acid synthesis from the development of multinuclearity of muscle cells in culture. *J. Biophys. Biochem. Cytol.* **8**, 333–343.

LASH, J. W. (1963) . Tissue interaction and specific metabolic responses: Chondrogenic induction and differentiation *In* "Cytodifferentiation and Macromolecular Synthesis" (M. Locke, ed.) , pp. 235–260. Academic Press, New York.

LAUFER, H. (1965) . Developmental studies of the dipteran salivary gland. III. Relationships between chromosomal puffing and cellular function during development. *In* "Developmental and Metabolic Control Mechanisms and Neoplasia," pp. 237–250. Williams & Wilkins, Baltimore, Maryland.

LEBLOND, C. P. (1964) . Classification of cell populations on the basis of their proliferative behavior. *Natl. Cancer Inst. Monograph* **14**, 119–150.

LEDERBERG, J. (1959) . Genes and antibodies. *Science* **129**, 1649–1653.

LEE, H. H., KAIGHN, M. E., AND EBERT, J. D. (1966) . Viral antigens in differentiating muscle colonies after infection with Rous sarcoma virus *in vitro*. *Proc. Natl. Acad. Sci. U.S.* **56**, 521–525.

LYON, M. F. (1961) . Gene action in the X-chromosome of the mouse (*Mus musculus* L.) . *Nature* **190**, 372–373.

McCARTHY, B. J., AND HOYER, B. H. (1964) . Identity of DNA and diversity of messenger RNA molecules in normal mouse tissues. *Proc. Natl. Acad. Sci. U.S.* **52**, 915–922.

MACH, B., AND VASSALLI, P. (1965) . Biosynthesis of RNA in antibody-producing tissues. *Proc. Natl. Acad. Sci. U.S.* **54**, 975–982.

MACPHERSON, I., AND STOKER, M. (1962) . Polyoma transformation of hamster cell clones—an investigation of genetic factors affecting cell competence. *Virology* **16**, 147–151.

MAKINODAN, T., AND ALBRIGHT, J. F. (1962) . Cellular variation during the immune response: One possible model of cellular differentiation. *J. Cell. Comp. Physiol.* **60**, *Suppl.* 1, 129–144.

MAKINODAN, T., AND ALBRIGHT, J. F. (1963) . Cytokinetics of antibody response. *In* "Immunopathology" Proc. 3rd Intern. Symp., pp. 99–112. Benno Schwabe, Basel.

MAKINODAN, T., AND PETERSON, W. J. (1964) . Growth and senescence of the primary antibody-forming potential of the spleen. *J. Immunol.* **93**, 886–896.

MANAKER, R. A., AND GROUPÉ, V. (1956) . Discrete foci of altered chicken embryo cells associated with Rous sarcoma virus in tissue culture. *Virology* **2**, 838–840.

MARKS, E. P., AND REINECKE, J. P. (1964) . Cytoplasmic interaction between macrophages and lymphocytic cells in antibody synthesis. *Science* **143**, 964–965.

MATIOLI, G. T., AND NIEWISCH, H. B. (1965) . Electrophoresis of hemoglobin in single erythrocytes. *Science* **150**, 1824–1826.

MEDINA, D., AND SACHS, L. (1965) . A cause of variation in clonal morphology of polyoma transformed hamster cells. *Virology* **27**, 398–408.

MEKORI, T., CHIECO-BIANCI, L., AND FELDMAN, M. (1965) . Production of clones of lymphoid cell populations. *Nature* **206**, 367–368.

MELLORS, R. C., AND MUNROE, J. S. (1960) . Cellular localization of Rous sarcoma virus as studied with fluorescent antibody. *J. Exptl. Med.* **112**, 963–974.

METZ, C. W. (1938) . Chromosome behavior, inheritance and sex determination in *Sciara*. *Am. Naturalist* **72**, 485–520.

MILLER, O. L. (1964). Fine structure of lampbrush chromosomes. *J. Cell. Biol.* **23,** 109A.

MONOD, J., CHANGEAUX, J.-P., AND JACOB, F. (1963). Allosteric proteins and cellular control systems. *J. Mol. Biol.* **6,** 306–329.

MOORE, M. A. S., AND OWEN, J. J. T. (1965). Chromosome marker studies on the development of the haemopoietic system in the chick embryo. *Nature* **208,** 956, 989–990.

MUELLER, G. C., AND KAJIWARA, K. (1965). Regulatory steps in the replication of mammalian cell nuclei. *In* "Developmental and Metabolic Control Mechanisms and Neoplasia," pp. 452–474. Williams & Wilkins, Baltimore, Maryland.

MUN, A. M., TARDENT, P., ERRICO, J., EBERT, J. D., DELANNEY, L., ARGYRIS, T. S. (1962). An analysis of the initial reaction in the sequence resulting in homologous splenomegaly in the chick embryo. *Biol. Bull.* **123,** 366–387.

NAKANO, M., AND BRAUN, W. (1966). Fluctuation tests with antibody-forming spleen-cell populations. *Science* **151,** 338–340.

NISONOFF, A., AND INMAN, F. P. (1965). Structural basis of the specificity of antibodies. *In* "Reproduction: Molecular, Subcellular, and Cellular" (M. Locke. ed.), pp. 39–64. Academic Press, New York.

NIU, M. C. (1964a). Mode of action of the exogenous ribonucleic acid in cell function. *Natl. Cancer Inst. Monograph* **13,** 167–177.

NIU, M. C. (1964b). RNA-induced changes in cells and embryos. *In* "Acidi Nucleici e Loro Funzione Biologica," pp. 352–371. Baselli, Milan.

NOSSAL, G. V. J., AUSTIN, C. M., AND ADA, G. L. (1965). Antigens in immunity. VII. Analysis of immunological memory. *Immunology* **9,** 333–348.

OKAZAKI, K., AND HOLTZER, H. (1965). An analysis of myogenesis *in vitro* using fluorescein-labeled antimyosin. *J. Histochem. Cytochem.* **13,** 726–739.

PALM, L. (1965). "Isoantigens and Cell Interactions." Wistar Inst. Press, Philadelphia, Pennsylvania.

PAVAN, C. (1965). Nucleic acid metabolism in polytene chromosomes and the problem of differentiation. *In* "Genetic Control of Differentiation," pp. 222–241. Brookhaven Natl. Lab., Upton, New York.

PERKINS, E. H., AND MAKINODAN, T. (1964). Relative pool size of potentially competent antibody-forming cells of primed and nonprimed spleen cells grown in *in vivo* culture. *J. Immunol.* **92,** 192–200.

PERNIS, B., CHIAPPINO, G., KELUS, A. S., AND GELL, P. G. H. (1965). Cellular localization of immunoglobulins with different allotypic specificities in rabbit lymphoid tissues. *J. Exptl. Med.* **122,** 853–876.

PLAYFAIR, J. H. L., PAPERMASTER, B. W., AND COLE, L. J. (1965). Focal antibody production by transferred spleen cells in irradiated mice. *Science* **149,** 998–1000.

PUCK, T. T., MARCUS, P. I., AND CIECIURA, S. J. (1956). Clonal growth of mammalian cells *in vitro*. Growth characteristics of colonies from single HeLa cells with and without a "feeder layer." *J. Exptl. Med.* **103,** 273–284.

PUTNAM, F. W., AND EASLEY, C. W. (1965). Structural studies of the immunoglobulins. I. The tryptic peptides of Bence-Jones proteins. *J. Biol. Chem.* **240,** 1626–1638.

RAPOLA, J., VAINIO, T., AND SAXEN, L. (1963). Viral susceptibility and embryonic differentiation. IV. An attempt to correlate viral susceptibility with the metabolism and proliferation in embryonic tissues. *J. Embryol. Exptl. Morphol.* **11,** 757–764.

RITOSSA, F. M., AND SPIEGELMAN, S. (1965). Localization of DNA complementary to ribosomal RNA in the nucleolus organizer region of *Drosophila melanogaster*. *Proc. Natl. Acad. Sci. U.S.* **53**, 737–745.

ROIZMAN, B. (1961). Virus infection of cells in mitosis. I. Observations on the recruitment of cells in karyokinesis into giant cells induced by herpes simplex virus and bearing on the site of virus antigen formation. *Virology* **13**, 387–401.

ROIZMAN, B., AND SCHLUEDERBERG, A. E. (1961). Virus infection of cells in mitosis. II. Measles virus infection of mitotic HEp-2 cells. *Proc. Soc. Exptl. Biol. Med.* **106**, 320–323.

RUBIN, H. (1956). An analysis of the apparent neutralization of the Rous sarcoma virus with antiserum to normal chick tissues. *Virology* **2**, 545–558.

RUBIN, H. (1961). Influence of tumor virus infection on the antigenicity and behavior of cells. *Cancer Res.* **21**, 1244–1253.

RUBIN, H., AND VOGT, P. K. (1962). An avian leukosis virus associated with stocks of Rous sarcoma virus. *Virology* **17**, 184–194.

RUDKIN, G. T., AND SCHULTZ, J. (1961). Disproportionate synthesis of DNA in polytene chromosome regions in *Drosophila melanogaster*. *Genetics* **46**, 893–894.

RUSSELL, L. B. (1964). Genetic and functional mosaicism in the mouse. *In* "The Role of Chromosomes in Development" (M. Locke, ed.), pp. 153–181. Academic Press, New York.

SACHS, L., AND MEDINA, D. (1961). *In vitro* transformation of normal cells by polyoma virus. *Nature* **189**, 457–458.

SACHS, L., MEDINA, D., AND BERWALD, Y. (1962). Cell transformation by polyoma virus in clones of hamster and mouse cells. *Virology* **17**, 491–493.

SADO, T., AND MAKINODAN, T. (1964). The cell cycle of blast cells involved in secondary antibody response. *J. Immunol.* **93**, 696–700.

SAXEN, L., VAINIO, T., AND TOIVONEN, S. (1963). Viral susceptibility and embryonic differentiation. I. The histopathology of mouse kidney rudiments infected with polyoma and vesicular stomatitis viruses *in vitro*. *Acta Pathol. Microbiol. Scand.* **58**, 191–204.

SCHIFF, J. A., AND EPSTEIN, H. T. (1965). The continuity of the chloroplast in *Euglena*. In "Reproduction: Molecular, Subcellular, and Cellular" (M. Locke, ed.), pp. 131–189. Academic Press, New York.

SCHULTZ, J. (1965). Genes, differentiation and animal development. *In* "Genetic Control of Differentiation," pp. 116–147. Brookhaven Natl. Lab., Upton, New York.

SILVERSTEIN, A. (1964). Ontogeny of the immune response. *Science* **144**, 1423–1428.

SMALL, P. A., JR., REISFELD, R. A., AND DRAY, S. (1966). Peptide maps of rabbit γG-immunoglobulin heavy chains controlled by allelic genes. *J. Mol. Biol.* **16**, 328–333.

SMITH, L. D. (1965). Transplantation of the nucleic of primordial germ cells into the enucleated eggs of *Rana pipiens*. *Proc. Natl. Acad. Sci. U.S.* **54**, 101–107.

SMITH, R. T., GOOD, R., AND MISCHER, P. (1966). "Ontogeny of Immunity," Univ. of Florida Press, Gainesville, Florida. In press.

SONNEBORN, T. M. (1960). The gene and cell differentiation. *Proc. Natl. Acad. Sci. U.S.* **46**, 149–165.

SONNEBORN, T. M. (1963). Does preformed cell structure play an essential role in cell heredity? In "The Nature of Biological Diversity" (J. M. Allen, ed.), pp. 165-221. McGraw-Hill, New York.

SONNEBORN, T. M. (1964). The differentiation of cells. *Proc. Natl. Acad. Sci. U.S.* **51**, 915-929.

SRB, A. M. (1965). Extrachromosomal heredity in fungi. In "Reproduction: Molecular, Subcellular, and Cellular" (M. Locke, ed.), pp. 191-216. Academic Press, New York.

STANNERS, C. P., TILL, J. E., AND SIMINOVITCH, L. (1963). Studies on the transformation of hamster embryo cells in culture by polyoma virus. I. Properties of transformed and normal cells. *Virology* **21**, 448-463.

STENT, G. S. (1964). The operon: on its third anniversary. *Science* **144**, 816-820.

STEWARD, F. C., MAPES, M. O., KENT, A. E., AND HOLSTEN, R. D. (1964). Growth and development of cultured plant cells. *Science* **143**, 20-27.

STOCKDALE, F., AND HOLTZER, H. (1961). DNA synthesis and myogenesis. *Exptl. Cell Res.* **24**, 508-520.

STOKER, M., AND ABEL, P. (1962). Conditions affecting transformation by polyoma virus. *Cold Spring Harbor Symp. Quant. Biol.* **27**, 375-386.

STOKER, M., AND MACPHERSON, I. (1961). Studies on transformation of hamster cells by polyoma virus *in vitro*. *Virology* **14**, 359-370.

SZILARD, L. (1960). The molecular basis of antibody formation. *Proc. Natl. Acad. Sci. U.S.* **46**, 293-302.

TAKATA, C., ALBRIGHT, J. F., AND YAMADA, T. (1965). Lens fiber differentiation and gamma crystallins: Immunofluorescent study of Wolffian regeneration. *Science* **147**, 1299-1301.

TEMIN, H. M. (1962). Separation of morphological conversion and virus production in Rous sarcoma virus infection. *Cold Spring Harbor Symp. Quant. Biol.* **27**, 407-414.

TEMIN, H. M. (1965). The mechanism of carcinogenesis by avian sarcoma viruses. I. Cell multiplication and differentiation. *J. Natl. Cancer Inst.* **35**, 679-692.

TEMIN, H. M., AND RUBIN, H. (1958). Characteristics of an assay for Rous sarcoma virus and Rous sarcoma cells in tissue culture. *Virology* **6**, 669-688.

TODARO, G. J., AND GREEN, H. (1966). Cell growth and the initiation of transformation by SV 40. *Proc. Natl. Acad. Sci. U.S.* **55**, 302-308.

TRAGER, G. W., AND RUBIN, H. (1964). Quantitative studies on cell transformation following infection with Rous sarcoma virus. *Natl. Cancer Inst. Monograph* **17**, 575-585.

URSO, P., AND MAKINODAN, T. (1963). The roles of cellular division and maturation in the formation of precipitating antibody. *J. Immunol.* **90**, 897-907.

VAINIO, T., SAXEN, L., AND TOIVONEN, S. (1963a). Viral susceptibility and embryonic differentiation. II. Immunofluorescence studies of viral infection in the developing mouse kidney *in vitro*. *Acta Pathol. Microbiol. Scand.* **58**, 205-211.

VAINIO, T., SAXEN, L., AND TOIVONEN, S. (1963b). Viral susceptibility and embryonic differentiation. III. Correlation between an inductive tissue interaction and the onset of viral resistance. *J. Natl. Cancer Inst.* **31**, 1533-1547.

VASIL, V., AND HILDEBRANDT, A. C. (1965). Differentiation of tobacco plants from single, isolated cells in microcultures. *Science* **150**, 889-892.

VOGT, M., AND DULBECCO, R. (1960). Virus-cell interaction with a tumor-producing virus. *Proc. Natl. Acad. Sci. U.S.* **46**, 365–370.

VOGT, M., AND DULBECCO, R. (1963). Steps in the neoplastic transformation of hamster embryo cells by polyoma virus. *Proc. Natl. Acad. Sci. U.S.* **49**, 171–179.

VOGT, M., DULBECCO, R., AND SMITH, B. (1966). Induction of cellular DNA synthesis by polyoma virus. III. Induction in productively infected cells. *Proc. Natl. Acad. Sci. U.S.* **55**, 956–960.

VOGT, P. K., AND RUBIN, H. (1961). Localization of infectious virus and viral antigen in chick fibroblasts during successive stages of infection with Rous sarcoma virus. *Virology* **13**, 528–544.

WADDINGTON, C. H. (1966). Mendel and the study of development. *Proc. Roy. Soc. (London)* **B164**, 219–229.

WEBER, C., AND BROWN, D. D. (1966). Studies on the genetic linkage of ribsomal and soluble RNA's. *Carnegie Inst. Wash , Yearbook* **65** (in press).

WEIL, R., MICHEL, M., AND RUSCHMANN, G. K. (1965). Induction of cellular DNA synthesis by polyoma virus. *Proc. Natl. Acad. Sci. U.S.* **53**, 1468–1475.

WEILER, E. (1965). Differential activity of the allelic gamma-globulin genes in anti-body-producing cells. *Proc. Natl. Acad. Sci. U.S.* **54**, 1765–1771.

WEILER, E., MELLETZ, E. W., AND BREUNINGER-PECK, E. (1965). Facilitation of immune hemolysis by an interaction between red cell-sensitizing antibody and gamma-globulin allotype antibody. *Proc. Natl. Acad. Sci. U.S.* **54**, 1310–1317.

WESSELLS, N. K. (1965). Morphology and proliferation during early feather development. *Develop. Biol.* **12**, 131–153.

WESSELLS, N. K., AND ROESSNER, K. D. (1965). Nonproliferation in dermal condensations of mouse vibrissae and pelage hairs. *Develop. Biol.* **12**, 419–433.

WESSELLS, N. K., AND WILT, F. H. (1965). Action of actinomycin D on exocrine pancreas cell differentiation. *J. Mol. Biol.* **13**, 767–799.

WILT, F. H. (1965). Regulation of the initiation of chick embryo hemoglobin synthesis. *J. Mol. Biol.* **12**, 331–341.

WINOCOUR, E., KAYE, A. M., AND STOLLAR, V. (1965). Synthesis and transmethylation of DNA in polyoma-infected cultures. *Virology* **27**, 156–169.

Dynamics of Determination*,†

ERNST HADORN

Zoologisch-vergleichend anatomisches Institut der Universität Zürich, Zürich, Switzerland

Determination can be defined as "a process which initiates a specific pathway of development by singling it out from among various possibilities for which a cellular system is competent" (Hadorn, 1965). It is not the aim of the following contribution to review and evaluate all aspects involved in such a concept of determination. Thus, I shall refrain from discussing the mechanisms of embryonic induction through which blastemas become differently determined. Nor shall I consider all the classic work on mosaic eggs which showed that during cleavage blastomeres become differently endowed and thus determined by pre-existing cytoplasmic constituents.

Rather, I shall limit this discussion mainly to cell systems of insects which have been already determined during embryogenesis, and I will ask among others the following questions: What kind of characteristics are fixed in such a state and to what extent is determination irreversible or open to change? The reason for avoiding a direct approach to the determining process itself at the outset is obvious: We want to escape from all the well-known difficulties. Although determination has been under investigation for more than half a century no real and definite insight into its initiating phase has been gained. We still ignore what happens inside a cell when it enters one pathway of development or another. We know neither the immediate effectors of the determining decision nor the primary carriers of a newly established state of determination. In such a situation it would be well to try to analyze the dynamic properties of a determined system. Thereby, we hope to obtain some indirect information about the preceding processes which have led to the cellular state under investigation.

The imaginal disks present in larvae of holometabolic insects, such

* Dedicated to Karl von Frisch on his eightieth birthday.
† Research supported by the Schweizerische Nationalfonds zur Förderung der wissenschaftlichen Forschung.

as *Drosophila,* have proven to be suitable objects for such an approach. We found that these disks contain a mosaic of many neighboring cell districts of which each is determined for the formation of different adult organs or body parts. When, for instance, fragments of a male genital disk taken from a fully grown larva are isolated and implanted into the body cavity of a metamorphosing host, only those parts of the genital apparatus become differentiated for which the isolated blastema had been specifically determined (Hadorn *et al.,* 1949). Thus, from central parts only sperm pumps and *ductus ejaculatorius* arise, and from certain lateral districts only anal plates. Likewise, fragments of wing disks will differentiate into patterns typical for the wing border, while other blastemas furnish the central area of the wing (Hadorn and Buck, 1962). The mosaic determination within a disk is moreover revealed by irradiation experiments (Ursprung, 1959; Nöthiger and Schubiger, 1966). Districts of determined cells can be killed by localized ultraviolet beams. This will result in the development of a genital apparatus from which certain elements such as anal plates, claspers, or penis parts are missing.

At this point we should ask a question of general importance. What carries such a specific determination? Is it a territory, a metabolic gradient, a prepattern (cf. Stern, 1965) or an embryonic field to which the individual cells are subordinated in such a way that they differentiate according to the supercellular system to which they happen to belong? Or are the different blastemas composed of cells each of which is specifically and individually determined? The decision between these two possibilties is important for the discussion I will present and interpret later.

The imaginal disks of *Drosophila* larvae provide a unique opportunity for investigation of this problem. We can disintegrate the blastemas and mix cells from differently determined districts of a disk, or cells from disks of different body segments, different sexes, or different species. Genes such as *yellow, ebony,* and *multiple wing hairs* are available for marking the cells in such mixtures (Hadorn *et al.,* 1959; Ursprung and Hadorn, 1962; Nöthiger, 1964; Garcia-Bellido, 1966). After aggregation the combinations are implanted into metamorphosing hosts. Here the cells are forced to differentiate into adult structures. Since bristles and hairs (trichomes) are unicellular products we can easily follow the developmental performance of each individual cell.

From the results so far obtained, we concluded that all cells are individually and differently determined. In no case did a cell from a wing disk cooperate in the formation of any structure of the genital apparatus (Nöthiger, 1964). Even in the most intimately mixed aggregates the different partners move apart and cells of the same region-specific type join, so that wing and genital structures differentiate separately side by side. A similar dissociation was observed in wing-leg mixtures (H. Tobler, unpublished). Cellular determination is not only fixed with respect to such rather general characteristics as "wingness" or "legness," however. Determination is also established with respect to the specific regions of a wing or leg.

Thus, cells from the distal part of a wing disk did not cooperate in the formation of patterns normally produced by more proximal wing blastemas (Garcia-Bellido, 1966). Again the mixed partners segregated before they differentiated separately into the regions for which they had been determined.

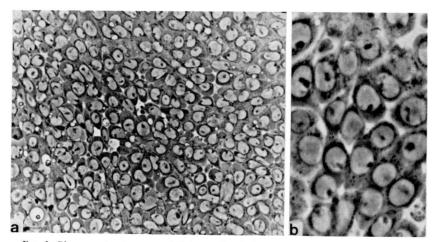

Fig. 1. Phase contrast aspect of living cells of the general type present in imaginal disks and in the permanent cultures. From P. Remensberger (unpublished). Magnification: a, 420×; b, 1000×.

Cells of the differently determined blastemas with which the mixtures were made are morphologically indistinguishable. They contain large nuclei each having a conspicuous nucleolus. There is relatively little cytoplasm (Fig. 1). The fact that cells in a blastema look equal might further indicate that they have all reached the same general level of determination. We have not studied the cytology of all our lines, but there is certainly no indication for the presence of some "more embryonic" interstitial cells which would not have been determined yet. The morphological aspect accords with the experimental results. We can exclude the existence of such "I cells."

Determination, as it occurs in the mosaic districts of the imaginal disks, involves alternatively at least such diverse regional properties as anal plates, claspers, or penis parts in genital anlagen, coxa, tibia, or tarsus in a leg disk, and different regions of the wing border or the central area of the wing. Within these regional blastemas there is no indication that I cells are present.

Each of these regions is further characterized by its own more specific pattern, however. In a limited area of the anterior wing border we find, for instance, three rows of differently shaped bristles which are arranged at definite distances (Hadorn *et al.,* 1959). When and how do the different cells of the border blastema become determined for their

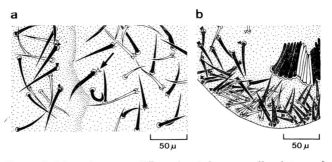

a   b

| 50 μ | 50 μ |

Fɪɢ. 2. Parts of chimaeric tarsus differentiated from a cell mixture of a *yellow* leg disk (light structures) and an *ebony* leg disk (dark structures). a: The arrow points to a chimaeric bristle-bract combination. b: Chimaeric sex comb. From H. Tobler (unpublished).

ultimate role within the region-specific pattern? Our mixtures provided no definite answer. We only know that cells determined for the triple row area find each other and are then able to cooperate in forming an integrated pattern. The same holds true for the blastema of the basitarsus. When cells of different leg disks are mixed, a chimaeric sex comb can be formed (Fig. 2b). We might again ask whether the final characteristic "sex comb cell" or the prefinal property "sex comb area" has been determined in the larval disk. The information gained from cell mixtures and even more so from the differentiating performance of the test fragments taken from permanently cultured blastemas (Hadorn, 1966) favors the concept of a "prefinal" regional determination. This means that the final role of each cell within a region-specific pattern would be determined after pupation at the very last moment, that is, immediately before adult differentiation begins. Cellular interaction of short range could govern the patterning.

We have at least one direct observation which supports this interpretation. Our collaborators H. Tobler (unpublished) and Garcia-Bellido (1966) intermingled leg primordia of *yellow* with *ebony* genotypes. They found that the cells determined for tibia or tarsus joined their fellows and cooperated in differentiating the respective leg segments (Fig. 2). In this body region the majority of the bristles are accompanied by short cuticular protuberances known as bracts. In some cases *yellow* bristles become paired with *ebony* bracts or vice versa (Fig. 2a). From this result it follows first that the "bristle bract tandem" cannot have arisen from a late-occurring differential mitosis of a common ancestral cell. We therefore consider these chimaeric pairs cases of induction. The epidermal cells of tibia and tarsus would be capable of reacting to the inductive and determining influence emanating from a bristle organ. As a matter of fact, we have never observed isolated bracts.

These findings on the bract-bristle dependence are of general interest because to my knowledge, this seems to be the first case in insects in which a pattern element has been shown to come into existence through an induction by neighboring elements. Moreover, the chimaeric bristle-bract pairing suggests a further generalization. Determination is revealed as a process which passes from a more general prefinal to a most specific final cellular state.

The prefinal state in which region-specific pathways leading to basitarsus, tibia, or coxa are determined could also have been established in a stepwise manner by passing through at least three stages or grades of specificity. A first decision must occur early in embryogenesis when some cells in the blastoderm become determined for immediate differentiation into larval organs, whereas other groups of cells are set apart for the various imaginal disks in which differentiation is repressed until metamorphosis (Hadorn, 1965). A second decision, later on, could involve differences between the diverse disks, and a third determining step might fix the properties of the different regional blastemas within a disk. We must confess that no direct experimental evidence is available which would prove that such a sequential determination leading from generality to specificity really occurs. It might well be that the first event which separates the imaginal cells could directly decide between disk-specific pathways, and even the different blastemas within a disk could be determined without passing through some more general preceding stages.

A *Drosophila* embryo can be treated 3 hours after fertilization with ether. In this early stage the future disk cells are still invisibly incorporated within a blastoderm of homogenous appearance. From such an experiment, flies of the *tetraptera* or *bithorax* type (Gloor, 1947) result. Apparently the cells which normally enter the metathoracic pathway become pushed into the pathway of another disk. We infer from this result that disk-specific characteristics must be determined even before the respective cell groups become visibly separated.

Later we shall consider the dynamics of determination as the result of differential gene activity. The concept of a stepwise determination would therefore imply the sequential engagement, first of the genes which control the most general properties, then the genes dealing with the determination of more and more specific events. Although such a system might be inferred from the phase-specific action of lethal factors (Hadorn, 1961), we hardly have any direct evidence on which a gene-conditioned sequential determination could be based. We should therefore leave open the question of the extent to which a first determining switch might already decide between region-specific pathways.

My colleagues working on vertebrate systems encountered the same problems and difficulties (cf. Waddington, 1962). Is a determined state which is typical only of the general characteristic "nervous system" ever in existence? Or is it that the regional qualities for different parts of the brain and the spinal cord are already established from the very beginning of induction? I do not believe that we have really escaped from this dilemma.

In many well-known developmental systems the cellular states of determination are immediately followed by specific differentiation; this is not true for the imaginal disks of insects, however. Here the cells remain undifferentiated throughout larval life. Their early fixed developmental program is held back and played through only after the onset of pupal metamorphosis. Before this performance the cells of the blastemas present in a disk divide, and we know that their determined properties are thereby maintained and passed over to all their daughter cells by cell heredity.

Now we are prepared to discuss experiments which will not only show us the phenomenon of stable replication of a determined state but also the changing hazards of cell heredity.

During the last four years we have succeeded in keeping cell populations derived from imaginal disks of fully grown larvae of *Drosophila* in permanent cultures (Hadorn, 1963, 1964, 1966). The determined blastemas are implanted into the abdomens of adult flies. The cells would normally have stopped dividing in the prepupae, but in this medium they proliferate continuously, and never differentiate into adult

structures. The omission of the pupal stage makes it possible to inter-
rupt development between determination and differentiation for various
long periods. When fragments of the cultures are transplanted back
into larvae which enter metamorphosis, such test pieces differentiate
normally into all those adult structures and organs for which they carry
a determination. Thus, our method allows us to test at any desired
moment the state of determination and the competence for differentiation present in permanently reproducing cell populations. The details
of this procedure have recently been fully described (Hadorn, 1966).

Among the various results we obtained, two phenomena have a direct
bearing on the topic of our present discussion. First, we found that a
proliferating blastema, which originally was determined for anal plates,
claspers, paragonia, or any other elements of the genital complex, will
furnish test pieces which differentiate into normal anal plates, etc. This
capacity can remain unchanged even after years of culturing, involving
passage through hundreds of cell generations. We conclude from these
results that the initial state of determination is either replicated or
newly re-established in each cell generation. Such an "autotypic" differentiation corresponds to the original prospective significance of the
determined cells. It is guided by an unchanging cell heredity.

In addition to this conservative behavior we observe regularly that in
parts of the cultures the state of determination becomes changed. Thus,
cells which were autotypically determined for anal plates or *ductus
ejaculatorius* can deliver blastemas which differentiate into head parts,
legs, or wings. Such "allotypic" differentiations are based on a newly
established state of determination which can also be propagated by its
own cell heredity. We call the process which leads from one type of
determination to another one transdetermination (Hadorn, 1965).

Let us first follow the sequence of determination and differentiation
in two lines which have been in culture for 3 years and 9 months (Fig.
3a,b). The cultures stand today (June 1966) in their ninety-seventh
transfer generation (Trg). Many hundreds of test implants (total of *n*)
furnish ample information with regard to all types of region-specific
differentiations.

Both lines were started with half a male genital disk which originally
contained all the blastemas for the various parts of the genital apparatus and the last abdominal segments. Among these autotypic elements
we will follow only the fate of the anal plate primordia (An). In both
lines all test implants at first furnish anal plates (100%). This state
of determination is then replicated in line *a* until Trg 70, whereas in

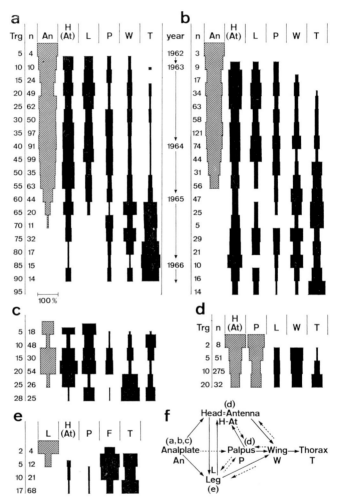

FIG. 3. Frequency and sequence of auto- and allotypic differentiations in test implants derived from various culture lines which were started with imaginal disks of
Drosophila melanogaster. Trg, transfer generations (the results of several Trg are
assembled as a group) ; n, number of test implants in each group of Trg; An, anal
plates; H (At), head structures (mainly antennal) ; L, leg parts; P, palpus; W, wing;
T, thorax. The blocks indicate the percentage of implants which differentiated into
one or the other autotypic (hatched) or allotypic structures (black). Scale of 100%
is given in a; a and b: male genital lines; c: female genital lines; d: antennal disk
lines; e: leg lines; f: scheme of transdetermination (cf. Hadorn, 1966) ; the starting
points of the different lines are indicated in brackets.

line *b* the anal plates disappear after Trg 55. The first allotypic structures are observed between Trg 6 and 10. Head parts (mainly antennae), legs, and palpus appear at about the same time and with similar frequencies. Wing blastemas are observed either later (*b*), or earlier, in only one among 10 test implants (*a*). Thorax is the last appearing allotypic differentiation. We observed it for the first time in just one implant at Trg 10 in line *a* and in Trg 19 in line *b*. In both lines the wing and the thorax blastemas later become more frequent. This increase was more excessive, however, for thorax than for wing.

From the distribution and association of all auto- and allotypic structures along the time axis of culturing observed in many lines and sublines, we concluded that transdetermination follows distinct sequences. A tentative scheme of transdetermination was therefore derived. It is shown in Fig. 3f. The facts on which it is based are fully documented in a recent publication (Hadorn, 1966). From autotypic anal plate blastemas, transdetermination of a first order leads to head (mainly antennae) or leg blastemas with about the same probability. There also seems to be a direct route in the direction of palpus. These new states of determination, once established, are further propagated by cell heredity over many transfer generations. From these three primordia we also observe offspring which become transdetermined further into wing anlagen (second order). Again the wing blastemas are partly maintained conservatively by cell heredity, and are partly transdetermined further into thorax primordia (third order). While some of the changing events proved to be reversible, according to our data so far, we are confident that the last, that is the thorax state, becomes replicated without further changes. As a whole, our scheme might explain why we eventually lose the starting anal plate blastema while the thorax end station becomes more and more frequent.

A corresponding sequence was found by G. Mindek (unpublished) who started a parallel experiment with female genital disks (Fig. 3c). In the first four transfer generations head and leg parts appear as allotypic structures. Wing and thorax arise only later. As in the lines of male disks, the anal plates also become lost, whereas wing and thorax reach high frequencies.

We might now ask what happens if we step into the sequential train at some later station. Gehring (1966) followed cultures which were founded with primordia of the antennal disk (Fig. 1d). Primordia from the first two transfer generations differentiated only into autotypic head (antennae) and palpus. In Trg 3 some allotypic leg and wing structures already appear. Moreover even thorax was traced in a few test implants. Its frequency increases, in accordance with our scheme, in the later transfer generations. Corresponding results were obtained on leg disks by G. Schubiger (unpublished, Fig. 3e). Again an increase in allotypic thorax appears in his lines. On the other hand, we see how the autotypic leg blastemas are lost rather early.

Only further experiments will show whether or not the directions and sequences of transdetermination as they are represented in Fig. 1f fully and correctly reflect the dynamics which are inherent as latent properties in already determined blastemas.

Before we discuss the possible events involved in transdetermination we should again stress the fact that our cultures are founded with blastemas within which each cell is specifically determined. It was shown that this is an unavoidable conclusion derived from the mixing experiments. One might nevertheless criticize our method because we started not with a single determined cell but rather with a whole blastema. Unfortunately we cannot make an isolated disk cell grow in the adult abdomen. Implants which do contain less than 100 cells cannot be recovered; apparently they are not able to maintain the metabolic equilibrium necessary for growth.

Our collaborator Dr. W. Gehring (unpublished), however, found a way to overcome this difficulty (Fig. 4). He irradiated young female larvae which are heterozygous for *yellow* (*y*) and *singed* (*sn*) at the age of 48 hours. This treatment can lead to the loss of one of the X chromosomes or to somatic crossing-over. In both cases single cells are obtained which have lost the + alleles. Such a cell will multiply during larval growth and constitute a mosaic area which is hemi- or homozygous for *y* and (or) *sn*. Irradiated disks are then dissected from 100-hour larvae and implanted into adult hosts. Here the blastemas increase by further cell division and thereby transdetermination does occur.

In test implants derived from such cultures the following categories of differentiation are met: (1) Autotypic structures such as antennae and maxillary palpus which show the wild phenotype. (2) Autotypic structures which are yellow and carry singed bristles. They must have stemmed from a "mutated" cell. In Fig. 4 a section of this type is shown which participates in forming an autotypic palpus. (3) Allotypic structures of the wild type which are of no interest in the present context. (4) Allotypic structures of the *y sn* genotype. Both wings (Fig. 4), leg parts, and later, thorax were observed. From the overall frequency with which the somatic elimination or crossing-over occurs it can be calculated that all y sn structures of a line stem from a single cell. It is thus proved that transdetermination to diverse blastemas can occur even in a clone initiated by a single determined cell.

We now ask what kind of external or internal conditions might initiate transdetermination in the cultured blastemas. First, we can exclude the adult medium as the causative agent. It was found that transdetermination occurs in larval hosts as well when fragments of disks are transplanted into younger larvae so that they can proliferate for a cer-

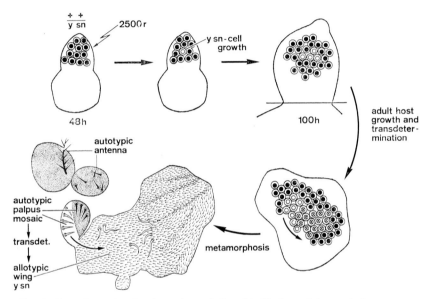

FIG. 4. Transdetermination in a clone. Cells with black nuclei are of the $++/y$ sn genotype. Cells with light nuclei are hemi- or homozygous for y sn. A cross indicates the transdetermined offspring within the y sn clone. As an example, a differentiated test implant is shown with auto- and allotypic structures, as explained in the text. After W. Gehring (unpublished).

tain time (Hadorn, 1963). Thus, we consider the adult hemolymph a neutral medium which just sustains and promotes growth.

Moreover, experience lets us assume that the state of determination does not change in a nondividing cell. The experimental evidence instead favors a concept according to which transdetermination occurs earlier or later in some of the dividing offspring of a determined cell population. Accordingly, the changes have been found to be dependent on the proliferating activity of a blastema (Gehring, 1966; Hadorn,

1966). Such a dependence has now been more directly analyzed by
H. Tobler (unpublished). He measured the growth rate of blastemas
which were cultured 4, 8, or 16 days in the adult abdomen. The different
fragments were then implanted into metamorphosing hosts. The rate
of transdetermination found was closely correlated with the rate of
proliferation (Fig. 5). However, the time during which a blastema re-

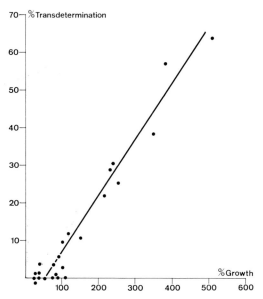

FIG. 5. Correlation between amount of growth and rate of transdetermination in
blastemas of leg and wing disk. From H. Tobler (unpublished).

mains exposed to the adult medium has no direct influence. This was
shown in the following experiments: In one series, genetically marked
leg and wing disks were intimately intermingled before they were cultured 16 days in an adult host. Such combined aggregates have a high
proliferation rate, and 53% of the test implants contained transdetermined areas. In the parallel series the two disks were first cultivated
separately for 16 days. Such intact disks grow relatively little. Only after
this culture time were the disks intermixed in the same way as in the
first experiment. The differentiation test showed transdetermined sectors
in only 3% of the combining blastemas.

    In accordance with all the available evidence we interpret transdeter-
mination as a process which is causally related to the dynamics of cell

proliferation. The following theoretical speculations are based on this concept.

We have seen that blastemas reproduce their state of determination without change over hundreds of cell generations. Similar systems are known in vertebrates in which, for instance, the cells in the *stratum germinativum* of the epidermis, or the stem cells of the bone marrow, maintain and reproduce their specific determination throughout life. On what conditions might such steady states be based? As indicated in Fig. 6 we propose a distinction between effectors of determination (E) and carriers of determination (C). The effectors correspond to Waddington's genotropic substances (1962). We might therefore call them genotropic effectors. Their specific nature is not known in any determining system of a higher organism. Small molecules, even ions, hormones, or any cytoplasmic or nuclear constituents could act as effectors. The genotropic effectors are considered to activate, to repress, or to derepress genes or gene teams (Fig. 6a).

We envisage any direct or remote products of gene activity which control a specific differentiation (D) as carriers of determination. Again we are embarrassed by our ignorance as to the nature of such carriers. mRNA, proteins, or other molecular species could play the carrier role.

When determined cells divide, the pre-existing carriers of determination become distributed to the daughter cells and thus diluted (black squares in Fig. 6). An unchanged state of determination can only be maintained if new carriers of the same quality are synthesized. Thus the rate of synthesis must compensate for dilution of the pre-existing carriers. New synthesis will also be necessary when the former carriers because of a short lifetime, are lost.

In our theoretical scheme the carriers are considered to influence their own synthesis through a feedback action on genotropic effectors. Thus, only a permanently supplemented population of carriers might guarantee the constancy of a gene-controlled state of determination. Unchanged cell heredity, as it is partly found in our lines, could only be maintained if the rate of cell division, on which the speed of dilution of pre-existing carriers depends, remains in equilibrium with the rate of synthesis of new carriers of the same type (Fig. 6a).

Figure 6b shows how such a steady equilibrium could become unbalanced. Here we assume a higher rate of cell division which, however, is not paralleled by an equally increased rate of carrier synthesis of the former type. The changed concentration of carriers could affect genotropic effectors in such a way that other gene systems come into action. A different population of carriers would then replace the former ones. Such a substitution results in transdetermination. The new state could now be propagated as long as the new rate of mitosis remains in equilibrium with the corresponding rate of new synthesis.

Such a scheme must of course remain to a large extent tentative and

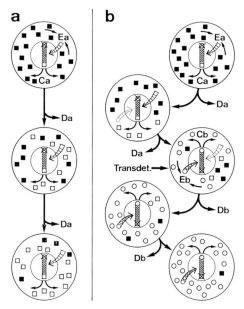

Fig. 6. Relation between rate of cell division and rate of synthesis of carriers of determination. a: Unchanged cell heredity. b: Dynamics leading to transdetermination. Ea,b, genotropic effectors; Ca,b, carriers of determination; Da,b, specific differentiation. Black squares, pre-existing carriers for a; light squares, newly synthesized carriers for a; Circles, carriers for the transdetermined state b. Within the nucleus two genes or gene teams are shown either active or repressed (cross).

hypothetical. We propose it nevertheless because it is in accordance with the well-established fact that transdetermination is correlated with the rate of cell proliferation. We have good reason to assume that in blastemas proliferation is different in distinct central or peripheral regions. Since no other external or internal factors which initiate transdetermination have been discovered thus far, we envisage a simple mechanism in which only such cell-intrinsic parameters as rates of division and changing concentrations of controlling and determining constituents are involved.

Moreover, I refrain from incorporating in our interpretation any further and more specific details which could be borrowed from molecular biology and microbial genetics. I wish, however, to call attention to a rather dubious passage in our dynamic scheme. Differentiation as a result of determination is always strictly alternative. This holds true also for the character-forming processes in transdetermined cell populations. The offspring of a genital blastema continue to form typical anal plates or they differentiate into completely normal parts of antennae, legs, or wings. No intergrades whatsoever between different structures have ever been observed.

We would like to know at what level this accuracy of alternative behavior becomes secured. Could the decision fall in the transcription phase in such a way that different populations of determining mRNA would always mutually exclude each other? Or are we right in assuming, as shown in Fig. 6b, that during a transitory phase genes for various alternative pathways can act side by side within the same cell?

It is true that changes at the transcription level are well known from operon systems in microorganisms, but these results are hardly of any help in our context because all information about bacteria is obtained from large populations and not from sequences of single cells. Furthermore, bacteria do not manifest the kind of alternative differentiation which occurs in multicellular creatures. We might therefore search for cases in plants and animals in which the presence of competing messengers has been found within the same cell.

Embryonic reticulocytes first synthesize foetal hemoglobin; later cell generations make the adult molecule. It has been claimed that during a transitory phase both hemoglobins are present in the same cell (Kleihauer *et al.*, 1957). If such a situation could also occur in blastemas which later differentiate alternatively, then the switching decision should not be placed at the transcription level. As a matter of fact Zetsche (1966), working with the unicellular alga *Acetabularia,* has most recently reported that rather long-lived competing messengers could exist side by side. He has shown how genes for stem and for hat formation produce their mRNA simultaneously. Although these carriers of alternative information are available at the same time, stem differentiation still begins first and only later on does the hat differentiate. Zetsche gives evidence that the control acts on the translation level. After such findings, a control of alternative pathways at any level remote from transcription should also be considered seriously as a possible mechanism acting in blastemas which are undergoing transdetermination. Once this perhaps short transitory phase is passed, however, only the new team of genes would be active in the synthesis of carriers of determination (Fig. 6b).

But are we certain that a whole "team of genes" is engaged when, for instance, the descendants of a leg blastema are transdetermined into a wing anlage? We need, certainly, specific carriers for coxa, tarsus, wing border, wing base, etc. There are dozens of genetic loci known in *Drosophila* controlling specific characters of differentiation either on legs or on wings. As mentioned above, transdetermination should therefore turn off all the leg genes and turn on all the wing genes. How could such a simple dynamic system as it is proposed in Fig. 6b control the action of so many different genes simultaneously? It would be of great help to the understanding of the phenomenon of transdetermination if all members of the gene team for legs would hang like cooperating puppets in a marionette theater on one and the same controlling wire. The cell state which initiates a transdetermination could act in such a system on only one controlling gene (cf. Gehring, 1966), and we would need only a few different dynamic states for the various transdetermining events which we have observed. Unfortunately, the existence of such controlling genes is not yet sufficiently established in multicellular organisms, unless homoiotic mutants are interpreted in this way.

In concluding this report I wish to confront what we have learned and derived from transdetermination, as it occurs in our cultures, with a few phenomena well known in genetics and experimental embryology. To begin with, there are the homoiotic mutants of *Drosophila*. Genes such as *aristapedia, proboscipedia* and *ophthalmopedia* act in parts of antennal, labial, or eye disks in such a way that differentiation becomes regionally diverted into the direction of tarsus and leg formation. Other allelic substitutions change the developmental fate of whole disks. Belonging to this type are the mutants of the famous *bithorax* complex locus studied and interpreted by Lewis (1964).

Both transdetermination and homoiotic mutants can lead to indistinguishable final results. Thus, a cultivated antennal blastema will earlier or later become transdetermined into a tarsus primordium (Gehring, 1966) and from proliferating labial disks some leg anlagen regularly develop (H. Wildermuth, unpublished). Such a correspondence is observed, although the starting situation is principally different. In mutants the genetic structure is changed, whereas transdetermination implies and requires only a change in gene activity. If, however, a gene of the *aristapedia* type acts by altering the normal autotypic rate of cell division within the growing antennal disc, then both switches toward an allotypic determination could be based on the same general principle: a change in equilibrium between the rate of cell division and the rate of synthesis.

Several of the homoiotic mutants have been phenocopied in wild-type systems. We have already mentioned that treatment with ether results in flies of the *tetraptera* or *bithorax* phenotype. Phenocopies of *aristapedia* were obtained with nitrogen mustard (Bodenstein and Abel-Malek, 1949), by sodium metaborate (Sang and McDonald, 1954), and with fluorouracil (Gehring, 1964). These findings corroborate the well-established fact that the most diverse agents can produce the same phenocopy (cf. Hadorn, 1961). Such a lack of specificity is to be expected if the applied agents interfere with some general cellular properties involved in rates of proliferation and rates of synthesis. On this assumption we have found a common basis for phenocopies and transdetermination. This correspondence becomes even more directly evident in an experiment of Vogt (1947). She treated *aristapedia* disks with colchicine and observed a shift of differentiation in favor of the arista. Waddington (1942) found that in *Drosophila* which had been X-rayed certain anlage systems reacted with an excessive proliferation. Consequently, he observed the differentiation of maxillary palpus in the eye region, of leg-like structures at the base of the antenna, and of "body skin" in the wing area. We interpret all these "transdeterminations" as the result of a change in the proliferation-synthesis dynamics.

Another experiment which strongly favors our concept of transdetermining mechanisms was just reported by Brändle and Schmidt (1964). In the moth *Plodia interpunctella* two main types of scales become differentiated on the wings. One type is found within two distinct cross bands, and the other covers the area between and outside the bands. After the localization of the future bands has been determined a different rate of mitosis is observed. It is retarded within the bands and speeded up outside the bands. If mitosis is locally stimulated by injection of kinetin, cells which are already determined for band scales now divide more rapidly and so become "transdetermined" into cells which will differentiate into scales characteristic of the areas outside the bands. The kinetin effect can be obtained only as long as the cells are still capable of dividing. It must therefore affect the proliferation dynamics and by doing so alters the state of determination.

Still another phenomenon directly related to transdetermination is occasionally met when adult arthropods regenerate certain body parts.

Amputated antennae can be replaced by legs, or eyes by antennae. A survey of the pertinent literature is given by Korschelt (1927). Again we can interpret such a homoiosis as the result of an allotypical rate of proliferation. It is rather obvious that in blastemas which grow out from an antennal stump, dynamic conditions might become effective similar to those in our cell cultures when transdeterminations from antennal toward leg primordia are initiated.

Finally, the dynamics of transdetermination, as we have encountered them in our cultures of *Drosophila* blastemas, should also be confronted with all of our knowledge of the mechanics which govern the initial determination in embryonic systems. Each egg cell contains populations of genotropic effectors and to a certain extent populations of preformed carriers also. Such carriers must be abundant in mosaic systems but scarce in eggs of the more regulative type. During cleavage these constituents become unevenly distributed to the various blastomeres. Such a segregation in space will lead to a wide variety of differing cellular states of determination. In already determined blastemas, which are, however, competent for transdetermining switchovers, a segregation in time reestablishes a new variety, possibly by means of different rates of proliferation and synthesis.

Further experiments will certainly modify and correct the theoretical scheme outlined in this report. We consider the present contribution merely an heuristic attempt which tries to collect various findings into a unifying developmental concept.

ACKNOWLEDGMENT

Many unpublished results are incorporated in this report. For these contributions I am grateful to my collaborators whose names are mentioned in the text.

REFERENCES

BODENSTEIN, D., AND ABEL-MALEK, A. (1949). The induction of aristopedia by nitrogen mustard in *Drosophila virilis. J. Exptl. Zool.* **111,** 95–115.

BRÄNDLE, K., AND SCHMIDT, K. (1964). Determination des Zeichnungsmusters von Plodia interpunctella (*Lepidopt.*) durch Entwicklungsverschiebung. *Z. Naturforsch.* **19**b, 759–763.

GARCIA-BELLIDO, A. (1966). Pattern reconstruction by dissociated imaginal disk cells of *Drosophila melanogaster. Develop. Biol.* (in press).

GEHRING, W. (1964). Phenocopies produced by 5-fluoro-uracil. *Drosophila Inform. Serv.* **39,** 102.

GEHRING, W. (1966). Uebertragung und Aenderung der Determinationsqualitäten in Antennenscheiben-Kulturen von *Drosophila melanogaster. J. Embryol. Exptl. Morphol.* **15,** 77–111.

GLOOR, H. (1947). Phänokopie-Versuche mit Aether an *Drosophila*. *Rev. Suisse Zool.* **54**, 637-712.

HADORN, E. (1961). "Developmental Genetics and Lethal Factors." Methuen, London.

HADORN, E. (1963). Differenzierungsleistungen wiederholt fragmentierter Teilstücke männlicher Genitalscheiben von *Drosophila melanogaster* nach Kultur *in vivo*. *Develop. Biol.* **7**, 617-629.

HADORN, E. (1964). Bedeutungseigene und bedeutungsfremde Entwicklungsleistungen proliferierender Primordien von *Drosophila* nach Dauerkultur *in vivo*. *Rev. Suisse Zool.* **71**, 99-115.

HADORN, E. (1965). Problems of determination and transdetermination. From: Genetic control of differentiation. *Brookhaven Symp. Biol.* **18**, 148-161.

HADORN, E. (1966). Konstanz, Wechsel und Typus der Determination und Differenzierung in Zellen aus männlichen Genitalanlagen von *Drosophila melanogaster* nach Dauerkultur *in vivo*. *Develop. Biol.* **14**, 424-509.

HADORN, E., AND BUCK, D. (1962). Ueber Entwicklungsleistungen transplantierter Teilstücke von Flügel-Imaginalscheiben von *Drosophila melanogaster*. *Rev. Suisse Zool.* **69**, 302-310.

HADORN, E., BERTANI, G., AND GALLERA, J. (1949). Regulationsfähigkeit und Feldorganisation der männlichen Genital-Imaginalscheibe von *Drosophila melanogaster*. *Arch. Entwicklungsmech. Organ.* **144**, 31-70.

HADORN, E., ANDERS, G., AND URSPRUNG, H. (1959). Konbinate aus teilweise dissoziierten Imaginalscheiben verschiedener Mutanten und Arten von *Drosophila*. *J. Exptl. Zool.* **142**, 159-175.

KLEIHAUER, E., BRAUN, H., AND BETKE, K. (1957). Demonstration von fetalem Hämoglobin in den Erythrocyten eines Blutausstrichs. *Klin. Wochschr.* **35**, 637-638.

KORSCHELT, E. (1927). "Regeneration and Transplantation: Regeneration," Band 1. Borntraeger, Berlin.

LEWIS, E. B. (1964). Genetic control and regulation of developmental pathways. *In* "The Role of Chromosomes in Development" (M. Locke, ed.), pp. 231-252. Academic Press, New York.

NÖTHIGER, R. (1964). Differenzierungsleistungen in Kombinaten, hergestellt aus Imaginalscheiben verschiedener Arten, Geschlechter und Körpersegmente von *Drosophila*. *Arch. Entwicklungsmech. Organ.* **155**, 269-301.

NÖTHIGER, R., AND SCHUBIGER, G. (1966). Developmental behaviour of fragments of symmetrical and asymmetrical imaginal discs of *Drosophila melanogaster* (Diptera). *J. Embryol. Exptl. Morphol.* **16**, 355-368.

SANG, J., AND McDONALD, J. (1954). Production of phenocopies in *Drosophila* using salts, particularly sodium metaborate. *J. Genet.* **52**, 392-412.

STERN, C. (1965). Entwicklung und die Genetik von Mustern. *Naturwissenschaften* **52**, 357-365.

URSPRUNG, H. (1959). Fragmentierungs- und Bestrahlungsversuche zur Bestimmung von Determinationszustand und Anlageplan der Genitalscheiben von *Drosophila melanogaster*. *Arch. Entwicklungsmech. Organ.* **151**, 504-558.

URSPRUNG, H., AND HADORN, E. (1962). Weitere Untersuchungen über Musterbildung in Kombinaten aus teilweise dissoziierten Flügel-Imaginalscheiben von *Drosophila melanogaster*. *Develop. Biol.* **4**, 40-66.

VOGT, M. (1947). Beeinflussung der Antennendifferenenzierung durch Colchicin bei der Drosophilamutante *Aristopedia*. *Experientia* **3**, 156.

WADDINGTON, C. H. (1942). Growth and determination in the development of *Drosophila*. *Nature* **149,** 264-265.

WADDINGTON, C. H. (1962). "New Patterns in Genetics and Development." Columbia Univ. Press, New York.

ZETSCHE, K. (1966). Regulation der zeitlichen Aufeinanderfolge von Differenzierungs-vorgängen bei *Acetabularia*. *Z. Naturforsch.* **21b,** 375-379.

Fields and Gradients

C. H. WADDINGTON

Institute of Animal Genetics, Edinburgh, Scotland

The task given me by the organizers of this symposium was to evaluate what has been going on in the last thirty years in connection with the problem of fields and gradients. I do not think it is a problem I would have chosen to discuss if I had been left a free agent. Even in the 1930's, when it was a relatively fashionable subject, it was one that I personally always felt very wary about, and little has happened since then that would encourage one to feel much bolder in tackling it. The notions of fields and gradients have always been theoretical concepts, and much of this discussion will necessarily be of a theoretical nature. There is of course a vast amount of factual information to which these concepts have been applied. I shall not be able to refer to more than a very small part of this, but I will try to select a few points which seem of importance in clarifying the theoretical ideas and exhibiting their strength and weakness.

The Basic Terminology

It is an unfortunate fact that the basic terminology of developmental biology has been in a state of considerable confusion throughout the whole of the modern period of about the last forty years, particularly in connection with processes of the kind to which one might apply the field concept. We may begin by considering the general character of these processes. The field idea was first brought into theoretical developmental discussions by authors such as Gurwitsch (1922), Weiss (1926, 1930), and Rudy (1931). They used it to refer to processes by which some complex, organized morphological shape is brought into existence. Gurwitsch, for instance, described how in fungi a tangled mass of hyphal threads becomes molded into a fruiting body with the well-known cap or umbrella shape of mushrooms and toadstools. The formation of this definite shape from the indefinite mass of threads was, for him, an example of a "field phenomenon." Similarly, Weiss discussed such processes as the formation, out of a more or less cylindrical condensation of early limb mesenchyme, of a typical vertebrate limb with one proximal bone, two more distal ones, and a set of typically five digits.

Such processes, by which complex systems of order develop out of rudiments which have a much less complex and less obviously orderly arrangement, are typical examples of "organization." This is a concept which is notoriously difficult to define. I shall not attempt the task, but it is necessary to point out that the conventional embryological terminology in connection with organization unfortunately became confused as a result of Spemann's combination of the notions of organization and induction. Spemann made the simple but very far-reaching discovery that one part of an embryo may influence the developmental performance carried out by a neighboring part. He spoke of this as embryonic induction, but then went on to refer to the region of the gastrula, which exerts these inductive influences in a particularly striking way in early development, as the "organization center." This almost inextricably tied together the notions of induction and organization.

It is quite true that in normal development, and in a great many experimental situations, they do take place side by side, and indeed may be connected with one another more closely than that phrase implies. It is also true, however, and of basic importance, that the two processes can be dissociated. We can have agents that "induce" but do not transmit any degree of organization (e.g., certain chemical substances). We can also have regions of tissue in which a process of organization occurs without any sign of induction being involved (the egg as a whole is the most striking example but there are many other smaller systems, such as the mesoderm mantle in an amphibian gastrula). A third of a century ago I introduced two words which I hoped would be substituted, in precise discussion, for induction and organization, and would resolve the confusion between then (Waddington and Schmidt, 1933; Waddington and Needham, 1936). I use "evocation" to mean "induction which does not transmit organization," and "individuation" to mean "organization (chemical as well as morphological) independently of whether or not it is induced." One can retain the word induction to refer more loosely to phenomena in which evocation and individuation are occurring simultaneously. I took the word individuation from psychology where it is used to refer to the way in which what are originally a series of separate muscular contractions and movements of bones become gradually molded into a coordinated and skillfully performed single action. This seems to me to have considerable formal similarities to processes by which a number of separate discrete masses of tissue, such as lumps of bone, muscle, nerve, etc., become molded into a normally organized functioning limb or other anatomical structure.

It is clear that the type of "field" which was the concern of the early authors is allied to the concept of individuation. It might indeed be called an "individuation field." Unfortunately, fairly soon after its introduction, the notion of a field became taken up by less critical authors who used it in a wide variety of senses in many of which it meant no more than "area." One of the first major textbooks of modern experimental embryology in the English language was "The Elements of Experimental Embryology" by J. S. Huxley and G. R. de Beer (1934). In reviewing their book I (Waddington, 1934) wrote as follows:

"One ambiguity in Huxley and de Beer's use of 'field' is obvious after a very cursory reading. In some contexts the field is thought of as actually affecting or limiting the differentiation of tissues within it; in others it merely means a place where something is happening and only implies location. The second use seems to be unnecessary and confusing, but it is common throughout the book, particularly in the first half. Thus one of the two references to Field in the Index refers to the following passage (p. 221) : "The determination and localisation of organ-rudiments is revealed sooner or later by the presence of chemodifferentiated material or morphogenetic substances in certain places which constitute what may be called *fields*, or areas of differentiation of organs." A sentence later there is a discussion of the "presumtive fore-limb area, or field." It would lead to a great increase in clarity if the word field was abandoned in this connection, and such a word as area, or region, used to mean location without implying any formative agency. There is, as a matter of fact, great need for some careful thinking on the various possible sorts of region which must be considered. In respect of any given organ, there are for instance, the region from which it normally develops (presumptive region) ; the region from which it will develop if the presumptive region and surrounding tissue is extirpated; the region isolated parts of which will develop into the organ; the region from which the organ can be formed in response to a specific, or a non-specific stimulus, and so on."

The point was taken up and elaborated by Needham (1942) in his great summary of the 1930's experimental embryology, "Biochemistry and Morphogenesis" (see pp. 127ff. and 286ff.). The confusion still crops up, however, and one finds it necessary to draw attention to the distinction between fields and districts even at the present time (Waddington, 1956, p. 23ff., Faber, 1965). For the purpose of this paper let us keep firmly in mind that what we shall be discussing are "individuation fields."

The Nature of Fields

In the 1930's, one of the points that most worried the more materialistically minded embryologists was the question: If there are fields, what are they fields of? Our feeling was that the field concept would only be useful scientifically if we had grounds for believing that we were talking of the distribution in space of one or a few potentially identifiable chemical substances. This outlook brought the idea of fields into some sort of connection with that of "axial gradients." This was the theory, advocated by Child (1915), that in many field phenomena the operative agent is distributed in one or more relatively simple continuous gradients. I will return to this theory later. Here I want to point out that it was by no means obvious exactly what the "operative agent" consisted of. Sometimes Child urged that it was the rate of cellular respiration, sometimes that it was a more general index of cellular metabolism as a whole, and sometimes that it was an even less precisely specifiable "morphogenetic potential."

I have gradually come to feel that this difficulty, of deciding what the field is a field of, does not have quite as much importance as I once thought. After all, physicists are happy to use the concepts of the electromagnetic or the gravitational fields, but would be very hard put to it to tell us exactly what electromagnetism or gravity is. The weakness of the embryological field theory is, I now think, of a different kind. Essentially it arises because there are so many different embryological fields. There is only one gravitational field and we can describe how it is modified by moving things about within it. But there is a different limb field for the forelimb and for the hindlimb of the same animal, and other fields for the forelimbs of different species. Thus, in developmental biology, we have not only to describe the field of a particular limb in a particular species, but also to try to understand the ways in which that field is modified in related species. It is mainly for this reason I think that the field concept becomes much more a way of asking questions than of answering them.

The Temporal Characteristics of Fields

Biologists as a whole—but I hope not the members of this Society— are all too often content to think of the structure of organs as spatial arrangements fixed in time. In fact, of course, in developmental biology we are always dealing with processes, not with states. A moment's thought is sufficient to convince one that the field is something which is extended in the time dimension. For instance, when a mass of developing tissue is disturbed in some way, perhaps by cutting out a part of it, and then, in a typical "field phenomenon," rearrangement occurs so that a normal situation is restored, the restoration does not take place back to the *status quo ante* the disturbance. The phenomenon consists in the developing system achieving a state which corresponds to a later condition of the field.

In forming a mental picture of a field we have, therefore, as a minimum to consider the three dimensions of space and the dimension of time. Even this, of course, is not enough, because we also have to consider the chemical characteristics of the different types of tissue involved. In considering a developing limb, it is not sufficient to outline the positions in space of the muscles, bones, nerves, etc., leaving out of account the fact that these tissues are different in their chemical constitution. Any precise description of a field must therefore require reference to a multidimensional space, which would have axes on which one could plot not only positons in time and the three dimensions of space but also the concentrations of essential chemical compounds. The branch of thought which deals with structures in multidimensional space is topology. An embryonic field is, I am afraid, essentially a topological notion. Not many biologists feel themselves much at home in this realm of thought and I certainly do not do so myself. In the past, although I have known that some of the ideas I wanted to express really involve multidimensional spaces, I have resisted trying to expound them in those terms. Fortunately in recent years however, several topological mathematicians, such as Zeeman (1965) and Thom (1966), have become interested in theoretical biology, and perhaps the time has now come to put these notions in terms which are at least somewhat more respectable mathematically.

The basic concept is, I think, one which I have called a "chreod." This is a word derived from two Greek roots which mean "it is necessary or fated" and "a path." The word refers to a region in a multidimensional configuration space. The region is extended along the time dimension and along the three axes of space, and also includes a number of other dimensions which allow one to represent the relevant variations in chemical composition. Such a region has a chreodic character when there is a hypersurface within it, extended in the time dimension, which acts as an "attractor" with respect to the neighboring vector fields (Fig. 1). This means that points in the neighborhood of this surface will tend, as time passes, to move back into it. The region over which the attractor hypersurface is fully effective is what Thom calls the "support of the chreod." The remaining part, over which its action is too weak to bring displaced points fully back to itself, he refers to as the "cone" of the chreod. Thom discusses how "catastrophes" may arise within the cone of a chreod, leading to the production of new vector fields which converge on another attractor hypersurface—all of which is a more mathematically refined way of referring to the process that we embryologists often speak of as "switching."

These topologically defined notions can be used to form concepts appropriate to several different aspects of developmental biology. If we omit the three dimensions of normal Newtonian space from our multi-dimensional configuration space, we can use the concept to consider only changes in chemical composition, and can represent such facts as the existence of discontinuities between the composition of, say, muscle cells and nerve cells. Alternatively, if we allow the three dimensions of space to be represented, we can form concepts to deal with definite spatial arrangements (changing, of course, in time) of chemically distinct masses of tissue. The point I want to make here is that the field is a notion of this kind: it is the concept of a chreod in which the attractor affects the three dimensions of Newtonian space as well as dimensions of chemical composition.

The Causal Complexity of the Field

Most of the earlier writers who employed the field concept seem to have considered that eventually it would be found that the effective causal basis for the processes going on within the field is the distribution of one or a very few morphogenetic substances. If this were the case, one could make an adequate conceptual model which involved no more than the three dimensions of space, that of time, and one or two further dimensions to represent the effective substances. Authors gradually realized, however, that this would represent a very drastic abstract

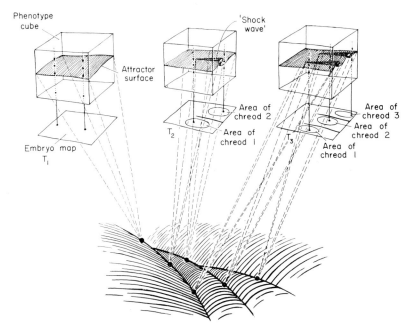

Fig. 1.   A drastically simplified illustration of how an embryo may be represented in multidimensional function space. The embryo at any given time, really three-dimensional, is shown reduced to an "embryo map" in two dimensions. To represent the constitution as well as the geometry of the embryo, we should have to specify for each point on this map a number of other coordinates giving concentrations of a few tens or hundreds of key compounds. These would lie in a multidimensional space, "the phenotype cube." At each point plotted in this space, processes would be going on tending to alter the constitution; these could be represented by vectors (indicated by the arrows on the lines projecting the embryo map into the phenotype cube). If there is a tendency to "regulation," the vector fields will converge on some (multidimensional) surface, the "attractor surface," which describes the condition of homeostasis at that time (upper left).

As time passes (T_1, T_2, T_3), the shape of the attractor surface changes (crudely speaking, homeostasis is around different points of stability). The most important changes are the division of the embryo into different regions (organs) each with its own "homeostatic" characteristics. This can be represented as foldings of the attractor surface. The situation can be represented, even more diagrammatically by mapping the attractor surface at each time down to one or more points (lower part). The sequence of points will form a branching line, and the vector fields associated sloping surfaces (bottom of figure). Any section (or even the whole) of this line, with its associated slopes, is a "chreod." The whole system has been referred to by the metaphor, "the epigenetic landscape" (Waddington, 1940b). (Based on discussions with Rene Thom and C. Zeeman.)

simplification of the true situation although it might be useful enough in particular connections. Weiss (1953), for instance, spoke of processes of development in terms of "molecular ecology," by which he meant changes in space and time of the distribution of many different types of molecule.

To provide a really solid factual basis for this type of concept would require that one could identify the various types of molecule involved. This is not yet possible. One can, however, make some approach toward that end by enlisting the aid of genetics. Each different genetic locus which produces a distinguishable phenotypic effect on a developing system does so, we believe, by controlling the formation of a specifically distinct type of protein. If, therefore, n different gene loci produce n or more different phenotypic alterations in a system, then we can deduce that at least n different protein species are causally affecting the developmental processes. It was in order to provide an actual example of such an analysis that at the end of the 1930's I took the trouble to look at the effects produced by a number of genes on a relatively simple morphogenetic field system—the wing of *Drosophila* —which had been well analyzed genetically (Waddington, 1940a). I looked at the effects of over 30 different genetic loci, each of which produced a characteristic phenotypic effect, and I described some 16 different developmental processes which were altered in various ways by the different genes. The broad outlines of the story have often been described since, and I will not repeat them here. The main point they make—that a field is the site of exceedingly complex interconnected reactions involving many different operative substances—is one that has been demonstrated repeatedly since that time, particularly by workers investigating development by studying the effects of genes.

One could use many examples, and more or less arbitrarily I will refer to a recently published study by Milaire (1966) on the developing limb bud in the mouse. In the developing vertebrate limb, as many workers have shown, there are reciprocal interactions between the ectoderm and mesoderm which change somewhat as time goes on. They are indicated in Fig. 2. Neither of these two reacting tissues is simple within itself. Quite a number of genes are known which affect either the mesoderm or the ectoderm or their interaction. Four described by Milaire are shown in Figs. 2 and 3, and there are many others. A similar situation is of course known in the chick, in which perhaps even more genetically determined disturbances of the pattern of the limb field have been studied developmentally.

To give another example of the basic complexity of the material substrate of a field, let us glance briefly at the gastrulation movements in the amphibia. It is well known that the whole region around the blastopore of an amphibian gastrula behaves as a morphogenetic field in the sense that, if pieces are removed and replaced with reversed

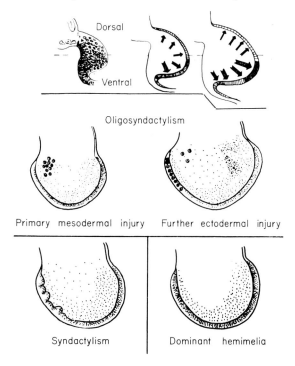

Fig. 2. The upper row shows the mesenchyme of the early limb bud exerting an influence on the overlying ectoderm, leading to the formation of an "apical ridge" (black). The lower diagrams show three different genetic effects. In oligosyndactyly, a primary defect in the mesenchyme causes an injury to the apical ectoderm, which then in turn affects the mesoderm. In syndactyly and dominant hemimelia there are two other distinct alterations to the mesoderm-ectoderm system of interactions. (After Milaire, 1966.)

orientation, they may show some tendency to continue their original movements but they are also affected by the direction of movements of their surroundings. In the 1930's I made several studies of these processes, showing for instance that the tendency to conserve the local direction of movement is much stronger in the rapidly developing egg of *Discoglossus* than in the more slowly gastrulating forms such as the newt, measuring the forces which the gastrulating tissues could exert, etc. The whole outlook on field theories at that time suggested that one should search for some single underlying mechanism, and we argued about whether this was to be found in changing adhesion of cell surfaces, in phenomena comparable to surface tension, or in the formation of orientated bundles of internal fibrils in the cells, etc. Recent electron microscope studies on the cells in the blastopore (Baker, 1965; Perry and Waddington, 1966) have shown that the processes bringing about the changes in cell shape, and thus the movement of the tissue as a whole, are highly complex (Fig. 4). They probably

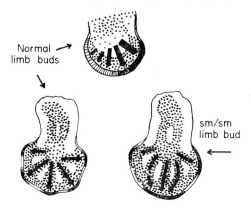

Normal →
limb buds

sm/sm
limb bud
←

FIG. 3. Another genetic effect on the limb field, which changes the manner of subdivision of the mesodermal factor which maintains the apical ectodermal ridge. (After Milaire, 1966.)

involve changes in cell adhesiveness, and certainly many alterations take place in the cell surface, some of them perhaps more or less passively (such as an accumulation of cortical material at the outer surface lining the blastopore groove); but others, such as the formation of flanges which become interwrapped with those of neighboring cells, seem to involve definite activity on the part of the cell concerned. Within the cell there is the appearance and orientation both of microfibrils and microtubules. There is also a sorting out of cell contents into zones, one of which contains a great accumulation of vesicles of a kind not at all common in cells of earlier or later stages. One can hardly avoid the conclusion that the global property of "gastrulation movements" does not have a single defined causal basis, but is to be regarded as a complex function involving many individual variables.

It follows from this discussion that a field is *essentially* a description of the causal structure of complex processes in which many different substances are fundamentally important. The field really does belong in a phase space with quite a considerable number of dimensions. It is a concept which can only be properly handled by a considerably more sophisticated type of thinking than embryologists contemplated when it was first introduced.

Abstractions from the Total Field Concept

We find, therefore, that if we try to define what we mean by a field, we are forced to envisage it as a chreodic region in a multidimensional space. One must then ask, having developed such a notion what can one do with it? I should like to suggest three things; each of them involves asking particular questions about particular aspects of the field rather than any further attempt to characterize the field as a whole.

(a) How strong is the field character? One of the most important characteristics of a field or a chreod is that there is a trajectory of "normal development" which acts as an attractor for neighboring trajectories, so that "regulation" takes place back toward normality. One can ask how strong is the attractiveness of the attractor, or, better, one can investigate experimentally how it can be altered. So far the main avenue of approach to this problem is through genetics. For instance, by selection through several generations, one can alter the degree to which a developing system is resistant to outside disturbing influences. In genetic language, one can select for or against the canalization of development of a particular character (Waddington, 1960; Waddington and Robertson, 1966). One can even obtain some relative measurement of the strength of canalization by selection experiments in which a phenotypic character is carried through a zone of canalization, and one can estimate how much selection pressure is necessary to pull it out of the canalization in comparison with the amount necessary to change it by a similar amount in a noncanalized zone. There is considerable literature on this type of experiment (Rendel, 1962; Rendel and Sheldon, 1960; Fraser and Kindred, 1960; Scharloo, 1964). I will not go into it here, since it is perhaps rather far away from the interests of most readers.

(b) What is the general nature of the interactions between processes within the field? There have been suggestions that the interactions might be largely electrical in nature (for instance, Lund, 1947). Nowadays these theories seem to have receded into the background except in special instances, such as the field concerned with the orientation of lamellae in the growth of bones (Becker *et al.*, 1964).

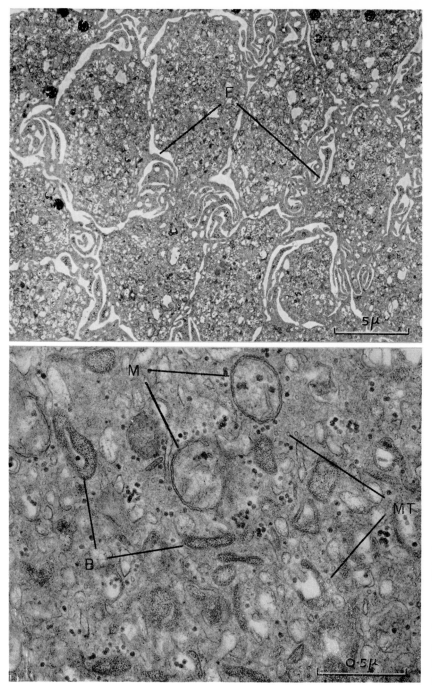

The other obvious type of interaction is, of course, chemical. Since the 1930's there have been many experimental studies aimed at investigating chemical interactions during field development. Perhaps the most profound and far-reaching of them has been Grobstein's well-known work (1962) on the interaction between the mesenchymal and epidermal components of several glands. Work by authors such as Moscona (1962), and Steinberg (1963), and others on the reaggregation of disaggregated cells, falls into the same general line of thought although they cannot, as a rule, come as close as Grobstein to characterizing the chemical nature of the interaction processes.

In many other recent analyses of morphogenetic field phenomena the analysis has had to stop at the level of the cell and its behavior (for instance, Gustafson and Wolpert's (1963) beautiful analysis of early sea urchin development). One presumes that the cellular behavior will ultimately find its explanation in terms of chemical processes proceeding within the cells and on their surfaces, rather than in purely physical ones such as electrostatic attractions, Van der Waal's and other long range forces, etc., although these must certainly play a part.

Studies of this kind are certainly the most fashionable and probably, at the present time, the most rewarding approaches to the investigation of fields. One must beware however of supposing that they are likely to provide us with more than a very general picture of the overall character of the processes going on within the field. The examples of genetic factors modifying the results of interaction between mesoderm and ectoderm in the limb system give us some warning of the limitations of what we are able to discover with present-day biochemical methods.

It may well be that there are other systems of interaction between the subregions of a field. Goodwin (1964) has recently argued that the cellular metabolic systems involving the synthesis of protein are likely, in general, to show periodic oscillatory phenomena. The oscillations from different regions of a field might not be in phase, and they then might influence one another. It is not inconceivable that this might provide a mechanism for the overall integration of a region into a unified field (Waddington, 1965).

Fig. 4. The complexity of the structural changes in the cells involved in the morphogenetic field of gastrulation in urodeles. Top: A transverse section of cells lining the blastopore showing the "flanges" by which the edges of the cells become wrapped around one another. Bottom: Higher powered view of cytoplasm showing microtubules (MT), the special beta-granules (B), as well as normal constituents such as mitochondria (M). (In collaboration with Margaret M. Perry.)

In considering the general mechanisms by which fields are integrated, it is important to remember that field phenomena may occur in masses of living material which are not subdivided into recognizable cellular subunits having interactions to which the field properties can hypothetically be referred. I am alluding not only to such fields of special character as those of the cortex of ciliates. These are not divided into cellular subunits, but they do have clearly defined subunits of another

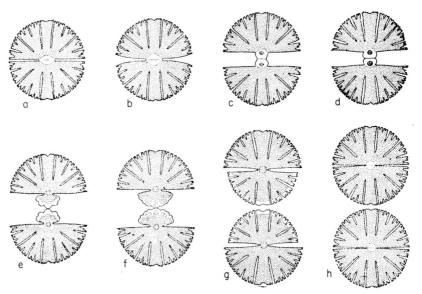

FIG. 5. The desmid *Micrasterias* has the form of a thin circular plate, made up of two semicircular half-cells connected by a narrow isthmus where the nucleus is located. On cell division, the newly expanding half-cells become molded into the normal pattern of five sublobes.

kind, the kineties or kinetosomes. There are still more challenging cases in which field phenomena occur within the body of a single cell in which no kind of subunit is obvious.

An example is the desmid *Micrasterias* (Kallio, 1960; Waddington, 1962, 1963; Selman, 1966). The field processes are concerned with the production of a regular pattern of lobes and sublobes in the outgrowing half-cells formed at cell division (Fig. 5). Normally there is a regular symmetrical five-lobed pattern, and if injuries are made there is regulation back to this pattern (Fig. 6b) although it may take several cell-generations before normality is restored (Fig. 7), and some races (presumed genetic, although no breeding is possible in this species) are found in which the number of lobes is permanently reduced (Fig. 6a). It seems to me extremely difficult to envisage a mechanism by which spatial arrangements of material on this scale of magnitude could be brought about. The conventional *deux ex machina* to be invoked is "local specialization of the cell surface"; but the pattern of the new half-cell is hardly affected by the pattern of the old surface. On the other hand, ultraviolet injuries to the nucleus, or inhibition of its action by actinomycin D, leads to an underdevelopment of the

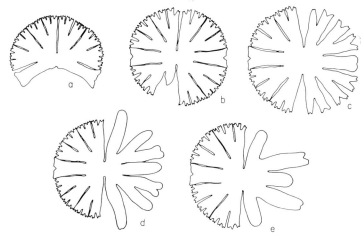

Fig. 6. *Micrasterias.* a:A race in which one of the side lobes is missing. b: If one side lobe is destroyed by localized ultraviolet irradiation of its surface, the normal pattern is nevertheless produced at the next division. c and d: Imperfect development of the minor details of pattern following localized irradiation of the nuclear region of a newly formed half-cell (irradiated half-cells on left, new ones on right). e: Similar underdevelopment following treatment with actinomycin D during the outgrowth of the half-cell on the right. (After Selman, 1966.)

pattern, although not to any topologically important alteration in it (Selman, 1966) (Fig. 6e). Here we have the problem of the causal mechanism of fields presented to us in the baldest possible way, and most of our usual ploys for avoiding the issue are ruled out. We just have to realize that we don't have an answer that makes sense.

(c) Third, one can concentrate attention on some geometrical aspect of the field and try to study the factors in it and their disposition in space. The "axial gradient" approach is of this kind.

At this stage progress can only be made in this direction if one is willing to accept a very drastic simplification of the nature of the field, and to formulate questions which involve only one or two selected major features of the whole complex field process. As an example of the kind of approach that has proved enlightening in recent years, one may mention the work of Webster and Wolpert (1966) on the field system in *Hydra*. They began by simplifying to the extent that they neglected two dimensions of space and considered the organism as simply a linear sequence of parts, namely hypostome (bearing tentacles), subhypostome, digestive region, peduncle, and basal disk. It has been known for a long

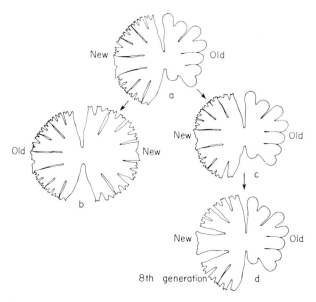

Fig. 7. *Micrasterias*. Ultraviolet treatment of a developing half-cell produced absence of one side lobe and reduction in complexity of the rest of the cell (right half, a). At the next division, this half-cell produced a relatively normal offspring (left half, a) which in turn produced quite normal cells at the next division (b). The original injured half continued to produce mildly defective offspring for several generations but eventually becomes more normal (c and d). (After Selman, 1966.)

time that if the animal is cut in parts, any section is capable of being reformed into the whole organism. The authors, however, abstracted from this complete reorganization the one precise question: How is a distinction made between the hypostome and the rest?

It was known that if a hypostome is transplanted into another position in the body it can cause the outgrowth of a new hydra from that region. Webster and Wolpert showed that this experimental method could be used to reveal the time at which a section of a regenerating hydra becomes determined to develop into a hypostome, which is much earlier than this development can be observed visually by the outgrowth of tentacles. They then demonstrated the existence of an "axial gradient" in the time necessary for this determination; it is less when the cut is made distally, and becomes progressively greater as the cut is made more proximally, i.e., farther and farther away from the original hypostome. This time gradient is a resultant of two underlying gradients of physiological action. Spiegelman (1945) had made the general point that any axial gradient system, in which a morphogenetic stimulatory activity falls off from a high point toward lower values, necessarily implies that there must also be some gradient in inhibitory actions, since otherwise the final result would be that the whole mass of tissue would eventually turn into a product characteristic of the top end of the gradient, even though the lower end might take longer to get there. A hypostome does indeed exert an inhibitory action which falls off with distance, tending to prevent the formation of another hypostome. This gradient of inhibition must be maintained by the continued activity of the hypostome, since the level of inhibition begins to fall as soon as the hypostome is removed (Fig. 8).

The gradient in inhibition operates on tissues which themselves have a gradient in threshold of reactivity to it, the threshold for inactivation being higher in more distal regions than in more proximal ones. This can be demonstrated by grafting different regions of the threshold gradient into the same region of the inactivation gradient, when it is found that the level of inactivation which can prevent hypostome formation by a promixal segment cannot do so for a more distal segment.

Such an analysis gives us some further understanding of the character of the factors operative in the field, together with some information about their spatial arrangement. It is important, however, to note the limitations as well as the successes of studies of this kind. An answer is provided only to a question about the distinction between the hypostome and the rest. Many other aspects of the field activity have been omitted; for instance, how the tentacles are formed and modeled, how the rest of the body is divided into digestive zone, peduncle, etc. Moreover, the factors that are revealed—inactivation tendencies and thresholds of reaction to these—are defined only operationally, and it is by no means clear how they should be interpreted in chemical terms. It would be relatively simple to interpret the inactivation tendencies as due to the production by the hypostome of diffusible inhibitory substance which could be destroyed by cells from other parts of the organism. This suggestion is not a necessary consequence of the facts, however. If we remember that a field is the site of exceedingly complex interacting processes, the "inhibitory activity" may be some complex function involving many processes and not capable of reduction to a single molecular species. It seems even less plausible that the reaction threshold could be expressed in terms of a single chemical substance; it seems much more likely to be the expression of a complex function.

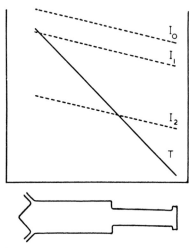

Fig. 8. Gradients of inhibition and threshold in *Hydra*. The animal is shown diagrammatically at the bottom. The threshold for inhibition is diagrammed by line T. Initially the level of inhibition is as indicated by I_0. On removal of the hypostome, this falls $(I_1, I_2 \ldots)$. A new hypostome is formed as soon as the level of inhibition at the cut surface falls below the threshold. (After Webster and Wolpert, 1966.)

Summary

The first requisite for discussing the embryological concepts of fields and gradients is to define as closely as possible what those terms are meant to imply. The fields commonly discussed in the physical sciences, such as the electromagnetic or gravitational fields, can be described by specifying for each point in a three-dimensional space some appropriate quantity (probably vectorial). An embryological field is essentially more complex in two ways: (a) Changes in time are among the fundamental characteristics of it and can never be omitted from its description; (b) The material substratum is essentially complex and cannot be described by a single parameter. An embryological field is therefore essentially a concept appropriate to the realm of discourse which deals in multidimensional spaces. Any attempt to reduce it to three or even four dimensions plus one field variable must be recognized as a drastic abstract simplification, which may perhaps be justified for certain particular purposes but must always be regarded with great caution. A field concept in the above sense could be used in connection with any developing system. In practice, the temptation to use it arises only in connection with systems which exhibit some general integration of the future developmental pathways followed by the different sub-regions within the whole; for systems, that is to say, which exhibit some degree of "regulation." Any such regulative properties can be expressed by specifying some "normal" developmental pathway within a multidimensional space and describing the manner in which it acts as an attractor for neighboring pathways. A region of phase space characterized by an attractor time trajectory has been called a chreod. A developmental field is essentially a chreod, whereas electromagnetic and stationary gravitational fields are not.

REFERENCES

BAKER, P. C. (1965). Fine structure and morphogenetic movements in the gastrula of the tree frog *Hyla regilla*. *J. Cell Biol.* **24**, 95–116.

BECKER, R. O., BASSETT, C. A., AND BACKMAN, C. H. (1964). Bioelectric factors controlling bone structure. In "Bone Biodynamics" (H. M. Frost, ed.), pp. 209–212. Little, Brown, Boston, Massachusetts.

CHILD, C. M. (1915). "Individuality in Organisms." Univ. of Chicago Press, Chicago, Illinois.

FABER, J. (1965). Autonomous morphogenetic activities of the amphibian regeneration blastema (discussion). In "Regeneration in Animals" (V. Kiortsis and H. A. L. Trampusch, eds.), pp. 404–419. North Holland Publ., Amsterdam.

FRASER, A. S., AND KINDRED, M. M. (1960). Selection for an invariant character, vibrissa number, in the house mouse. *Australian J. Biol. Sci.* **13**, 48–58.

GOODWIN, B. (1964). "Temporal Organization in Cells." Academic Press, New York.

GROBSTEIN, C. (1962). Interaction processes in cytodifferentiation. *J. Cellular Comp. Physiol.* **60**, Suppl. 1, 35–48.

GURWITSCH, A. (1922). Über den Begrift des embryonalen Feldes. *Arch. Entwicklungsmech. Organ.* **51**, 383–415.

GUSTAFSON, T., AND WOLPERT, L. (1963). The cellular basis of morphogenesis and sea urchin development. *Intern. Rev. Cytol.* **15**, 139–213.

HUXLEY, J. S., AND DE BEER, G. R. (1934). "The Elements of Experimental Embryology." Cambridge Univ. Press, London and New York.

KALLIO, P. (1960). Morphogenesis of *Micrasterias americana* in clone culture. *Nature* **187**, 164.

LUND, E. J. (1947). "Bioelectric Fields and Growth." Univ. of Texas Press, Austin, Texas.

MILAIRE, J. (1966). Aspects of limb morphogenesis in mammals. In "Organogenesis" (R. de Haan and H. Ursprung, eds.), pp. 283–300. Holt, New York.

MOSCONA, A. A. (1962). Analysis of cell recombination in experimental synthesis of tissues *in vitro*. *J. Cellular Comp. Physiol.* **60**, Suppl. 1, 65–81.

NEEDHAM, J. (1942). "Biochemistry and Morphogenesis." Cambridge Univ. Press, London and New York.

PERRY, M. M., AND WADDINGTON, C. H. (1966). Ultrastructure of the blastopore cells in the newt. *J. Embryol. Exptl. Morphol.* **15**, 317–330.

RENDEL, J. M. (1962). The relationship between gene and phenotype. *J. Theoret. Biol.* **2**, 296–308.

RENDEL, J. M., AND SHELDON, B. L. (1960). Selection for canalisation of the scute phenotype in *Drosophila melanogaster. Australian J. Biol. Sci.* **13**, 46–57.

RUDY, H. (1931). "Die biologische Feldtheorie." Borntraeger, Berlin.

SCHARLOO, W. (1964). Mutant expression and canalisation. *Nature* **203**, 1095–1096.

SELMAN, G. (1966). Experimental evidence for the nuclear control of differentiation in Microasterias. *J. Embryol. Exp. Morph.* **16**, 333–349.

SPIEGELMAN, S. (1945). Physiological competition as a regulatory mechanism in morphogenesis. *Q. Rev. Biol.* **20**, 121–146.

STEINBERG, M. S. (1963). Reconstruction of tissues by dissociated cells. *Science* **141**, 401–408.

THOM, R. (1966). Personal communication.

WADDINGTON, C. H. (1934). Morphogenetic fields. *Sci. Prog.* **114**, 336–346.

WADDINGTON, C. H. (1940a). The genetical control of wing development in *Drosophila. J. Genet.* **41**, 75–139.

WADDINGTON, C. H. (1940b). "Organisers and Genes." Cambridge Univ. Press, London and New York.

WADDINGTON, C. H. (1956). "The Principles of Embryology." Allen & Unwin, London.

WADDINGTON, C. H. (1960). Experiments on canalising selection. *Genet. Res.* **1**, 140–150.

WADDINGTON, C. H. (1962). "New Patterns in Genetics and Development." Columbia Univ. Press, New York.

WADDINGTON, C. H. (1963). Ultrastructural aspects of cellular differentiation. *Symp. Soc. Exptl. Biol.* **17**, 85–97.

WADDINGTON, C. H. (1965). Autogenous cellular periodicities as (a) Temporal templates and (b) the basis of "morphogenetic fields." *J. Theoret. Biol.* **8**, 367–369.

WADDINGTON, C. H., AND NEEDHAM, J. (1936). Evocation individuation and competence in amphibian organiser action. *Koninkl. Ned. Akad. Wetenschap. Proc.* **39**, 887–890.

WADDINGTON, C. H., AND SCHMIDT, G. A. (1933). Induction by heteroplastic grafts of the primitive streak in birds. *Wilhelm Roux Arch. Entwicklungsmech. Organ.* **128**, 522–563.

WADDINGTON, C. H., AND ROBERTSON, E. (1966). Selection for developmental canalisation. *Genet. Res.* **7**, 303–312.

WEBSTER, G., AND WOLPERT, L. (1966). Studies on pattern formation in *Hydra*, Parts I–III. *J. Embryol. Exptl. Morphol.* **16**, 91–141.

WEISS, P. (1926). "Morphodynamik." Borntraeger, Berlin.

WEISS, P. (1930). "Entwicklungsphysiologie der Tiere." Steinkopf, Darmstadt.

WEISS, P. (1953). Some introductory remarks on the cellular basis of differentiation. *J. Embryol. Exptl. Morphol.* **1**, 181–211.

ZEEMAN, E. C. (1965). Topology of the brain. *In* "Mathematics and Computer Science in Biology and Medicine," pp. 277–292. H. M. S. O., London.

Morphogenetic Cell Movements

J. P. TRINKAUS

Department of Biology, Yale University, New Haven, Connecticut

Introduction

About twenty-five years ago, when the Society for the Study of Development and Growth was founded, the normal course of the cell movements of gastrulation was understood in detail in only one form, the amphibian. The work of Vogt (1929) on these movements was at once pioneering and definitive, and in its completeness is one of the true classics of twentieth-century biology. The essential features of echinoderm invagination were also appreciated at that time, although important details remained to be studied (Hörstadius, 1939). Efforts had been made to follow cell movements in the meroblastic eggs of the teleosts, *Salmo* (Pasteels, 1936) and *Fundulus* (Oppenheimer, 1936), and of the chick (Wetzel, 1929), but although clear progress has been made, the results were incomplete. In other forms, our understanding of morphogenetic movements during early development was miniscule; often it rested more on concepts of comparative embryology, based mainly on amphibian gastrulation, than on detailed studies of the egg in question. The thoroughness with which amphibian gastrulation was understood clearly contrasted with the knowledge of gastrulation in all other forms. The intensive research devoted to gastrulation in the Amphibia appears to have been due primarily to the vital need to understand normal morphogenetic movements in the egg which at that time was the primary experimental material of the developmental analyst. In addition, however, its cells lent themselves exceptionally well to the technique of vital staining. Whatever the reasons, the work was slow in starting elsewhere. It wasn't until the 1940's and the 1950's that the chick received the attention it deserved (Spratt, 1946, 1954; Malan, 1953). Only during the last decade has sea urchin gastrulation been subjected to intensive study (Dan, 1960; Gustafson and Wolpert, 1963); and only this year have papers appeared which properly scrutinize teleost gastrulation (Ballard, 1966a,b,c). Significantly, in all these cases

125

2

2

important and sometimes unsuspected differences from the amphibian have been found.

Gastrulation involves mainly (but by no means exclusively) the spreading and folding of cohesive sheets of cells. So, indeed, do many other well-known morphogenetic movements, such as invagination of the optic vesicle, outpocketing of pharyngeal endoderm to form pharyngeal pouches, and branching of the ureteric bud, to name a few. This is not the only mode of locomotion available to metazoan cells, however. Some move as individuals, wending their way through the interstices of the developing embryo to accumulate at destinations near and far. Neural crest cells and germ cells were already famous for this capacity in the early decades of this century, but although their origins and derivatives were well understood, little was known of the paths traversed. In recent years, modern marking methods have been utilized to track these cells and have shown that they use varied means in gaining their destinations. Neural crest cells of the chick and primordial germ cells of the mouse, for example, move by preferred paths between the cells of more or less densely packed tissues (Weston, 1963; Mintz, 1959; see also Chibon, 1966). Chick germ cells, on the other hand, are wafted passively and dispersed randomly by the circulating blood during an important phase of their migrations (Simon, 1960; Meyer, 1964). The primary and secondary mesenchyme cells of sea urchin eggs have long been recognized as morphogenetically important, but only recently, with the application of time-lapse cinemicrography, have we been given a realistic appreciation of their activities (Gustafson and Wolpert, 1963).

Even though important details have been lacking and many forms remain unanalyzed to this day, it has been clear for some time that during early development cells may move extensively in highly ordered ways to found tissues and organs far from their original location. These morphogenetic cell movements, which occur mainly during gastrulation and the immediately succeeding phases of development, have attracted attention for years as one of the most wondrous phenomena of development. As such, they seemed for a long time to be so complex as to defy analysis, and in fact were subject to little. Studies of the mechanism of these cell movements prior to 1941 were largely speculative and often based more on model systems than on the developing embryo. There were some notable exceptions, however, in which the behavior of moving cells and cell masses was studied in isolation. Roux (1895) studied the behavior of isolated cells in primitive cell culture years ago and thought he observed that gastrula cells attracted each other, an observation which has since proved false (Voightlander, 1932; Kuhl, 1937; Lucey and Curtis, 1959). Harrison (1914) noted that tissue cells do not swim in the medium as do spermatozoa, but require a solid substratum on which to move. Weiss (1934) observed the behavior of cells under varying conditions of the substratum in culture and developed the concept of contact guidance, according to which the substratum imposes its orientations on the cells moving over it. Contact guidance is probably of importance in certain oriented cell movements during development and will receive additional attention later in this paper. One of the most exciting discoveries in the early years of this century was the ability of dissociated sponge cells to reaggregate and reconstitute small sponges (Wilson, 1907). The careful tracking of individual amoebocytes by Galtsoff (1923) indicated that cell movements and cell-to-cell adhesions are important in reaggregation, but due to the difficulty of distinguishing cell types, the problem of cell origin in the reconstituents remained unsolved (as indeed it still is today). Finally, in 1939 Holtfreter published his penetrating study of the contact affinities of isolated germ layers of amphibian eggs. By demonstrating that the germ layers adhere to each other differentially in a way that relates to normal morphogenesis, Holtfreter made a discovery that has served to light the way ever since. These were some of the investigations which, along with those on the normal course of morphogenetic movements, laid the basis for a concerted attack on the mechanism of such cell movements.

My discussion of morphogenetic cell movements will deal exclusively with animal cells, for in the matter of locomotion animal cells differ strikingly from plant cells. Herein perhaps lies the most fundamental difference between plant and animal morphogenesis. The cellular slime molds, and certain other lower plants, are of course notable exceptions to this rule and have been the subject of intensive investigation. Even so, I will not discuss them. These studies have been reviewed extensively elsewhere; indeed, they have several times been the subject of papers in these symposia. In the context of a review of progress during the last twenty-five years, however, it is significant to note that the first clear demonstration of chemotaxis in the slime molds was published less than twenty years ago (Bonner, 1947).

Study of the mechanism of the cellular movements of morphogenesis is a thoroughly modern subject in the sense that it is only in modern times that morphogenetic movements have been investigated directly and extensively *in vivo*. Naturally, modern work is based on foundations constructed in the past, but the prior work that has been most useful are the concrete studies of cell and tissue behavior; the models and speculations have been of little help. Much is owed to Paul Weiss for his early recognition that individual cell behavior lies at the basis of mass movements, and that it is to the cells and their behavior under artificially controlled conditions that one must ultimately turn if complex cellular movements within the organism are ever to be understood. Modern investigation of mechanism began with a frontal attack by Holtfreter (1943a,b, 1944) on what appeared to be the most impregnable bastion of them all—amphibian gastrulation. It is not that gastrulation is more complex in the amphibian egg, or indeed that the process of gastrulation is more complex than other morphogenetic movements, it is just that amphibian gastrulation was by far the best known mass movement and hence appeared to be the most complex. In any case, the boldness of Holtfreter's attack and the progress which he made gave inspiration to less courageous souls and as a result studies on several other eggs began soon afterward. It is of interest that the ensuing studies of the mechanism of the mass cellular movements during embryogenesis occurred largely independently of contemporaneous studies of cell behavior in culture, which have contributed substantially to our understanding of the factors controlling cell movement. The last two decades have seen enormous advances in our ability to culture cells and control their conditions of growth, and this has led to certain fundamental discoveries. It is appropriate, therefore, that some of the results of these studies be reviewed before we consider the mechanisms of morphogenetic cell movements.

Cell Movements in Culture

Contact Guidance

Although Harrison (1914) noticed many years ago that cells tend to orient along discontinuities in the substratum, the significance of this observation was not properly appreciated until Paul Weiss (1934, 1945) systematically investigated the question. He found that fibroblasts orient preferentially in culture on glass or plastic fibers, in grooves scored in the glass substratum and even along lines of stress in a plasma clot. These observations were historically important because they were a convincing demonstration of the essential role of the substratum in the control of cell movements. They had morphogenetic significance in providing a means whereby a simple physical change in a common substratum could orient individual cells or cell masses adherent to it. The possibility that the substratum acts to orient cells *in vivo* is supported by a number of observations: pigment cells and nerve axons orient along blood vessels; regenerating nerve axons grow out along a path laid down by the degenerating cut axon and along myotome boundaries; heart-forming mesoderm cell clusters orient on the oriented endoderm over which they are moving (DeHaan, 1963); neural crest cells move down the sides of the neural tube, regardless of its orientation in the embryo (Weston, 1963); melanocytes extend long dendritic processes along oriented rows of barbule cells. Weiss termed this influence of the substratum *contact guidance,* and everyone agrees that it is probably a fundamental mechanism in the control of cell movements. Important problems remain, however. It is not clear how cells orient along a glass fiber or groove. It seems unlikely that the glass offers orientations to which cells respond. P. Weiss (1961) has suggested that cells exude macromolecular materials which coat the substratum and form a sort of "ground mat" which spreads along the interface between the cell and its substratum. According to Weiss, the micellar network of such a mat could be oriented by the fiber or groove and give orientation to the cells. Rosenberg (1962) has found that cells in culture do indeed release macromolecular materials which coat the substratum. It remains to be determined, however, whether or not the postulated orientations in the ground mat actually occur and, if so, whether or not the cells orient to them as suggested. In the case of orientation in grooves, it is possible that the observed cellular orientation has nothing to do with orientations in the substratum. The increased surface area of the sub-stratum could increase the chances for cell adhesion and formation of a ruffled membrane (see below). In this case, cells would be guided by contact with the substratum, but not necessarily by its orientations. Rosenberg (1963) has shown that cells which adhere to one substratum more readily than to another can detect the former even though sep-arated from it by several molecular layers of the latter, and will accu-mulate preferentially and orient in grooves in which the covering layer is thinner. Here the cells are guided by differential contact with the substratum, but not by its orientations (see also Carter, 1965). Another difficulty with the theory of contact guidance concerns its application *in vivo.* Concrete evidence that cells are actually orienting to micellar orientations in their natural substrata is still lacking, even in places in which such orientations seem likely. Finally, it is necessary to em-phasize that even though orientations of the substratum may guide cells, it can of itself give only orientation, not direction. Supplementary factors are required for this.

The Ruffled Membrane

The movement of fibroblasts in culture has been intensively studied with phase, interference, and surface contact microscopy by Abercrombie and Ambrose (1958), Ambrose (1961), and Abercrombie (1961), and the following picture emerges. Fibroblasts flatten on the substratum and glide over it without gross deformation or evident protoplasmic flow. They appear to move by means of waves of adhesive contact with the substratum. The leading edge of such a moving fibroblast consists of an exceedingly thin, fanlike membrane, 5–10 μ wide which is closely applied to the substratum. The upper surface of this membrane undergoes continual, delicate folding movements or ruffles which beat backward. The under surface is attached intermittently to the substratum in order to gain traction. Wherever a large ruffled membrane is detected, the cell is generally moving in that direction. Where a new one forms, the cell soon begins to move in that direction. It appears, therefore, that the ruffled membrane is the locomotive organ of the cell. Although epithelial cells have been studied less, they too appear to move by means of leading ruffled membranes (Vaughan and Trinkaus, 1966). Since the ruffled membrane, or some modification of it, seems also to be the means of movement of many cells engaged in morphogenetic cell movements, an understanding of its formation and mechanism of operation is indispensable to the subject of this paper. The manner of its adhesion to the glass substratum is not yet understood, but Curtis (1964) has recently made a good start on this. He examined the points of adhesion of the ruffled membrane with interference reflection microscopy and found the closest approach of the cell surface to the glass was approximately 100 Å, the classic gap separating adhering epithelial cells from each other. Compression waves at or between the attachments undoubtedly assure cell movement, but they have not yet been detected. In this context it is of interest that glycerol-extracted fibroblasts contract in the presence of ATP in a manner reminiscent of skeletal muscle fibers (Hoffmann–Berling, 1959). The sequence of events leading to the formation of a ruffled membrane is still undetermined, but it has been established that its formation is inhibited by the presence of a large ruffled membrane elsewhere on the cell surface (Weiss and Garber, 1952) and by contact with another fibroblast (Abercrombie and Heaysman, 1953).

Contact Inhibition

The discovery that the ruffled membrane of a fibroblast is paralyzed when it contacts another fibroblast came as part of a time-lapse cinematographic study of fibroblast movement (Abercrombie and Heaysman 1953, 1954), in which it was shown that a fibroblast stops moving when it encounters another fibroblast. This constitutes impressive evidence that the ruffled membrane is indeed a locomotive organ, but it also reveals an aspect of the social behavior of fibroblasts that can explain certain mass cell movements. Abercrombie and Heaysman termed this phenomenon "contact inhibition" and showed that it probably lies at the basis of "zone of outgrowth" formation around an explant in culture. Contact inhibition is now well known and has been discussed in several recent reviews (e.g., Abercrombie, 1961, 1964a,b; Curtis, 1962a; Trinkaus, 1965), hence there is no need to reiterate the evidence in detail. When a fibroblast is inhibited by contact with another fibroblast, its ruffled membrane is paralyzed. With the inhibition of this ruffled membrane the free surface of the cell is liberated (Weiss and Garber, 1952); it can now form a new ruffled membrane and usually does so. The new ruffled membrane eventually provides sufficient momentum to pull the fibroblast away. The cell will then migrate more or less at random until it encounters another fibroblast, is again contact inhibited, and so on. One can readily see how such behavior will cause the most peripheral cells of an explant to break away, and in doing so free a surface of the cells behind so that they too can form ruffled membranes and eventually move out on their own. Since fibroblasts will not move over each other, but only into a cell-free space, they tend to form a monolayer. This explains how an explant comes to be surrounded by an ever-widening monolayer of fibroblasts.

As far as we know, fibroblasts ordinarily do not move about *in vivo* (Weston and Abercrombie, 1967). This could well be due to contact inhibition. The possibility that contact inhibition applies to several kinds of cells and operates *in vivo* as well as in tissue culture was strengthened when Abercrombie *et al.* (1957) found that certain sarcoma cells which are invasive *in vivo,* hence noncontact-inhibiting, are similarly not contact inhibited by fibroblasts in culture. They move over them as readily as over the glass substratum.

The means by which one cell surface paralyzes the ruffled membrane of another cell by contact is not understood. There are a number of possibilities (Abercrombie, 1961), but we are not yet in a position to distinguish among them. Comparison of the contact relations of contact-inhibiting cells and noncontact-inhibiting cells in the electron microscope may yield interesting leads and is clearly a possibility that deserves close attention (see below, p. 165–166).

Spreading of Cell Sheets

The spreading of epithelial cell sheets has been studied both in culture and in the closing of wounds. It has long been established that such a sheet spreads as a unit, with individual cells maintaining their positions within the sheet. Moreover, a sheet will invariably spread, provided it adheres to the substratum and has a free edge. It was pointed out a long time ago by Rand (1915) that an epithelium "will not tolerate a free edge" and seeks to close it off. The prime movers in the spreading of an epithelial sheet appear to be the marginal cells. This conclusion is based on three lines of evidence. (1) The free edges of the marginal cells show marked ruffled membrane activity. This has been observed many times (Lewis, 1922; Holmes, 1914; Vaughan and Trinkaus, 1966). (2) It is a common observation of all who have cultured tissues that a spreading epithelial sheet is attached to the substratum most firmly, or even only, at its margin, for when the margin of a sheet is detached from the glass the whole sheet usually retracts. Since adhesion to the substratum is necessary for the spreading of cells, it would appear that the most active spreading region is at the margin. (3) At the onset of spreading of a wound epithelium only the marginal cells show movement (Lash, 1955). Nonmarginal cells join the advance at progressively later times, the delay in mobilization increasing with their distance from the edge of the sheet. The observation of Lash would suggest that the nonmarginal cells spread passively in response to the pull of the advancing margin. Yet all cells of an epithelial sheet are known to possess the power of ruffled membrane formation and movement. If the sheet is cut anywhere, it will readhere after retraction, and begin spreading at its new margin. This raises an important question. Are the submarginal cells only passively pulled or are they active participants? Vaughan and I (Vaughan and Trinkaus, 1966) investigated this problem with time-lapse cinemicrography of spreading epithelial sheets in culture and found that when local portions of the margin spread more than the rest, the cells between such outgrowths came to be markedly stretched and tangentially oriented. In addition, the submarginal cells of the outgrowth region became radially oriented with respect to the main cell mass. This is clear evidence that cells lacking ruffled membranes, whether marginal or submarginal, respond passively to the pull of the outward spreading, membrane-active portions of the margin. This, however, is not the whole story. Although cells of the sheets are usually closely adherent to each other all around their circumference, they frequently appear to be pulled apart, as if the tension from the spreading margin is too great. When this occurs, there is a local retraction and a large gap opens up, often as large as one or two cells. After a brief pause, membrane activity is seen to commence at the free edges of the gap and the cells move together, closing the gap. When the gap is near the margin (as it almost always is), membrane activity occurs only on the free centrifugal cell surface. A free rear surface of a cell of the leading edge does not form a ruffled membrane. Possibly, the already established ruffled membranes at the front of the free edge cells inhibit the formation of membrane activity at their rear ends (Weiss and Garber, 1952). It appears from these observations that the submarginal cells of a sheet both stretch passively and spread actively. They are passively stretched by the actively spreading margin, but they also spread actively intermittently to close gaps that occasionally open up between them due to tension in the sheet.

When the margin of a spreading sheet contacts the margin of another sheet, ruffled membrane activity ceases and the sheet stops spreading. Conversely, when the contacts of cells within a sheet are broken, ruffled membranes form at the free cell borders and the cells move to close the gap. When the cells contact each other again, ruffled membrane activity ceases. This is the behavior of a contact inhibiting system. It therefore seems reasonable to consider that the movement of epithelial cells, like that of fibroblasts, is inhibited by contact with other cells. Why then do epithelial cells show less tendency to break away from the mass and move about as individuals? Presumably their adhesive contacts are firmer. It is also possible that epithelial cells have less efficient ruffled membranes. These are important questions that need investigation. Direct measurement of adhesiveness (cf. Coman, 1944; Weiss, 1962a,b; Steinberg, 1964; Curtis, 1966) and observations of cell contact relationships at the fine-structural level (cf. Robertson, 1964; Baker, 1965; Overton, 1962; Trinkaus and Lentz, 1966) are obvious first approaches. It would also be of interest to know whether epithelial cells are contact-inhibited only by other epithelial cells or by fibroblasts as well. If they require contact with other epithelial cells, will all epithelia work equally well, or might specificity be involved (cf. Chiakulas, 1952)?

Type-Specific Cell Segregation

The well-known phenomenon of reconstitution of organs and organisms by aggregates of dissociated cells has been subjected to intensive analysis during the last decade. In a number of instances it has been shown to be due to type-specific segregation of the various cell types (Townes and Holtfreter, 1955; Moscona, 1957; Curtis, 1960; Trinkaus, 1961, 1963b; Steinberg, 1962a). There are two components of this sorting out: cell movement within the aggregate and differential adhesion. What brings cells of a particular tissue or organ type together is a problem that has excited the imagination of many. The work on this problem has been reviewed several times recently, indeed twice in these symposia (Moscona, 1959, 1962, 1965; Curtis, 1960, 1962a; Steinberg, 1964; Abercrombie, 1964b; Trinkaus, 1965). There is, therefore, no need to consider the matter in detail in this paper. Instead, I will confine myself to a brief summary of certain relevant results and a few comments.

Both Curtis (1960) and Steinberg (1963) have pointed out that all theories of segregation must account for both the eventual cohesion of cells of similar type to form homonomic sectors within the aggregate, and the positioning of these sectors in a concentric pattern peculiar to each combination (Townes and Holtfreter, 1955; Trinkaus and Groves, 1955; Moscona, 1957). Any mechanism which explains positioning will explain sorting out. Three hypotheses have been proposed to account for positioning. All three recognize that all cells are mutually adhesive at first (Fig. 1).

The old notion that directed movements of cells could be caused by their movement along a gradient in concentration of some metabolite has been invoked by Stefanelli *et al.* (1961) and Townes and Holtfreter (1955) to account for sorting out. They suggested that the internally segregating component of a mixed aggregate might be attracted to the point of highest concentration of a generally produced metabolite in the center of the aggregate, or alternatively, toward the periphery of the aggregate by a metabolite present in the medium. Steinberg (1963, 1964) has pointed out that in either case the internally segregating component would tend to form a single sector at the center of the aggregate (Fig. 1). Since this rarely occurs, chemotaxis by a generally produced metabolite is not favored. The pattern of sorting out also does not favor chemotaxis (Steinberg, 1964). The first small clusters of the internal component to form are located randomly within the aggregate (Trinkaus, 1961; Steinberg, 1963, 1964; Trinkaus and Lentz, 1964).

Another form of chemotaxis would require the internally segregating cells to move toward a concentration of a substance (s) that they and only they produce. Obtaining critical evidence for this hypothesis is a more difficult matter. If the mixture of cell types in the aggregate is random at the onset of segregation, the hypothetical attractant will be in highest concentration in the central region of the aggregate, and the same pattern of sorting out would be expected as for the first type of chemotaxis.

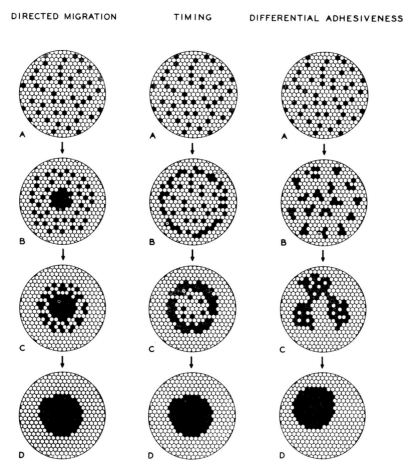

Fig. 1. The time course of segregation, as it would appear ideally, if brought about through directed migration (chemotaxis), timing, or differential adhesiveness. (From Steinberg, 1964.)

However, the mixture of cells is in fact rarely truly random (see Trinkaus, 1961). A nonrandom mixture would have foci of attraction wherever there is a higher initial concentration of the internally segregating cells and would consequently give some of the results typically obtained, i.e., several clusters forming at random within the aggregate (Trinkaus, 1961; Steinberg, 1963, 1964; Trinkaus and Lentz, 1964). In order to acquire critical evidence for the second form of chemotaxis the movements of individual cells must be observed. If they are chemotactically attracted to cells of the same type, they should move directly toward a cluster of such cells whenever they come within the sensitive range. Monahan and I (unpublished) have recently followed the movements of individual chick retinal pigment cells sorting out from heart cells with time-lapse cinemicrography and have found that individual pigment cells move away from a nearby cluster of pigment cells as well as toward it, and two pigment cells which have been observed to move toward each other and apparently come into contact may reverse themselves and move apart again. It would appear from these observations that the second form of chemotaxis does not control the segregation of retinal pigment cells from heart cells, the one case in which individual cell behavior has been examined, and is therefore not a good working hypothesis at present for explaining cell segregation in general.

Curtis (1960, 1961, 1962a,b) has proposed that the cell surface is changed by the dissociating agent in such a manner that the cells become less adhesive. These less adhesive cells are thought to move about within the aggregate until they recover from the effects of the dissociating agent; their adhesiveness then supposedly rises. If it be further assumed that cell motility increases with shear, then there will be less motility at the surface of the aggregate, where there is less shear, and the cells which regain their adhesiveness first will tend to be trapped at the surface of the aggregate. As other cells of the same type, also with increased adhesiveness, contact these immobile cells, they also will be trapped. In this manner the first cells to recover their adhesiveness will accumulate at the surface and will herd the other cells inward toward the center of the aggregate where they will form a single central cluster. The fact that the internally segregating cells rarely form a cluster in the center and often segregate into two or more clusters argues against the ideal operation of Curtis' "timing hypothesis." In addition, Townes and Holtfreter (1955), Steinberg (1962c), and Bresch (1955) have shown that the same patterns of positioning result if intact pieces of the same organs are joined *in vitro*. Since there can be no effect of dissociation in these combinations, the postulated effect of the dissociating agent is thrown into question. Curtis (1961, 1962b) has performed some ingenious experiments in which he found that if the internally segregating cells are dissociated before the others and allowed to "recover" before association into an aggregate, the positioning could be reversed. These results suggest that the dissociating agent may well affect the sorting out of cells, but do not necessarily support the thesis that the effect is differential. Moreover, there is no direct evidence that the dissociating agent reduces adhesiveness. In short, the timing hypothesis lacks consistent support. It has been useful in calling attention to the largely unanalyzed effects of dissociating agents on the surface properties of cells, but is inadequate as an explanation of sorting out. In addition, the timing hypothesis has limited appeal for those concerned with morphogenetic movements, because it requires an artificial effect to explain the tendency of cells to assume normal topographical relationships in mixed aggregates, e.g., mesoderm within ectoderm and cartilage within muscle.

This is not the case with the differential adhesion hypothesis of Steinberg (1962a,b,c, 1963, 1964). It proposes that cells segregate and assume characteristic positioning in mixed aggregates as a result of random mobility and innate quantitative differences in their general surface adhesiveness. Cells tend to maximize their adhesion to each other. Hence the more cohesive cells of a population will tend to cohere to each other within the aggregate and exclude those which are less cohesive toward the periphery. Equilibrium, i.e., maximal adhesion, will be reached ideally when all of the more cohesive cells cohere in a sphere imbedded within and engulfed by a sphere of less cohesive cells. On the basis of this hypothesis one can make a number of testable predictions (Steinberg, 1964). (1) The cluster or clusters of the internally segregating cells need be neither central nor single. They only need be internal. As I have already pointed out, clusters of the internally segregating cells are in fact rarely central or single. (2) The minimal demand on cells of the internally segregating (more adhesive) component is that they leave the surface of the aggregate. When the proportion of internally to externally segregating component is low, they do indeed all leave the surface, if only the distance of 1 cell diameter. (3) Unlike the other two hypotheses, the differential adhesion hypothesis does not require that cells migrate great distances. We have followed the sorting out of the internally segregating retinal pigment cells from heart cells by photographing them every few hours (Trinkaus and Lentz, 1964)

and with time-lapse cinemicrography (Trinkaus and Monahan, unpublished), and have found that the pigment cells actually migrate
very short distances; no movements of more than 30–50 μ have been
observed.* Thus it is predictable that the lower the proportion of internally segregating cells the poorer the sorting out. Steinberg (1964) found
this to be true for aggregates of neural retina and heart cells and we
for aggregates of retinal pigment cells and heart cells (Trinkaus, 1965).
(4) If segregation and positioning are due to quantitative differences,
the cells which constitute the internally segregating component in one
combination may constitute the externally segregating component in
another. Steinberg (1963) found this to be true for an extensive series
of combinations. (5) If segregation is due to innate differences between
the cells, they need not be dissociated in order to achieve the positioning
characteristic for each combination. As already pointed out, Townes and
Holtfreter (1955), Bresch (1955), and Steinberg (1962c, 1964) have all
found this to be true. (6) Sorting out often stops short of completeness.
Instead of all cells of the internally segregating component cohering in
a single, internally located, spherical cluster they often form a number
of clusters. Given the tendency of cells to maximize their adhesions, this
should not take place unless clusters of internally segregating cells are
unable to move within the aggregate. We have shown in observations of
sorting out in living aggregates that clusters of internally segregating
retinal pigment cells do not move (Trinkaus and Lentz, 1964).

It is clear that the selective adhesion hypothesis explains more of the
results of sorting out than the other hypotheses. In consequence, it seems
likely that it, or some modification of it, will turn out to be the correct
explanation of how cell segregation occurs in mixed aggregates. This is
not to say that chemotaxis of one kind or another does not occur under
certain circumstances. It simply is inadequate of itself to account for
the results. Nor should this conclusion be taken to imply that trypsin,
EDTA, and other dissociating agents do not have significant effects on
the adhesive and motile properties of the cell surface. It is just that
cells seem to recover rapidly from whatever effect these agents have,
and participate in the sorting out process primarily in terms of their
innate surface properties. It must be emphasized that there is as yet no
direct evidence for the postulated quantitative differences in adhesiveness. Efforts have been made to measure adhesiveness by a number of

* This distance is so short that it seems possible that sorting out is not brought
about by free migration of cells, but through the competition of retractable filopodial
processes. The cellular mobility of Steinberg's hypothesis may be mainly the mobility
of the processes (cf. Weston and Abercrombie, 1967).

means, but the results do not yield to uniform interpretation (Taylor, 1961; P. Weiss, 1961; L. Weiss, 1961, 1962b; Steinberg, 1964; Curtis, 1966). The measurement of cell surface adhesiveness and the relation of the results to cell movement, cell arrangements, and cell contact relations at the fine-structural level are obviously matters of extreme importance, not only for understanding the behavior of cells in mixed aggregates, but for understanding morphogenetic cell movements as well. One final point should be made concerning the interpretation of the manner in which cells sort out. Abercrombie (1964b) has pointed out that any factor which reduces the probability of separation, once cells have collided, could theoretically serve instead of adhesion. For example, there could be an inhibition of locomotion or increased resistance of the adhering membranes to rupture (L. Weiss, 1962a; L. Weiss and Lachmann, 1964).

Conclusions

A number of general conclusions relevant to the mechanisms of morphogenetic cell movements may be drawn from these *in vitro* studies. (1) Cells from both embryos and adults have the power of locomotion at their disposal. This potential is of course put to its fullest use during embryogenesis. In the case of adult tissue cells, the power to move appears to be utilized only during the exceptional circumstances of wound closure, regeneration, and in cell and tissue culture. (In the last circumstance special treatments may sometimes be required to free adult cells from the trap of intercellular materials in which they are often enmeshed before they can express their locomotor capacity.) The migratory activities of the amoebocytes of the blood and lymph have been excluded from this discussion. (2) The translocation of cells depends upon two closely related properties: a locomotor organ such as a ruffled membrane and adhesiveness for the substratum. (3) The properties of the substratum are vitally important, both to provide cells with a surface on which they can gain traction during movement and for cell orientation. (4) The movements of fibroblasts are inhibited by contact with each other *in vitro*. This apparently also applies to epithelial cells. (5) Tissue and organ specificity of cell adhesions can be explained on the basis of quantitative differences in adhesiveness (or ability to break away, once adhered). Qualitative differences in cell surface properties is not a necessary postulate. (6) There is no evidence for the operation of chemotaxis in directing the movements of fibroblasts and epithelial cells in tissue culture and in the sorting out of cells within a cell aggregate.

Unsolved Problems

A number of problems have arisen from these investigations which will need close attention in the near future.

(1) We really don't understand what causes the formation of a ruffled membrane at a free surface of a cell. The orientation of the substratum may promote formation of a ruffled membrane, as in contact guidance. But how does it do it? How is a ruffled membrane paralyzed by contact with the surface of another cell?

(2) The apparent absence of contact inhibition in the movement of cells over each other as they sort out in mixed aggregates has hardly been analyzed (cf. Abercrombie, 1964b) and there is as yet no coherent unifying theory for the two modes of behavior.

(3) There has been but little effort to study the possible role of contact inhibition in the control of cell movements *in vivo*. The transparent embryos and larvae of many forms should be ideal material for such studies with time-lapse cinemicrography (see our studies of *Fundulus*, p. 153–155).

(4) Although contact guidance is established as an important effect of the substratum on cell behavior that could have morphogenetic significance, it is not yet established whether it is always due to orientations of the substratum substructure or perhaps also to trapping caused by increased substratum adhesiveness (see Carter, 1965). Moreover, the evidence that contact guidance is at work *in vivo* is as yet only suggestive. Careful study of the substrata over which cells normally move is required.

(5) There is now considerable evidence that cells of germ layers, organs, and certain tissues sort out in mixed aggregates, but in the case of most organs we have no information as to whether their different tissue types are sorting out from each other (Trinkaus, 1965, p. 70). Weiss and Taylor (1960), for example, have shown that a suspension of dissociated liver cells cultured on the chorioallantoic membrane will form liver tissues with an organization that remarkably resembles the normal. Are the individual tissue types sorting out here? We have no evidence as yet. In the case of metanephric kidney, Okada (1965) has demonstrated with fluorescent antibody labeling that secretory tubule cells sort out from all other kidney cells. Other studies like this are needed.

(6) Criteria for adhesiveness, such as the tendency of certain cells to adhere together in a sheet, degree of flattening on the substratum

(Lieberman and Ove, 1958; Trinkaus, 1963a; Carter, 1965), the amount of membrane closely applied to that of an adjacent cell (Okazaki *et al.,* 1962; Gustafson and Wolpert, 1963), and the amount of pull by glass needles (Coman, 1944) or turbulence required to pull cells apart or off substrata (L. Weiss, 1961), have thus far sufficed to demonstrate the importance of different degrees of adhesiveness for certain cell movements and collective behavior. In many instances, however, we do not know whether cells are adhering more or less readily, because the variations in adhesiveness may be too small to be detected by our methods of measurement. More precise quantitative methods must be developed to detect and measure such variations. Only then will we be able to test directly the differential adhesion hypothesis of Steinberg, analyze the relative strengths with which fibroblasts adhere to glass and other fibroblasts, assess delicate adhesive changes during critical phases of embryogenesis and compare neoplastic and normal cells.

(7) A major area of contemporary interest is the physics and chemistry of the relations between two cells as they approach one another and enter into stable topographical relations (Abercrombie and Ambrose, 1962; Curtis, 1962a, 1966; Grobstein, 1961; Humphreys, 1963; Lansing and Zollinger, 1965; Moscona, 1959; Pethica, 1961; Rappaport and Howze, 1966; Rosenberg, 1962; Steinberg, 1964; L. Weiss, 1962a,b; P. Weiss, 1961). Studies on the nature of the cell surface and of the forces that hold cells together have increased with the growing realization of the overriding importance of cell surface properties in cell movement and contact in both normal cell differentiation and carcinogenesis (cf. Rubin, this volume). Jones and Elsdale (1963), for example, have shown that cells of an early amphibian embryo adhere and flatten on the glass in culture before they begin visible cytodifferentiation, and Holtfreter (1944), Gustafson and Wolpert (1963), and I (Trinkaus, 1963a) have shown that a change in surface properties of cells is a prelude to the mass movements of cells in gastrulation. Among the questions to be asked, the most important are those which attempt to provide explanations on the physico-chemical level for cell contact activities which are already reasonably well-understood at the level of the cell. There has been insufficient focusing of all the possible techniques on particular cell contact relationships. It is only by concentrating techniques that we can begin to bridge the gap between research at the molecular and cellular levels of organization. For example, what changes at the fine-structural level accompany changes in cell locomotion and contact? What changes in chemical and physical properties

accompany both? The electron microscope has been applied to the study of cell contacts as they relate to cell movements only in a minimal way. Some of the first results reveal striking structural correlations with the observed behavior of cells in culture and during morphogenesis (Balinsky, 1960; Dollander, 1961; Overton, 1962; Bellairs, 1963; Baker, 1965; Lesseps, 1963; Robertson, 1964; Cloney, 1966; Trinkaus and Lentz, 1967; Hilfer and Hilfer, 1966; Perry and Waddington, 1966), and confirm the need for concerted observation at the fine-structural level of cell contacts in the presence and absence of contact inhibition, during different phases of sorting out, and at the time of morphogenetic movements.

Mechanism of Morphogenetic Cell Movements

Morphogenetic cell movements have been studied with a view to elucidating mechanism principally in four kinds of embryos: amphibian, echinoderm, chick and teleost. The first studied was that of the amphibian. The studies on other forms soon followed. I shall not consider amphibian, echinoderm, and chick movements in detail, since I have recently reviewed them (Trinkaus, 1965), but will confine myself to brief summaries of our current understanding and a few comments on possible fruitful avenues of future investigation. I will give teleost epiboly more extended treatment, inasmuch as it has preoccupied me now for several years and I feel in a better position to handle it in detail.

Amphibian Gastrulation

By a combination of observations and dissections of normally gastrulating embryos, microsurgery, and culturing of germ layers and dissociated cells, Holtfreter (1943a,b, 1944) was able to point to several salient features of gastrulation. On the basis of these, and with the later theoretical considerations of Steinberg (1964), the following picture emerges. Invagination begins as the superficial endodermal cells of the blastoporal region actively sink into the deep endoderm to form elongate bottle cells. Their outer ends are tightly coherent, hence, as they sink in, the surface becomes indented and adjacent endoderm cells are drawn in also. In this manner, a beginning archenteron is formed. The prospective mesoderm follows, possibly in part because of an inherent tendency to stretch in an anteroposterior direction (Schechtman, 1934; Holtfreter, 1944), and spreads on the highly adhesive undersurface of the ectoderm. The ectodermal cells acquire an inherent tendency to spread and expand collectively in a sheet over the invaginating presumptive mesoderm, replacing it as it disappears from the surface. Ectodermal cells are presumed to have low average cohesiveness because of their nonadhesive outer surfaces. The superficial endoderm appears to possess properties similar to the ectoderm and in consequence spreads extensively to line the archenteron and aid in its enlargement. The greater spreading tendency of the ectoderm limits the spreading of the endoderm in lining the archenteron and thus prevents a reversal of involution.

Holtfreter (1943a) thought that an extraneous layer or "coat" is applied to the outer surfaces of all cells which are superficial at the onset of gastrulation and postulated that this coat unifies them into a cohesive sheet and is responsible for the nonadhesive quality of their outer surfaces. He also thought that the outer ends of the bottle cells are stuck to the coat and hence remain at the surface, while the rest of the cell is burrowing into the interior. It is apparent now that the concept of the coat was based on insufficient evidence (Trinkaus, 1965). A search for a surface coat with the electron microscope has given varied results. In some studies a coat was visualized (Dollander, 1961; Wartenberg and Schmidt, 1961), but in others it was not (Karasaki, 1959; Balinsky, 1960; Baker, 1965). The absence of a coat in electron micrographs could be attributed to the difficulty in detecting mucopolysaccharides (of which the postulated coat would probably be composed) with the methods used. Hence the matter is not yet settled. On the other hand, the electron micrographs revealed other specializations that conceivably could account for certain properties attributed to the coat. All superficial cells are united toward the distal end of their opposed surfaces by what appear to be zonal close junctions. These may aid cohesion into a cell sheet. Baker (1965) has found that bottle cells have long villous projections at their outer ends, which interdigitate with the outer surfaces of adjacent cells. Perhaps it is these that anchor the bottle cells to the archenteron surface (see also Perry and Waddington, 1966).

A useful feature of this picture of amphibian gastrulation is its heuristic value. It calls attention to the possible crucial importance of postulated differences in surface adhesiveness. Finding means of measuring cellular adhesiveness, therefore, should have the highest priority in future studies of amphibian gastrulation. It would also be of interest to know what surface specializations characterize the contacts of cells in movement, both those that move as individuals and as members of a sheet. A careful study of the behavior of cells of different regions in cell culture is also required. When do they acquire the capacity to spread and how do they do it? It seems certain that the bottle cells play an essential role, yet we don't know what causes them to extend into the interior. The answer to this question will probably indicate why some cells in the region of the marginal zone form bottle cells and others do not.

Echinoderm Invagination

The exceptional transparency of some echinoderm eggs has been taken advantage of by Dan and Okazaki and Gustafson, Kinnander and Wolpert (reviewed in Dan, 1960, Gustafson and Wolpert, 1963) to follow the cell movement of gastrulation in intimate detail. Their results have led to a more complete understanding of gastrulation than we have in any other form. Kinnander and Gustafson (1960) showed with time-lapse cinemicrography that the beginning of invagination is accompanied by a rounding up and pulsatory activity of the columnar cells of the vegetal plate on their inner borders, suggesting a reduction in adhesiveness. Their outer borders, however, remain tightly adherent to the hyaline plasma layer. If contact between columnar cells is reduced, a sheet will inevitably increase in area. Gustafson and Wolpert (1963) postulate that the vegetal plate is confined by the tightly constructed blastocoel wall (Balinsky, 1959) and therefore cannot spread as a flat sheet. If this is true, it is bound to curve, and since the reduced cell contact is on the inner side of the plate, it will curve in that direction. Thus invagination begins.

This concept may well be correct, but it bears some scrutiny. Moore and Burt (1939) performed an experiment several years ago that is relevant. They showed that the first $1/4$ to $1/3$ of invagination can take place after removal of the animal half of the egg. This suggests that changes intrinsic to the vegetal plate are responsible for primary invagination, and is consistent with the observation that invagination begins with a change in the surface properties of its cells. It also indicates, however, that the blastocoel wall need not be intact for invagination to begin and raises questions about the postulated confining role of the wall of the blastocoel. In light of this, it would be of interest to see if the activities of the vegetal plate cells of isolated vegetal halves are similar to those of intact eggs. The Moore and Burt experiment also eliminates the possibility that the change in surface behavior of vegetal plate cells is due to a change in the blastocoelic fluid (unless of course the effect has taken place prior to cutting away the animal half of the egg).

The primary phase of gastrulation comes to a halt when the archenteron tip is about one-third of the way to the animal pole. The second phase of invagination is always associated with the formation of filopodia spun out by the secondary mesenchyme cells which form at the tip of the archenteron. These filopodia extend to the inner surface of the blastocoel wall where they adhere and exert contractile tension. The Japanese and Swedish workers independently proposed that these filopodia exert sufficient tension to stretch and pull the archenteron to the animal pole (Dan and Okazaki, 1956; Gustafson and Kinnander, 1956). This hypothesis has been carefully tested experimentally and by time-lapse cinematographic observation of normal invagination, and appears to be correct for the last half of invagination when the majority of secondary mesenchyme filopodia attach to the blastocoel wall in the general area of the animal pole. The situation has not been as clear, however, for the beginning of the secondary phase (Trinkaus, 1965). At the completion of the first phase of invagination the archenteron tip is only one-third of the way to the animal pole and is actually nearest the lateral and vegetal surfaces of the blastocoel wall. If filopodia attach at random, they might be expected to adhere predominantly to these regions. Published photomicrographs of Gustafson and Wolpert (1963) and studies of my own on the egg of the sea urchin, *Lytechinus variegatus,* appeared to confirm this expectation. In such circumstances the first phase of secondary invagination should be opposed by the tension of these filopodia. I investigated this situation in gastrulas of *Paracentrotus lividus* (a species used occasionally by Gustafson and his co-workers) and found that in this species filopodia attach predominantly to the animal pole region at all times, even at the very beginning of the secondary phase. This is consistent with the hypothesis of Dan and Gustafson and support it as a complete explanation of the secondary phase of invagination. The filopodia of the secondary mesenchyme apparently adhere preferentially to the blastocoel wall in the general area of the animal pole, and by their collective contractile tension stretch the archenteron until its clinging secondary mesenchyme cells reach the animal pole. Perhaps the inner surface is more adhesive in the region of the animal pole. The ever-shortening filopodia also serve to anchor the stretched archenteron, for when they are broken by compressing the egg during invagination, the archenteron immediately retracts (Trinkaus, unpublished).

It begins to appear that movement by means of the contraction of adhering filopodia may be a major means of cell locomotion during early development (see below). It is therefore of importance to study

this type of movement as closely as possible. The transparency of echinoderm eggs make their primary and secondary mesenchyme cells prime
material for such studies, and interesting progress has already been made
(Gustafson and Wolpert, 1961; Okazaki *et al.*, 1962). How do the contacts of primary mesenchyme cells change and what kind of attachments
are made by the tips of the secondary mesenchyme filopodia, studied at
both the optical and fine-structural level? How do the tips of the
filopodia move over their substratum? Is it proper to consider such
filopodia as elongate ruffled membranes (Trinkaus, 1965)? Is there any
way of measuring the tension in the filopodia? What binds secondary
mesenchyme cells to the tip of the archenteron so that the contraction
of their filopodia can exert tension on the archenteron wall? Gustafson
and Wolpert (1963) have proposed that gastrulation may be explained
in terms of three cell properties: random motility, filopodial contraction,
and differential adhesiveness. This is a good working hypothesis. A
major effort of future studies must be to find independent means of
studying the adhesiveness of different regions of the inner surface of
the blastocoel wall during secondary invagination and of the vegetal
plate cells during primary invagination.

Chick Epiboly

The epibolic spreading of the area opaca of the chick blastoderm over
the yolk is an impressive aspect of chick morphogenesis. It was therefore
puzzling that chick blastoderms did not spread in culture when explanted to plasma or agar substrata (Waddington, 1932; Spratt, 1946).
The answer was found recently by New (1959). The margin of the
area opaca normally adheres tightly to the overlying vitelline membrane
and New showed that when a cultured blastoderm is inverted and
placed on the inner surface of its vitelline membrane, it adheres to it
and spreads over it at the normal rate.

It is clear that here too, as in the spreading of other sheets, the
nature of the substratum is important. With this in mind, Bellairs *et al.*
(1963) examined the fine structure and chemical composition of the
vitelline membrane and found it to be composed of two layers that
differ structurally and chemically. Both are composed of protein, but
the protein of the inner layer resembles materials which have been
found in connective tissue accompanying collagen. This is of interest,
because although a blastoderm margin will adhere to both the outer
and inner surfaces of the vitelline membrane, it will spread only over
the inner surface (New, 1959). These results suggest that the precise

nature of the inner membrane is crucial. This may well be true for normal epiboly, but it is not the only substratum that will support spreading. Spratt (1963) found that a cellulose ester polypore filter will serve almost as well. New found that the tautness of the membrane is also quite important. A flaccid vitelline membrane will not support epiboly and a local increase in tautness will cause increased local spreading, raising the possibility that the blastoderm may be guided by stress lines in its substratum. There is no evidence, however, that there is an animal-vegetal orientation in the membrane which guides normal expansion of the blastoderm. Even if there is one, it is unimportant for epiboly. A blastoderm placed endoderm-down on the vitelline membrane will curl under and spread backward in an animal direction.

The spreading of a blastoderm under the vitelline membrane, like other spreading cell sheets, depends primarily on the strong adhesion of its margin. The remainder of the blastoderm is either nonadherent or very lightly adherent. Unlike other spreading sheets, such as an epithelial sheet in culture and the spreading *Fundulus* blastoderm (see below), apparently the only cells of the chick blastoderm which will spread are those *normally* at the margin. This observation suggests that the marginal cells are intrinsically different. Bellairs (1963) has examined these cells in the electron microscope and found that each extends a long, thin process (or processes) out onto the vitelline membrane. Individual processes may be as much as 500μ long and as little as $\frac{1}{4} \mu$ deep. The extreme edge of the blastoderm is only as thick as a single process, but further medially there is a gradual increase in thickness where individual processes overlap one another. Only marginal cells have been observed to extend such processes. These processes are no doubt part of the locomotor organ of the cell. Bellairs suggests that they probably contract and pull the blastoderm with them. Significantly, the margin of the blastoderm adheres so tightly to the vitelline membrane that cells and membrane remain attached throughout the fixation procedure. Projections from the upper surface of a process are occasionally observed extending up into the vitelline membrane and may help to anchor the process to the membrane. Like other hyaline cytoplasmic extensions (see p. 156 and Figs. 10 and 11) these processes lack mitochondria, endoplasmic reticulum, Golgi formations and, intracellular yolk droplets. Bellairs and New (1962) have found marginal cells to be highly phagocytic. In view of their obvious importance it would be of interest to observe the surface activities of these cells in the living state in greater detail. Hopefully this could be done in culture, under more favorable optical conditions than on the vitelline membrane.

New (1959) has suggested that the mechanical tension imposed by the spreading margin is necessary for blastoderm expansion. If tension were not necessary, he contends, the rate of expansion would sometimes overtake the rate of movement of the attached edge. This does not occur. An alternative interpretation is that the mechanical tension is not a cause of expansion but an inevitable consequence of the actively spreading margin pulling and expanding the relatively passive nonmarginal regions. This interpretation is supported by two facts: (1) blastoderm expansion occurs only when the margin is spreading (2) the marginal region of the blastoderm will spread in isolation (Schlesinger, 1958). This would also explain why the ectoderm near the margin increases in thickness, from 1 cell to 3–4 cells thick, when a blastoderm adheres to the outer surface of the vitelline membrane (New, 1959). In this case, cell division apparently continues, but since the margin is not spreading and expanding the blastoderm, the cells are allowed to pile up. Time-lapse cinemicrography of the activities of nonmarginal cells during epiboly should yield information on just how passive the nonmarginal cells are (if appropriate optical conditions can be devised). Since the blastoderm is placed under considerable tension by the pull of its actively spreading margin, the nonmarginal cells must be tightly adherent, or they would be pulled apart. It is therefore significant that the ectodermal cells, which form a cohesive sheet throughout epiboly, are joined to each other by "terminal bars," or close junctions at 18 hours incubation, when the ectoderm is 1 cell thick (Bellairs, 1963; Overton, 1962). At this time, desmosomes are uncommon, but by 3 days, when the ectoderm is 2 or more cells deep, desmosomes are common, uniting not only cells lying side by side, but also those lying on top of each other.

Cell division goes on during epiboly, primarily near the margin of the blastoderm, but it is not necessary for blastoderm expansion. A blastoderm will continue spreading after mitoses have been inhibited (Bellairs, 1954) and with no increase in protein (New, 1959). There is therefore no support for the suggestion that rapidly dividing cells cause spreading by pushing from behind (Spratt, 1963).

I have discussed elsewhere (Trinkaus, 1965) the spreading of the hypoblast, the involation of the mesentoblast and the migration of precardiac mesoderm, and since I have nothing further to add at this time, will not consider them in this paper.

Teleost Epiboly

The attractiveness of teleost eggs for studies on the mechanism of morphogenetic movements has rested on two features: the transparency of the eggs and the great extent of their epiboly. During blastula stages, a blastoderm consisting of a few thousand cells surmounts a fluid yolk sphere several times its size. Then, as gastrulation begins, it flattens and spreads down over the yolk, finally to encompass it completely. Three separate structures participate in this epibolic spreading (Trinkaus, 1965) (Fig. 2): the enveloping layer of the blastoderm, a precocious,

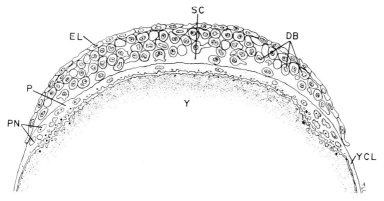

Fig. 2. Diagram of an early gastrula (stage 12). The blastoderm is flattened and extends over one-third of the yolk sphere as a result of epiboly. The cells of the enveloping layer (EL) are flattened and closely united. Lobopodia extend from some of the blastomeres (DB). The basal membrane of the periblast (P) does not contain as many projections into the yolk as in cleavage stages, and granules and vacuoles are not as numerous. SC, segmentation cavity; PN, periblast nucleus; Y, yolk; YCL, yolk cytoplasmic layer. The clear area immediately beneath the periblast and yolk cytoplasmic layer is a region where yolk is apparently being digested. 140×. (From Lentz and Trinkaus, 1967.)

cohesive epithelium that forms the outer membrane of the blastoderm; the deep cells of the blastoderm, which engage in extensive morphogenetic movements beneath the spreading enveloping layer; and the periblast, a syncytial layer at the surface of the yolk, beneath the deep cells and the enveloping layer. The role of these parts in the mechanism of epiboly has been studied both in the trout (Devillers, 1960) and in *Fundulus* (Trinkaus, 1965). My discussion will concern itself principally with our investigations of epiboly in the egg of *Fundulus heteroclitus* (Trinkaus, 1949, 1951, 1963a, 1965; Trinkaus and Ebstein,

1967; Lentz and Trinkaus, 1967; Trinkaus and Lentz, 1967). Studies on trout epiboly have been reviewed elsewhere (Devillers, 1960; Trinkaus, 1965).

The periblast is an ideal substratum for the spreading blastoderm; it spreads beneath it throughout epiboly and in addition possesses the capacity to spread independently of the blastoderm. If a blastoderm is removed, the periblast can complete epiboly in its absence. The blastoderm, however, appears to require the periblast as its substratum. In both normal epiboly and under experimental conditions a blastoderm spreads over the periblast to the periblast margin, but it never spreads beyond the margin of the periblast to move over the yolk cytoplasmic layer (Figs. 3 and 4).

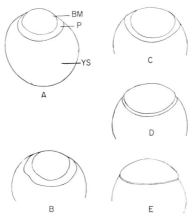

Fig. 3.   Epiboly of blastoderm and periblast (stage 10 to 11 + +). Note the decrease in width of the marginal periblast during the first stages of blastoderm expansion (from B to E). Time intervals since A are: B, 175 minutes; C, 245 minutes; D, 365 minutes; E, 450 minutes. BM, blastoderm; P, periblast; YS, yolk sphere. (From Trinkaus, 1951.)

The cells of the blastoderm seem to have an intrinsic capacity for spreading at the time of gastrulation. Partial blastoderms will spread on the periblast and even complete epiboly, regardless of their original position on the periblast. Such a partial blastoderm often approximately doubles its normal extent of expansion, a dramatic demonstration that the capacity of the blastoderm for expansion is much greater than is normally expressed. The spreading of parts of the blastoderm directed attention to its cells. To begin analysis at the cellular level, blastoderms were dissociated into suspensions of separate cells and cultured on glass.

Under these conditions, gastrula cells tend to flatten rapidly on the glass substratum, while blastula cells remain spherical with protruding lobopodia (Fig. 5). This correlation of cell spreading *in vitro* with the onset of epiboly *in vivo* suggests that changes in the surface properties of the blastoderm cells, such as an increase in their adhesiveness, lie at the basis of blastoderm epiboly. Late blastula cells behave differently from early blastula cells. They flatten slightly at first, but more extensively with increased time in culture, when control eggs are beginning epiboly. This observation suggests that the processes which change cell behavior *in vivo* begin in the late blastula stage and continue *in vitro*, regardless of the change in environmental conditions.

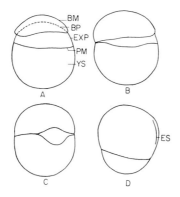

FIG. 4. Re-expansion of a reattached blastoderm of an early gastrula over the periblast in *Fundulus heteroclitus*. Time intervals since severance of the marginal connections of the blastoderm to the margin of the periblast: A, 30 minutes; B, 105 minutes; C, 330 minutes; D, 480 minutes. BM, blastoderm; BP, periblast underneath the blastoderm; ES, embryonic shield; EXP, exposed periblast; PM, margin of periblast; YS, yolk sphere. (Modified from Trinkaus, 1951.)

We may conclude from all this that the blastoderm and its constituent cells acquire the intrinsic capacity for spreading during late blastula stages and that this spreading capacity is expressed during gastrulation by epiboly over its natural substratum, the expanding periblast. Although cell division continues throughout epiboly, it is not necessary for the process. Kessel (1960) has shown that epiboly will continue until completion, even though mitoses are blocked. From what we know of other spreading cell sheets, it comes as no surprise that the manner of adhesion of the blastoderm to its periblast substratum is crucial. When the marginal adhesion between the enveloping layer and the periblast (Fig. 4) is severed during epiboly, the blastoderm promptly retracts, indicating that it is under tension and that marginal cells adhere more strongly to the periblast than do nonmarginal cells. This recalls other spreading epithelial sheets and suggests that the marginal cells may be the prime movers in epiboly, exerting tension on the blasto-

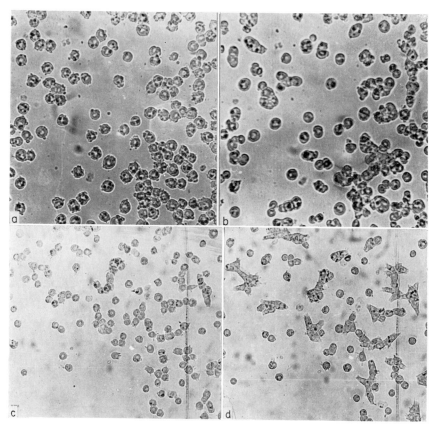

FIG. 5. Behavior of *Fundulus* cells in culture. A: Blastula cells (stage 8-9) ; 29 minutes in culture; note many lobopodia; no cells are flattened. B: Same cells as in A; 5 hours in culture; note continued aggregation; a few cell clusters are slightly flattened. C: Early gastrula cells (stage 11⅓) ; 18 minutes in culture; cells are already flattened. D: Same cells as in C; 1 hour in culture; note aggregation; cells are extensively flattened. 300×. (From Trinkaus, 1963a.)

derm by their outward spreading. This could explain why rate of linear advance is the best parameter of blastoderm epiboly (Milkman and Trinkaus, 1953). In this regard, it is significant that when the enveloping layer lacks a free edge, as in isolates of whole blastoderms, it spreads little, if at all (Trinkaus and Drake, 1956). The spreading activity of the marginal cells is certainly of central importance for blastoderm expansion. It should be emphasized, however, that a capacity for strong adhesion to the periblast is not an exclusive property of cells which are normally at the margin (as is the case for the chick blastoderm). Removal of part of a blastoderm results in adhesion of cells at the free cut surface to the periblast. In other words, when central cells become marginal, they too adhere more tightly. The partial blastoderm now spreads over the exposed periblast. Although the marginal cells of the blastoderm are the only cells which normally adhere strongly to the periblast, they are not the only ones to adhere. The lowermost deep cells also adhere somewhat, as shown by the tendency of some of them to remain stuck to the periblast when a blastoderm is removed. The degree of adhesiveness, however, apparently is low. They are readily brushed off with a hair loop.

It was obvious at this juncture that a knowledge of the surface activities of the cells within the blastoderm and their contact relations to each other and the periblast is basic to an understanding of the mechanism of *Fundulus* epiboly. For this reason we recently inaugurated a correlated time-lapse cinematographic and fine-structural study of cell surface activities and cell contacts within normally developing blastoderms. Time-lapse cinematography (Trinkaus and Lentz, 1967; Trinkaus and Ebstein, 1967) reveals a changing pattern of surface behavior on the part of the deep blastomeres. During early cleavage, blastomeres show no surface activity, but at about the 64-cell stage gentle undulations become evident. As cleavage continues and the segmentation cavity is formed, deep blastomeres gradually form protruding, rounded, hyaline lobopodia, with ever increasing frequency (Fig. 6). By the middle of the blastula stage, elongate lobopodia appear and both rounded and elongate lobopodia form quite rapidly and frequently, every few minutes, and are withdrawn soon after they appear. A new one then forms elsewhere on the cell surface and it in turn is withdrawn. These lobopodia apparently do not adhere to other cells during early and middle blastula. Their rapid formation and withdrawal without adhesions causes the cells to change shape constantly in one place, with no translocation, and transform the blastoderm into a jostling mass of surface-active cells.

During the late blastula, just before the beginning of epiboly, lobopodia can be observed adhering to the surfaces of other cells. When this occurs, the lobopodium is stretched either into an elongate filo-

podium or a spreading membranous fan (Fig. 7). These adhesions give
the cell traction, so that as the processes retract, cells are pulled in the
direction of the adhesion. Thus, translocation of deep cells begins.
With the onset of epiboly, this locomotory behavior gradually increases,
so that by the onset of epiboly most deep cells appear to be involved.
At first the cell movements appear to be mainly random and cause the
deep cells to occupy the expanding space beneath the spreading enveloping layer. These movements soon take on a directional component,

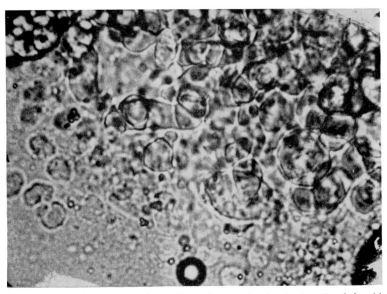

FIGS. 6–9. Printed from time-lapse film of normally developing *Fundulus* blastoderms. Bright-field optics. 100×.

FIG. 6. Deep blastomeres of a blastula (stage 9½). Most cells possess short
lobopodia, two being apparent in profile. Translocation of the deep cells has not
yet begun. The margin of the blastoderm where it joins the periblast stretches
diagonally across the lower portion of the field. Three adjacent periblast nuclei
may be seen at the lower left. From Trinkaus and Lentz, 1967.)

however, as the germ ring forms and cells converge dorsally to form the
embryonic shield. The increased adhesiveness of the cell surfaces toward
the end of the blastula stage and during gastrulation was predictable
from the observation that these cells tend to flatten on the glass in
culture (Trinkaus, 1963a), and supports the conclusion that increased
flattening on a plane surface in culture is a sign of increased adhesiveness.

Cells of the enveloping layer also show much membrane activity during epiboly. There is no cell displacement, however. All remain together in a cohesive layer (Figs. 8 and 9). This confirms for *Fundulus* the observation of Ballard (1966a) in the trout that stained cells do not leave the enveloping layer to engage in involution. Enveloping layer cells contract and expand and show surface undulations. Occasionally, the surfaces of two adjacent cells appear to separate over a part of the

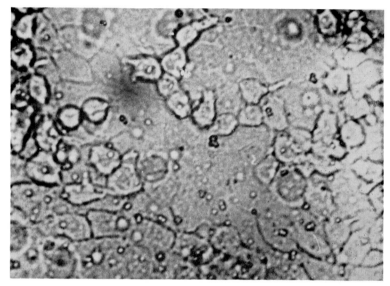

FIG. 7.   Deep blastomeres of a middle gastrula (stage 12½) near the ventral blastoderm margin. An elongate lobopodium is adhering to another at its tip. Another blastomere possesses an adhering fanlike process derived from a short lobopodium. These cells are actively motile. At the upper left, the outlines of the flattened cells of the enveloping layer may be discerned, slightly out of the plane of focus. (From Trinkaus and Lentz, 1967.)

area of contact (Fig. 9). Cells bordering such a gap often appear to show ruffled membrane activity or send processes across the gap (Fig. 9). These gaps are short-lived and close again in several minutes. During early epiboly, the marginal cells of the enveloping layer actively crawl over the periblast until they reach the region of its margin. From then on they remain close to the periblast margin. The free surfaces of these marginal cells show extensive ruffled membrane activity. Sometimes marginal cells retract slightly and then move again toward the periblast margin, with associated membrane activity.

The fine-structural studies of *Fundulus* epiboly were performed in collaboration with Dr. Thomas L. Lentz of the Department of Anatomy of Yale University and are described in full in Lentz and Trinkaus (1967) and Trinkaus and Lentz (1967).

The fine-structural observations correlate closely with the low power time-lapse observations of living deep blastomeres. Lobopodia are evident and their hyaline appearance is confirmed and explained. They are relatively free of organelles (as are those of the chick, see p. 147). In early and middle blastulas, close contacts of lobopodia with other cells are rare, an observation which is consistent with their evident lack of adhesiveness at this time (Fig. 10). During late blastula and

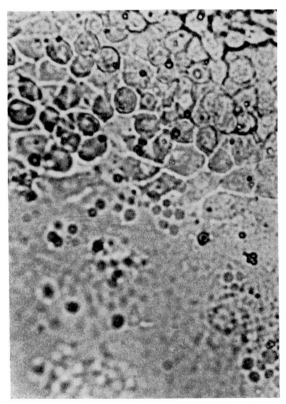

Fɪɢ. 8. Cells at the lateral margin of a midgastrula (stage 12½). Marginal cells of the flattened enveloping layer are visible where they adhere to the periblast. Note that the enveloping layer cells also adhere closely to each other. The margin of the periblast is located just beyond the margin of the enveloping layer, but is not visible in this micrograph. (From Trinkaus and Lentz, 1967.)

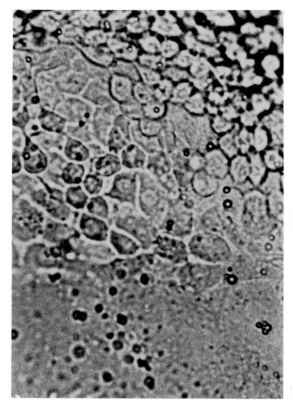

FIG. 9. The same region of the blastoderm shown in Fig. 8, 14½ minutes later, showing the progress of epiboly or downward migration of the enveloping layer and periblast over the yolk sphere. A gap has formed temporarily between three cells of the enveloping layer in the center. Note that thin suface extensions appear to connect two of the cells. At the left, filopodia of deep cells are in focus. (From Trinkaus and Lentz, 1967.)

gastrula stages, however, 200-Å contacts of lobopodia with other cells appear regularly (Fig. 11). The appearance of 200-Å contacts at a time when lobopodia attach to other blastomeres is evidence that these contacts are adhesive. A few close (60–75 Å) junctions have been observed between deep cells, but no desmosomes. This contrasts with the enveloping layer (see below), in which close junctions are invariably present and desmosomes appear during gastrulation. If close junctions and desmosomes are more adhesive junctions, we would expect to find them where cells remain bound together in a sheet. For cells that are constantly in locomotion, like deep cells, however, adhesion is needed only to gain traction for movement (Abercrombie and Ambrose, 1962; Trinkaus, 1965) ; and the adhesion must not be too strong, otherwise the cells would be immobilized. The 200-Å contacts apparently represent just this kind of adhesion. It is of interest in this context that Curtis (1964) has recently observed that moving fibroblasts make junctions of ca. 100 Å with the glass substratum.

We were not able to determine the relation of the lowermost deep cells to the periblast in films of living eggs. The electron micrographs of this relation, however, are clear. They reveal no tight or extensive

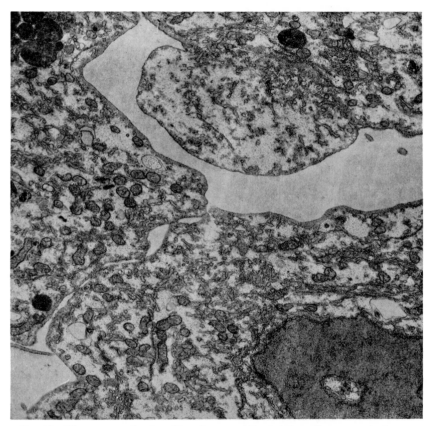

Fig. 10. Blastomeres of a late blastula stage 10) . A lobopodium extends from one of the blastomeres (upper right) into the segmentation cavity. Note that the lobopodium is not in contact with adjacent cells. The cytoplasm of the lobopodium contains fewer organelles than the cell proper. A thin band of condensed material separates the lobopodium from the remainder of the cell. 13,500×. (From Lentz and Trinkaus, 1967.)

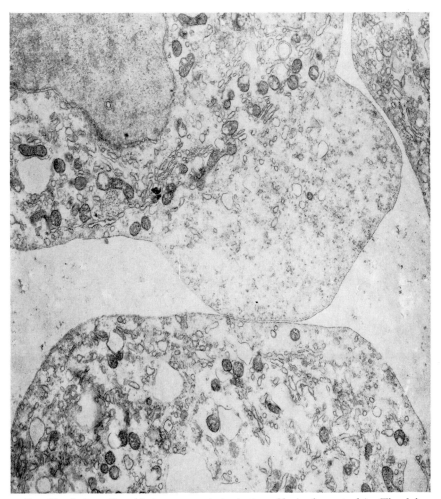

FIG. 11. Lobopodium-blastomere contact at stage 11 (early gastrula). The lobopodium is relatively free of organelles, containing a few vesicles and polyribosomes. In the zone of contact the adjacent plasma membranes are parallel, and separated by a gap of 200 Å. 21,500×. (From Trinkaus and Lentz, 1967.)

junctions, just some blastomeres lying on the top of microvilli which protrude from the upper surface of the periblast (Fig. 12). This is consistent with the apparent low adhesiveness of deep cells for the periblast revealed by dissections. If deep cells utilize the periblast as a substratum for movement, they must crawl over the tips of the periblast microvilli.

Cells of the enveloping layer are invariably bound together apically by junctions with an intercellular gap of ca. 60–75 Å (Fig. 13). For convenience, this junction is referred to as a close junction. Only a few junctions other than *zonulae occludentes* (Farquhar and Palade, 1963) have been observed, in which the intercellular space is less than 150 Å (Balinsky, 1959, 1960; Hama, 1960, 1965; Lesseps, 1963; Robertson, 1961), and the majority of these occur either in embryonic tissues or certain synapses. During blastula stages this apical close junction is the sole close contact between adjacent cells. A widened intercellular space occurs below the junction. During epiboly, however, when the

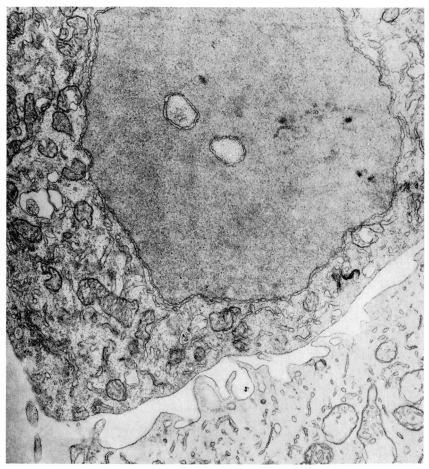

FIG. 12.   Blastomere-periblast contact. The blastomere lying in the segmentation cavity forms no specialized junctions with the periblast, but appears to brush the tips of some of the periblast microvilli. 21,000×. (From Trinkaus and Lentz, 1967.)

enveloping layer becomes increasingly stretched, the apical junction is supplemented by an initial zone in which the plasma membranes are separated by a gap of 120 Å and by desmosomes (Fig. 13). Additional close (60–75 Å) junctions and septate desmosomes are occasionally added to these. Most proximally the unit membranes diverge to produce a wider intercellular space. In many places, during epiboly, the unit membranes of adjacent cells follow a zig-zag course so that cytoplasmic processes interdigitate with one another.

In spite of the constant surface activity of enveloping layer cells seen in the time-lapse films, these cells remain in close contact most of the time. Presumably, their contact specializations, revealed in the electron microscope, are responsible for this. In the films, however, the surfaces of two adjacent cells occasionally appear to separate and then close again. These separations were not apparent in our electron micrographs. There are several possible explanations for this apparent contradiction (Trinkaus and Lentz, 1967), but we are not yet in a position to choose among them.

The contact relations of the marginal cells of the enveloping layer with the periblast are of special interest, since the only tight adhesive connection of the blastoderm to the periblast is at this region. Moreover, the marginal cells of the enveloping layer show ruffled membrane activity at their outer edges, as they spread over the expanding periblast. The junction between the periblast and the enveloping layer is identical to that uniting enveloping layer cells—a close junction with a gap of 60–75 Å, followed by regions in which the unit membranes are separated by 120 Å or more. If these cells form intermittent adhesions, as appears to be the case from the films, the cells must form close junctions, separate again and form junctions anew, in a matter of minutes. If this process occurs in a stepwise fashion, with a distal junction forming before the proximal contact is disrupted, at least one region of contact would always be present between enveloping layer and periblast, as is the case in the electron micrographs. Other possibilities are discussed in Trinkaus and Lentz (1967).

The electron microscope has enabled us to settle another matter, which has been puzzling for years. The yolk sphere of teleost eggs is contained by a membrane termed the yolk gel layer (Trinkaus, 1949), which has remarkable contractile properties. Lewis (1949a,b) thought that contraction of this membrane was the primary force in epiboly. The usefulness of this hypothesis was greatly diminished by experimental testing in *Fundulus* (Trinkaus, 1951, 1965), but the layer has nevertheless been recognized as essential for preservation of the normal

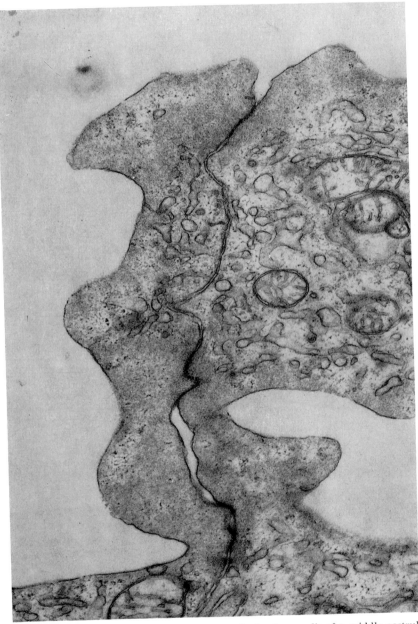

FIG. 13. Contact specializations between enveloping layer cells of a middle gastrula (stage 12⅓). In the initial junction and intermittently in other regions, the plasma

topography of the egg and thus, in an indirect way, for epiboly as well. The electron micrographs show that the yolk gel layer is actually a cytoplasmic layer, continuous with and an extension of the periblast (Trinkaus and Lentz, 1967). This discovery requires a new view of the spreading of the periblast in epiboly. The yolk layer was thought to solate at its juncture with the periblast, as it is gradually replaced in epiboly (Trinkaus, 1951). Since carbon marking experiments have shown that the yolk cytoplasmic layer does not contract during epiboly (Trinkaus, 1951), it now appears that periblast cytoplasm flows into the yolk cytoplasmic layer causing it to thicken and adding some organelles. In consequence, periblast epiboly appears not as the spreading of a layer with abrupt margins over the noncytoplasmic surface of the yolk, but as a controlled flow of cytoplasm from the thicker animal part of an intact cytoplasmic layer (the periblast) into its thinner vegetal part (the yolk cytoplasmic layer). This discovery raises an interesting question. The periblast appears to be a specific substratum for the blastoderm, limiting the rate of blastoderm epiboly by its own rate of spreading. If the periblast and yolk cytoplasmic layer are merely thick and thin parts of the same protoplasmic layer, why doesn't the enveloping layer push beyond the margin of the periblast during epiboly? We don't have the answer as yet, but it may be significant that the activity and structure of the outer surfaces of the two layers are markedly different. The exposed marginal surface of the periblast is highly active, with many villous projections, while the outer surface of the yolk cytoplasmic layer is characteristically quiescent and smooth.

It was once thought that an extraneous layer or "coat" was applied to the outer surfaces of enveloping layer cells in teleost eggs and functioned to unite them into a cohesive layer (Devillers, 1948; Trinkaus, 1949), but it has since been pointed out that the concept was based on insufficient evidence. Our fine-structural study of *Fundulus* development has revealed no extraneous material applied to the outer surfaces of enveloping layer cells, even though the material was fixed in a way that would likely show the presence of a mucopolysaccharide layer. As

---

membranes are closely apposed. Below the first contact, the plasma membranes are parallel, and separated by a distance of 120 Å. Another region of close apposition of plasma membranes occurs after which the membranes diverge to form an intercellular lake and then converge again. Below this last region of close contact a small desmosome occurs. Fibrils occur in the cytoplasm adjacent to the first two close junctions. The surface of the enveloping layer contains blunt undulations. The hyaloplasm beneath the plasma membranes is denser and contains fewer organelles than in deeper portions of the cells. 26,000×. (From Trinkaus and Lentz, 1966.)

in other eggs, the enveloping layer cells appear to be united by zonal close junctions and desmosomes.

The new information made available by time-lapse cinemicrography and electron microscopy requires a re-examination of our concept of the mechanism of *Fundulus* epiboly (Trinkaus and Lentz, 1967). The enveloping layer spreads like an epithelial sheet. Cells do not change position relative to each other and are bound together by close junctions and desmosomes. The crucial importance of the blastoderm margin (Trinkaus, 1965) and of the enveloping layer (Devillers *et al.*, 1957) has been confirmed. Like other epithelial layers, the enveloping layer seems to expand over its substratum (the spreading periblast) as a result of the activities of its marginal cells. These form close junctional adhesive contacts with the periblast and appear to spread over it as a result of ruffled membrane activity at their free margins. The strong adhesive contacts of the enveloping layer cells with each other communicate the pull of the outward (and downward) moving marginal cells to the entire enveloping layer. Nonmarginal cells are not completely passive, however. Their surfaces are in constant activity and when occasionally they partially separate, no doubt as a result of tension in the stretched membrane, they appear to form ruffled membranes and move together again to close the gap. Marginal cells, therefore, appear to be the prime movers, by their active spreading and their adhesion to the spreading periblast, but other cells are potentially active at all times and sporadically aid in the spreading of the sheet by tiny spreading movements of their own. Thus, cells at any cut surface of the enveloping layer will spread on the periblast. The tendency of enveloping layer cells to form a ruffled membrane only when an edge is free of contact with other cells, and then to spread in the direction of the ruffling membrane, and the absence of overlapping of cells, suggest that the enveloping layer is a contact inhibiting system. When the enveloping layer has spread entirely over the yolk, its marginal cells contact each other in closing the blastopore. As expected of a contact inhibiting system, their spreading now ceases. During closure of the blastopore the marginal cells of the enveloping layer are stretched into spindle shapes radiating from the point of blastopore closure, confirming an active pulling role of the marginal region of the periblast at this time. The mechanism of periblast epiboly is still not understood, although now it appears to involve a controlled flow of cytoplasm from the thicker periblast into the thinner yolk cytoplasmic layer.

The deep cells of the blastoderm translocate differently. They are not contact inhibiting. They are not bound together to form cohesive sheets, but move about over one another, and probably over the underlying periblast as well. At first, they appear to move largely at random, filling in space in the expanding segmentation cavity. Later, the movements of those in the germ ring near the blastoderm margin become directional and converge dorsally to form the embryonic shield. The deep blastomeres appear to acquire their capacity to move in two stages: (1) the formation of nonadhesive lobopodia during early blastula stages; and (2) an increase in surface adhesiveness during late blastula and early gastrula stages. There are three kinds of evidence for the increased adhesiveness toward the beginning of gastrulation: the tendency of dissociated gastrula cells to adhere and flatten on glass in cell cultures; adhesion of lobopodia to other cells in time-lapse films of normal development, with the consequent formation of taut filopodia and fans; the appearance of 200-Å junctions where lobopodia contact other cell surfaces. The lobopodium is the initial organ of locomotion and the increased adhesiveness gives it traction and converts it into a filopodium or fan. When an adhering filopodium or fan contracts, it pulls the cell along. The uppermost deep cells are closely applied (200 Å) to the under surface of the enveloping layer, while some of the lowermost cells are in close relation to the microvilli of the periblast. Deep cells, therefore, move by adhering to each other, to the inner surface of the enveloping layer, and probably also to the periblast.

Inasmuch as the cells of the enveloping layer appear to be contact inhibiting and the deep cells are certainly noncontact inhibiting, it is important to take note of their contact relations at the fine-structural level. During gastrulation, cells of the enveloping layer form one or more close junctions, 120-Å junctions, and desmosomal junctions with each other. In addition, cytoplasmic processes of adjacent cells may interdigitate. Deep cells, on the other hand, predominantly form only the classic 150–200-Å junction with each other, very occasionally adding a close junction. The contrast in contact relations of the two kinds of cells is arresting and emphasizes the need for similar comparative studies of other contact inhibiting and noncontact inhibiting systems. Perhaps ruffled membranes of contact inhibiting cells are paralyzed by contact with other such cells because of their tendency to form highly adhesive contact specializations with each other.

It is now evident that cells must differentiate in *Fundulus* in order for gastrulation to occur. Our correlated cell culture, cinematographic, and fine-structural studies have shown that changes in cell surface activity take place prior to gastrulation and that these changes constitute preparation for the cell movements of gastrulation. Study of the fine

structure of nuclei and cytoplasm of blastomeres during blastulation
reveals differentiations here as well (Lentz and Trinkaus, 1967). During
cleavage, the blastomeres are relatively undifferentiated: the hyaloplasm
is of low density, ribosomes and membranous elements comprising the
endoplasmic reticulum are sparse, and mitochondria are relatively simple structurally. Beginning with the early blastula stage, however, the
blastomeres show an increase in nuclear and cytoplasmic specializations.
The nucleolus appears as a mass of fine fibrillar material. Then, toward
the end of the blastula stage, dense granules, resembling cytoplasmic
ribosomes, appear within it. At the same time, nuclear chromatin material shows a tendency to aggregate into small clumps and interchromatin
granules become more numerous. These changes are like those described
by Karasaki (1965) for the egg of *Triturus*. In the cytoplasm, ribosomes, especially polyribosomes, become more numerous when the
nucleolus is first noted. Membranous elements of the endoplasmic reticulum also increase in number and the Golgi apparatus and mitochondria become more complex. The changes in surface activity of the
blastomeres occurring during this period presumably have their basis
in these nuclear and cytoplasmic differentiations, for such differentiations involve elaboration of the synthetic machinery of the cell. (Some
idea of the increase in differentiation of the cytoplasm can be gained
from examination of Fig. 12. The cytoplasm of the periblast is relatively
undifferentiated during cleavage, as is that of the blastomeres, but,
unlike the blastomeres, the periblast remains undifferentiated during
blastula and gastrula stages. In Fig. 12, the differentiated cytoplasm of
a deep cell of a gastrula is contrasted with the undifferentiated cytoplasm
of the periblast.)

Our latest studies of *Fundulus* epiboly have answered some questions,
but, inevitably, they have also spawned a whole family of new ones.
(1) How exactly does a filopodium or a fan of a deep cell operate as
an organ of locomotion? Do they terminate in ruffled membranes which
resemble ruffled membranes of fibroblasts? The same question may be
asked about the ruffled membranes of cells of the enveloping layer.
High-power microscopy of both kinds of cells *in vitro,* under more
favorable optical conditions, may permit the requisite observations. We
also need information on the manner in which marginal cells of the
enveloping layer begin to spread. It has been difficult to obtain adequate
photographs of this, because the mass of deep cells near the margin
impede observation of the enveloping layer at this stage. (2) If the
marginal cells of the enveloping layer are indeed the prime movers in
epiboly, nonmarginal cells should join the spreading progressively later,

as their distance from the margin increases. Also, separations between cells of the enveloping layer should appear first and more frequently near the margin, where the tension is greater. Quantitative studies of normal epiboly should give the answers. (3) The periblast also needs further study. Since the yolk cytoplasmic layer does not contract during epiboly, it would appear that the periblast spreads by a wave of surface activity (accompanied by cytoplasmic flow), which continually converts the yolk cytoplasmic layer into marginal periblast. If this is true, marks placed on the surface of an exposed periblast should remain in place and not spread with the margin. (4) Finally, we have as yet no knowledge of the chemical events on which changes in cell behavior essential to gastrulation depend. Now that we know some of the changes in surface activity and cell fine structure that occur prior to and during beginning phases of gastrulation, we are in a position to begin the biochemical analyses that may provide a molecular basis for these mass cell movements.

Epilogue

Certain general patterns appear to be emerging from studies on the mechanism of morphogenetic cell movements. In the first place, cells commence locomotion in various ways. (a) Primary mesenchyme of sea urchins and deep cells of teleosts appear to move by similar mechanisms. They begin by forming lobopodia. Then, as these protrusions adhere to other cells, they form filopodia and fans and cell movement begins, apparently as a result of contraction of the adhering processes. The similarity of behavior of these cells from widely separated phyla suggests that this mechanism of locomotion may be general for noncontact inhibiting cells (which move as individuals). Elongate cytoplasmic processes also appear to be essential for movement of marginal cells of the chick blastoderm and for dissociated sponge cells (Sindelar and Burnett, 1966). The tips of all of these processes may function like ruffled membranes. For cells which are flattened, like enveloping layer cells of teleosts, ruffled membranes, similar to those of fibroblasts *in vitro,* seem to be the organs of locomotion. (b) Changes in the surface adhesiveness of cells appear to be of general importance in morphogenetic movements. There is evidence for this in the case of the amphibian gastrula, the primary mesenchyme of the sea urchin and the cells of *Fundulus* blastoderms. (c) Acquisition of contact inhibition may be the change that sets certain cohesive systems in motion. This appears to be true for epiboly of the enveloping layer of teleosts and may also be true for the ectoderm of the chick and for the initial dispersal of cells of the neural crest. (d) An entirely different means of moving sheets of cells is by differential contraction of one surface of the sheet (Lewis, 1947). Cloney (1966) has just presented evidence that contraction of the tail ectoderm of ascidian larvae is due to oriented filaments in the apical cytoplasm of each cell. This might also be the mechanism for the formation of bottle cells at the onset of amphibian invagination (Waddington, 1940; Baker, 1965), for the formation of cone-shaped cells in the folding of a neural plate, and for many other foldings and invaginations during development.

Once cells have begun to move, the essential problem is to discover the means by which they are directed, or, lacking direction, the means by which they accumulate in specific loci. (a) The problem is relatively simple for the ectoderm of the chick and for the enveloping layer of the teleost, because of the topography of the situation. All that is required for the directional movement of epiboly is that the free edge spread centrifugally, given the proper substratum. In a sense, this is also true of the epiboly of amphibian ectoderm. In order to move in an oriented fashion, it need only spread to replace the mesoderm and endoderm as they undergo involution. In the case of amphibian ectoderm, however, there is no free edge; hence the mechanism by which the sheet spreads is obscure. (b) It is clear that contact guidance is not a necessary postulate for the directional epibolic spreading of fish, amphibian, and chick eggs, and there is no evidence for it. On the other hand, contact with underlying oriented endoderm cells may orient the migration of heart clusters in the chick. (c) In cases in which cells move randomly, regional differences in adhesiveness could trap them and thus account for their accumulation and arrangement in particular destinations. Although there is only one instance in which there is some evidence for this (trapping of primary mesenchyme of sea urchin eggs to form the mesenchyme ring), it is a hopeful idea. Carter (1965) has demonstrated that when cells in culture are presented with a gradient of increasing adhesiveness of the substratum they will move up it. (d) Folding of a sheet in a particular direction could be effected by differential contraction of the cytoplasm at the distal or proximal surface of the cells. The former would cause invagination and the latter evagination (as in an exogastrula). It would be interesting to compare cytoplasmic fine structure during the two contrasting processes.

A consistent picture seems to be emerging from structural studies of cell adhesions. When adhesions are less firm, the opposing plasma membranes appear to be held together by generally distributed adhesive sites.

When adhesions become firmer, specialized junctions appear. Overton (1962) showed that the first adhesions of dissociated chick blastoderm cells in a reaggregate lack desmosomes. These appear later, as the aggregate becomes tighter and cell movement presumably diminishes. Moving deep cells of *Fundulus* lack specialized junctions, while enveloping layer cells, which cohere firmly to form a sheet, have close junctions at first and then during epiboly add desmosomes and septate desmosomes.

Contemporary work in electrophysiology shows that cells with tight junctional and septate desmosomal contacts are electrotonically coupled (Loewenstein *et al.,* 1965; Bennett *et al.,* 1967). This discovery is potentially of considerable importance for the developmental biologist. It suggests that these junctional complexes not only aid cell-to-cell adhesion and the consequent formation of sheets and tissues, but in addition provide a means of electrical and chemical communication between cells so that the cell mass acts as a unit. This has obvious significance as a possible mechanism for simultaneous differentiation of cells within a mass, whether this differentiation be concerned with classic histogenesis or the mass cell movements which precede histogenesis.

In this paper, I have tried to show that substantial advances have been made in the area of morphogenetic cell movements during the last twenty-five years. Nevertheless, in comparison with many other areas of biology, the progress has been small. This is due in part to insufficient attention and in part to separation of analyses in this area from other studies in the broad area of cell contacts and cell movements. This disjunction seems now to be over. Indeed, one of the invigorating aspects of work on mechanisms of morphogenetic movements in the last few years has been the way in which studies in this area have begun to converge with studies on cell contacts and cell movements *in vitro,* in mixed aggregates, and at the level of fine structure. With this have come new techniques and an inevitable broadening of perspective. As a consequence, many questions are now better defined. This bodes well for the future. The next years should see elucidation of much that is at present mysterious in the mechanisms of morphogenetic cell movements.

Acknowledgment

The original work of the author and the writing of this paper have been supported by grants from the National Science Foundation. The Higgins Fund of Yale University supported some of the earlier work on *Fundulus* epiboly. The work of Dr. Thomas L. Lentz was supported by grants from the National Cancer Institute (TICA-5055) and from the National Institute of Arthritis and Metabolic Diseases (AM-03688), National Institutes of Health, United States Public Health Service. My observations on invagination in *Paracentrotus lividus* were made at La Station

Marine d'Endoume et Centre d'Océanographie, Marseille. It is a pleasure to record my indebtedness to Professor Jean-Marie Pérès, Director of the Station, for his hospitality during my stay.

REFERENCES

ABERCROMBIE, M. (1961) . The bases of the locomotory behaviour of fibroblasts. *Exptl. Cell Res. Suppl.* **8,** 188–198.

ABERCROMBIE, M. (1964a) . Behavior of cells toward one another. *Advan. Biol. Skin* **5,** 95–112.

ABERCROMBIE, M. (1964b) . Cell contacts in morphogenesis. *Arch. Biol.* **75,** 351–367.

ABERCROMBIE, M., AND AMBROSE, E. J. (1958) . Interference microscope studies of cell contacts in tissue culture. *Exptl. Cell. Res.* **15,** 332–345.

ABERCROMBIE, M., AND AMBROSE, E. J. (1962) . The surface properties of cancer cells: A review. *Cancer Res.* **22,** 525–548.

ABERCROMBIE, M., AND HEAYSMAN, J. E. M. (1953) . Observations on the social behaviour of cells in tissue culture. I. Speed of movement of chick heart fibroblasts in relation to their mutual contacts. *Exptl. Cell Res.* **5,** 111–131.

ABERCROMBIE, M., AND HEAYSMAN, J. E. M. (1954) . Observations on the social behaviour of cells in tissue culture. II. Monolayering of fibroblasts. *Exptl. Cell Res.* **6,** 293–306.

ABERCROMBIE, M., HEAYSMAN, J. E. M., AND KARTHAUSER, H. M. (1957) . Social behaviour of cells in tissue culture. III. Mutual influence of sarcoma cells and fibroblasts. *Exptl. Cell Res.* **13,** 276–291.

AMBROSE, E. J. (1961) . The movements of fibrocytes. *Exptl. Cell Res. Suppl.* **8,** 54–73.

BAKER, P. C. (1965) . Fine structure and morphogenic movements in the gastrula of the treefrog, *Hyla regilla. J. Cell Biol.* **24,** 95–116.

BALINSKY, B. I. (1959) . An electron microscopic investigation of the mechanisms of adhesion of the cells in a sea urchin blastula and gastrula. *Exptl. Cell Res.* **16,** 429–433.

BALINSKY, B. I. (1960) . Ultrastructural mechanisms of gastrulation and neurulation. Symposium on germ cells and development, *Inst. Intern. Embryol. Fondaz. A. Baselli.* pp. 550–563.

BALLARD, W. W. (1966a) . The role of the cellular envelope in the morphogenetic movements of teleost embryos. *J. Exptl. Zool.* **161,** 193–200.

BALLARD, W. W. (1966b) . Origin of the hypoblast in *Salmo.* I. Does the blastodisc edge turn inward? *J. Exptl. Zool.* **161,** 201–210.

BALLARD, W. W. (1966c) . Origin of the hypoblast in *Salmo.* II. Outward movement of deep central cells. *J. Exptl. Zool.* **161,** 211–220.

BELLAIRS, R. (1954) . The effects of folic acid antagonists on embryonic development. *Ciba Found. Symp. Chem. Biol. Pteridines,* 356–365.

BELLAIRS, R. (1963) . Differentiation of the yolk sac of the chick studied by electron microscopy. *J. Embryol. Exptl. Morphol.* **11,** 201–225.

BELLAIRS, R., AND NEW, D. A. T. (1962) . Phagocytosis in the chick blastoderm. *Exptl. Cell Res.* **26,** 275–279.

BELLAIRS, R., HARKNESS, M., AND HARKNESS, R. D. (1963) . The vitelline membrane of the hen's egg: a chemical and electron microscopical study. *J. Ultrastruct. Res.* **8,** 339–359.

BENNETT, M. V. L., PAPPAS, G. D., NAKAJIMA, Y., AND GIMENEZ, M. (1967) . Physiology and ultrastructure of electrotonic junctions. IV Medullary electromotor nuclei in gymnotid fish. *J. Neurophysiol.* **27** (in press).

BONNER, J. T. (1947). Evidence for the formation of cell aggregates by chemotaxis in the development of the slime mold, *Dictyostelium discoideum. J. Exptl. Zool.* **106**, 1–26.

BRESCH, D. (1955). Recherches préliminaires sur des associations d'organes embryonnaires de poulet en culture *in vitro. Bull. Biol. France Belg.* **89**, 179–188.

CARTER, S. B. (1965) Principles of cell motility: the direction of cell movement and cancer invasion. *Nature* **208**, 1183–1187.

CHIAKULAS, J. J. (1952). The role of tissue specificity in the healing of epithelial wounds. *J. Exptl. Zool.* **121**, 383–417.

CHIBON, P. (1966). Analyse expérimentale de la régionalisation et des capacités morphogénétiques de la crête neurale chez l'Amphibien Urodele *Pleurodeles waltlii* Michah. *Mém. Soc. Zool. France* **36**, 5–107.

CLONEY, R. A. (1966). Cytoplasmic filaments and cell movements: epidermal cells during ascidian metamorphosis. *J. Ultrastruct. Res.* **14**, 300–328.

COMAN, D. R. (1944). Decreased mutual adhesiveness, a property of cells from squamous cell carcinomas. *Cancer Res.* **4**, 625–629.

CURTIS, A. S. G. (1960). Cell contacts: some physical considerations. *Am. Naturalist* **94**, 37–56.

CURTIS, A. S. G. (1961). Timing mechanisms in the specific adhesion of cells. *Exptl. Cell Res. Suppl.* **8**, 107–122.

CURTIS, A. S. G. (1962a). Cell contact and adhesion *Biol. Rev. Cambridge Phil. Soc.* **37**, 82–129.

CURTIS, A. S. G. (1962b). Pattern and mechanism in the reaggregation of sponges. *Nature* **196**, 245–248.

CURTIS, A. S. G. (1964). The mechanism of adhesion of cells to glass. A study by interference reflection microscopy. *J. Cell. Biol.* **20**, 199–215.

CURTIS, A. S. G. (1966). Cell adhesion. *Sci. Progr. (London)* **54**, 61–86.

DAN, K. (1960). Cyto-embryology of echinoderms and amphibia. *Intern. Rev. Cytol.* **9**, 321–367.

DAN, K., AND OKAZAKI, K. (1956). Cyto-embryological studies of sea urchins. III. Role of the secondary mesenchyme cells in the formation of the primitive gut in sea urchin larvae. *Biol. Bull.* **110**, 29–42.

DeHAAN, R. L. (1963). Migration patterns of the precardiac mesoderm in the early chick embryo. *Exptl. Cell Res.* **29**, 544–560.

DEVILLERS, C. (1948). Le cortex de l'oeuf de Truite. *Ann. Sta. Centrale Hydrobiol. Appl.* **2**, 229–249.

DEVILLERS, C. (1960). Structural and dynamic aspects of the development of the teleostean egg. *Advan. Morphogenesis* **1**, 379–428.

DEVILLERS, C., COLAS, J., AND RICHARD, L. (1957). Différenciation *in vitro* de blasto- dermes de Truite *(Salmo irideus)* dépourvus de couche enveloppante. *J. Embryol. Exptl. Morphol.* **5**, 264–273.

DOLLANDER, A. (1961). Conceptions actuelles et terminologie relatives à certains aspects de l'organisation corticale de l'oeuf d'amphibien. *Arch. Anat. Histol. Embryol.* **44**, Suppl., 93–103.

FARQUHAR, M. G., AND PALADE, G. E. (1963). Junctional complexes in various epi- thelia. *J. Cell Biol.* **17**, 375.

GALTSOFF, P. S. (1923). The amoeboid movement of dissociated sponge cells. *Biol. Bull.* **45**, 153–161.

GROBSTEIN, C. (1961). Cell contact in relation to embryonic induction. *Exptl. Cell Res. Suppl.* **8**, 234–245.

GUSTAFSON, T., AND KINNANDER, H. (1956). Microaquaria for time-lapse, cinematographic studies of morphogenesis in swimming larvae and observations on sea urchin gastrulation. *Exptl. Cell Res.* **11**, 36–51.

GUSTAFSON, T., AND WOLPERT, L. (1961). Studies on the cellular basis of morphogenesis in the sea urchin embryo. Directed movements of primary mesenchyme cells in normal and vegetalized larvae. *Exptl. Cell Res.* **24**, 64–79.

GUSTAFSON, T., AND WOLPERT, L. (1963). The cellular basis of morphogenesis and sea urchin development. *Intern. Rev. Cytol.* **15**, 139–214.

HAMA, K. (1960). The fine structure of the desmosomes in frog mesothelium. *J. Biophys. Biochem. Cytol.* **7**, 575.

HAMA, K. (1965). Invertebrate synapses and other types of transmissional cell contacts. *Neurosci. Res. Progr. Bull.* **3** (4), 31.

HARRISON, R. G. (1914). The reaction of embryonic cells to solid structures. *J. Exptl. Zool.* **17**, 521–544.

HILFER, S. R., AND HILFER, E. K. (1966). Effects of dissociating agents on the fine structure of embryonic chick thyroid cells. *J. Morph.* **119**, 217–232.

HÖRSTADIUS, S. (1939). The mechanics of sea urchin development, studied by operative methods. *Biol. Rev. Cambridge Phil. Soc.* **14**, 132–179.

HOFFMANN–BERLING, H. (1959). The role of cell structures in cell movements. *In* "Cell, Organism and Milieu" (D. Rudnick, ed.), pp. 45–62. Ronald Press, New York.

HOLMES, S. J. (1914). The behavior of the epidermis of amphibians when cultured outside the body. *J. Exptl. Zool.* **17**, 281–295.

HOLTFRETER, J. (1939). Gewebeaffinität, ein Mittel der Embryonalen Formbildung. *Arch. Exptl. Zellforsch.* **23**, 169–209.

HOLTFRETER, J. (1943a). Properties and functions of the surface coat in amphibian embryos. *J. Exptl. Zool.* **93**, 251–323.

HOLTFRETER, J. (1943b). A study of the mechanics of gastrulation: Part I. *J. Exptl. Zool.* **94**, 261–318.

HOLTFRETER, J. (1944). A study of the mechanics of gastrulation: Part II. *J. Exptl. Zool.* **95**, 171–212.

HUMPHREYS, T. (1963). Chemical dissolution and *in vitro* reconstruction of sponge cell adhesions. *Develop. Biol.* **8**, 27–47.

JONES, K. W., AND ELSDALE, T. R. (1963). The culture of small aggregates of amphibian embryonic cells *in vitro*. *J. Embryol. Exptl. Morphol.* **11**, 135–154.

KARASAKI, S. (1959). Electron microscopic studies on cytoplasmic structures of ectoderm cells of the *Triturus* embryo during the early phase of differentiation. *Embryologia (Nagoya)* **4**, 247–272.

KARASAKI, S. (1965). Electron microscopic examination of the sites of nuclear RNA synthesis during amphibian embryogenesis. *J. Cell Biol.* **26**, 937–958.

KESSEL, R. G. (1960). The role of cell division in gastrulation of *Fundulus heteroclitus*. *Exptl. Cell Res.* **20**, 277–282.

KINNANDER, H., AND GUSTAFSON, T. (1960). Further studies on the cellular bases of gastrulation in sea urchin larva. *Exptl. Cell Res.* **19**, 218–290.

KUHL, W. (1937). Untersuchungen über das Verhalten Künstlick Getrennter Fur-chungszellen und Zellaggregate einiger Amphibienarten mit Hilfe des Zetraffer films (Laufbild-und Teilbold analyse). *Arch. Entwicklungsmech. Organ.* **136,** 593–671.

LANSING, A. I., AND ZOLLINGER, W. K., JR. (1965). Some characteristics of liver cell membranes. *Biol. Bull.* **129,** 411–412.

LASH, J. W. (1955). Studies on wound closure in urodeles. *J. Exptl. Zool.* **128,** 13–28.

LENTZ, T. L., AND TRINKAUS, J. P. (1967). A fine structural study of cytodifferentiation during cleavage, blastula, and gastrula stages of *Fundulus heteroclitus. J. Cell Biol.* (in press).

LESSEPS, R. J. (1963). Cell surface projections: their role in the aggregation of embryonic chick cells as revealed by electron microscopy. *J. Exptl. Zool.* **153,** 171–182.

LEWIS, W. H. (1922). The adhesive quality of cells. *Anat. Record* **23,** 387–392.

LEWIS, W. H. (1947). Mechanics of Invagination. *Anat. Record* **97,** 139–156.

LEWIS, W. H. (1949a). Superficial gel layers of cells and eggs and their role in early development. *Sobretiro Anales Inst. Biol.* **20,** 1–14.

LEWIS, W. H. (1949b). Gel layers of cells and eggs and their roles in early develop-ment. *Lecture Ser. Roscoe B. Jackson Mem. Lab.* 59–77.

LIEBERMAN, I., AND OVE, P. (1958). A protein growth factor for mammalian cells in culture. *J. Biol. Chem.* **233,** 637–642.

LOEWENSTEIN, W. R., SOCOLAR, S. J., HIGASHINO, S., KANNO, Y., AND DAVIDSON, N. (1965). Intercellular communication: renal, urinary bladder, sensory, and salivary gland cells. *Science* **149,** 295–298.

LUCEY, E. C. A., AND CURTIS, A. S. G. (1959). Time-lapse film study of cell reaggrega-tion. *Med. Biol. Illust.* **9,** 86–93.

MALAN, M. E. (1953). The elongation of the primitive streak and the localization of the presumptive chorda-mesoderm on the early chick blastoderm studied by means of coloured marks with nile blue sulphate. *Arch. Biol.* **64,** 149–182.

MEYER, D. B. (1964). The migration of primordial germ cells in the chick embryo. *Develop. Biol.* **10,** 154–190.

MILKMAN, R., AND TRINKAUS, J. P. (1953). Site of action of epibolic forces in the egg of *Fundulus heteroclitus. Anat. Record* **117,** 558–559.

MINTZ, B. (1959). Continuity of the female germ cell line from embryo to adult. *Arch. Anat. Microscop. Morphol. Exptl.* **48,** Suppl., 155–172.

MOORE, A. R., AND BURT, A. S. (1939). On the locus and nature of the forces causing gastrulation in the embryos of *Dendraster excentricus. J. Exptl. Zool.* **82,** 159–171.

MOSCONA, A. A. (1957). The development *in vitro* of chimaeric aggregates of dis-sociated embryonic chick and mouse cells. *Proc. Natl. Acad. Sci. U.S.* **43,** 184–194.

MOSCONA, A. A. (1959). Patterns and mechanisms of tissue reconstruction from dis-sociated cells. *In* "Developing Cell Systems and Their Control" (D. Rudnick, ed.), pp. 45–70. Ronald Press, New York.

MOSCONA, A. A. (1962). Analysis of cell recombinations in experimental synthesis of tissues *in vitro. J. Cellular Comp. Physiol.* **60,** Suppl., 65–80.

MOSCONA, A. A. (1965). Recombination of dissociated cells and the development of cell aggregates. *In* "Cells and Tissues in Culture" (E. N. Willmer, ed.), pp. 489–529. Academic Press, New York.

NEW, D. A. T. (1959) . The adhesive properties and expansion of the chick blastoderm. *J. Exptl. Embryol. Morphol.* **7,** 146–164.

OKADA, T. S. (1965) . Immunohistological studies on the reconstitution of nephric tubules from dissociated cells. *J. Embryol. Exptl. Morphol.* **13,** 299–307.

OKAZAKI, K., FUKUSHI, T., AND DAN, K. (1962) . Cyto-embryological studies of sea urchins. IV. Correlation between the shape of ectodermal cells and the arrangement of the primary mesenchyme cells in sea urchin larvae. *Acta Embryol. Morphol. Exptl.* **5,** 17–51.

OPPENHEIMER, J. M. (1936) . Processes of localization in developing *Fundulus. J. Exptl. Zool.* **73,** 405–444.

OVERTON, J. (1962) . Desmosome development in normal and reassociating cells in the early chick blastoderm. *Develop. Biol.* **4,** 532–548.

PASTEELS, J. (1936) . Études sur la gastrulation des vertébrés méroblastiques. I. Téléostéens. *Arch. Biol.* **47,** 205–308.

PASTEELS, J. (1937) . Études sur la gastrulation des vertébrés meroblastiques. III Oiseaux. IV Conclusions générales. *Arch. Biol.* **48,** 381–488.

PERRY, M. M., AND WADDINGTON, C. H. (1966) . Ultrastructure of the blastopore cells in the newt. *J. Embryol. Exp. Morphol.* **15,** 317–330.

PETHICA, B. A. (1961) . The physical chemistry of cell adhesion. *Exptl. Cell. Res. Suppl.* **8,** 123–140.

RAND, H. W. (1915) . Wound enclosure in actinian tentacles with reference to the problem of organization. *Arch. Entwicklungsmech. Organ.* **41,** 159–214.

RAPPAPORT, C., AND HOWZE, G. B. (1966) . Dissociation of adult mouse liver by sodium tetraphenylboron, a potassium complexing agent. *Proc. Soc. Exptl. Biol. Med.* **121,** 1010–1016.

ROBERTSON, J. D. (1961) . The unit membrane. *In* "Electron Microscopy in Anatomy" (J. D. Boyd, F. R. Johnson, and J. D. Lever, eds.) , p. 74. London.

ROBERTSON, J. D. (1964) . Unit membranes: a review with recent new studies of experimental alterations and a new subunit structure in synaptic membranes. *In* "Cellular Membranes in Development" (M. Locke, ed.) , pp. 1–81. Academic Press, New York.

ROSENBERG, M. D. (1962) . Long-range interactions between cells and substratum. *Proc. Natl. Acad. Sci. U.S.* **48,** 1342–1349.

ROSENBERG, M. D. (1963) . Cell guidance by alterations in monomolecular films. *Science* **139,** 411–412.

ROUX, W. (1895) . Über den "Cytotropismus" der Furchungs-zellen des Grasfrosches (*Rana fusca*) . *Arch. Entwicklungsmech. Organ.* **1,** 43–68.

RUBIN, H. (1966) . Fact and theory about the cell surface in carcinogenesis. *In* "Major Problems in Developmental Biology" (M. Locke, ed.) , pp. 317–340. Academic Press, New York.

SCHECHTMAN, A. M. (1934) . Unipolar ingression in *Triturus torosus:* a hitherto undescribed movement in the pregastrular stages of a urodele. *Univ. Calif. (Berkeley) Publ. in Zoology* **39,** 303–309.

SCHLESINGER, A. G. (1958) . The structural significance of the avian yolk in embryogenesis. *J. Exptl. Zool.* **138,** 223–258.

SIMON, D. (1960) . Contribution à l'étude de la circulation et du transport des gonocytes primaires dans les blastodermes d'oiseau cultivés *in vitro. Arch. Anat. Microscop. Morphol. Exptl.* **49,** 93–176.

SINDELAR, W. F., AND BURNETT, A. L. (1966). A time-lapse photographic analysis of sponge cell reaggregation. *Soc. Gen. Physiologists. Abstr. Short Papers*, Sept. 1966. Woods Hole, Massachusetts.

SPRATT, N. T., JR. (1946). Formation of the primitive streak in the explanted chick blastoderm marked with carbon particles. *J. Exptl. Zool.* **103**, 259–304.

SPRATT, N. T., JR. (1954). Studies on the organizer center of the early chick embryo. [Symposium Devel. Growth. 13: 209–232.] *Aspects of Synthesis and Order in Growth.* D. Rudnick, ed. Princeton, pp. 209–232.

SPRATT, N. T., JR. (1963). Role of the substratum, supracellular continuity, and differential growth in morphogenetic cell movements. *Develop. Biol.* **1**, 51–63.

STEFANELLI, A., ZACCHEI, A. M., AND CHEHERINI, V. (1961). Ricostituzioni retiniche *in vitro* dopo disagregazione dell'abozzo oculare di embrione di pollo. *Acta Embryol. Morphl. Exptl.* **4**, 47–55.

STEINBERG, M. S. (1962a). On the mechanism of tissue reconstruction by dissociated cells. I. Population kinetics, differential adhesiveness, and the absence of directed migration. *Proc. Natl. Acad. Sci. U.S.* **48**, 1577–1582.

STEINBERG, M. S (1962b). On the mechanism of tissue reconstruction by dissociated cells. II. Time-course of events. *Science* **137**, 762–763.

STEINBERG, M. S. (1962c). On the mechanism of tissue reconstruction by dissociated cells. III. Free energy relations and the reorganization of fused, heteronomic tissue fragments. *Proc. Natl. Acad. Sci. U.S.* **48**, 1769–1776.

STEINBERG, M. S. (1963). Reconstruction of tissues by dissociated cells. *Science* **141**, 401–408.

STEINBERG, M. S. (1964). The problem of adhesive selectivity in cellular interactions. *In* "Cellular Membranes in Development" (M. Locke, ed.), pp. 321–366. Academic Press, New York.

TAYLOR, A. C. (1961). Attachment and spreading of cells in culture. *Exptl. Cell Res. Suppl.* **8**, 154–173.

TOWNES, P. L., AND HOLTFRETER, J. (1955). Directed movements and selective adhesion of embryonic amphibian cells. *J. Exptl. Zool.* **128**, 53–120.

TRINKAUS, J. P. (1949). The surface gel layer of *Fundulus* eggs in relation to epiboly. *Proc. Natl. Acad. Sci. U.S.* **35**, 218–225.

TRINKAUS, J. P. (1951). A study of the mechanism of epiboly in the egg of *Fundulus heteroclitus*. *J. Exptl. Zool.* **118**, 269–319.

TRINKAUS, J. P. (1961). Affinity relationships in heterotypic cell aggregates. *La Culture Organotypique.* Paris: Coloq. Intern. *Centre Natl. Rech. Sci.* No. 101. pp. 209–226.

TRINKAUS, J. P. (1963a). The cellular basis of *Fundulus* epiboly. Adhesivity of blastula and gastrula cells in culture. *Develop. Biol.* **7**, 513–532.

TRINKAUS, J. P. (1963b). Behavior of dissociated retinal pigment cells in heterotypic cell aggregates. *Ann. N. Y. Acad. Sci..* **100**, 413–434.

TRINKAUS, J. P. (1965). Mechanisms of morphogenetic movements. *In* "Organogenesis" (R. L. DeHaan and H. Ursprung, eds.), pp. 55–104. Holt, New York.

TRINKAUS, J. P., AND DRAKE, J. W. (1956). Exogenous control of morphogenesis in isolated *Fundulus* blastoderms by nutrient chemical factors. *J. Exptl. Zool.* **132**, 311–342.

TRINKAUS, J. P., AND EBSTEIN, R. (1967). A time-lapse cinematographic study of cell movements during epiboly of *Fundulus heteroclitus*. In preparation.

TRINKAUS, J. P., AND GROVES, P. W. (1955). Differentiation on culture of mixed aggregates of dissociated tissue cells. *Proc. Natl. Acad. Sci. U.S.* **41**, 787–795.

TRINKAUS, J. P., AND LENTZ, J. P. (1964). Direct observation of type-specific segregation in mixed cell aggregates. *Develop. Biol.* **9**, 115–136.

TRINKAUS, J. P., AND LENTZ, T. L. (1967). Surface specializations of *Fundulus* cells and their relation to cell movements during gastrulation. *J. Cell Biol.* (in press).

VAUGHAN, R. B., AND TRINKAUS, J. P. (1966). Movements of epithelial cell sheets *in vitro*. *J. Cell Sci.* **1** (in press). Will be in Vol. 1 No. 4, December.

VOGT, W. (1929). Gestaltungsanalyse am Amphibienkeim mit Örtlicher Vitalfärbung. II. Teil. Gastrulation und Mesodermbildung bei Urodelen und Anuren. *Arch. Entwicklungsmech. Organ.* **120**, 384–706.

VOIGHTLANDER, G. (1932). Neue untersuchungen über den "Cytotropismus der Furchenzellen. *Arch. Entwicklungsmech. Organ.* **127**, 151–215.

WADDINGTON, C. H. (1932). Experiments on the development of chick and duck embryos cultivated *in vitro*. *Phil. Trans. Roy. Soc. London* **B221**, 179–230.

WADDINGTON, C. H. (1940). "Organizers and Genes." Cambridge Univ. Press, London and New York.

WARTENBERG, H., AND SCHMIDT, W. (1961). Elektronenmikroskopische untersuchungen der strukturellen Veränderungen im Rindenbereich des Amphibieneies im Ovar und nach der Befurchtung. *Z. Zellforsch. Mikroskop. Anat.* **54**, 118–146.

WEISS, L. (1961). The measurement of cell adhesion. *Exp. Cell Res. Suppl.* **8**, 141–153.

WEISS, L. (1962a). Cell movement and cell surfaces: a working hypothesis *J. Theoret. Biol.* **2**, 236–250.

WEISS, L. (1962b). The mammalian tissue cell surface. *Biochem. Soc. Symp.* (*Cambridge, Engl.*) **22**, 32–54.

WEISS, L., AND LACHMANN, P. J. (1964). The origin of an antigenic zone surrounding HeLa cells cultured on glass. *Exptl. Cell Res.* **36**, 86–91.

WEISS, P. (1934). *In vitro* experiments on the factors determining the course of the outgrowing nerve fiber. *J. Exptl. Zool.* **68**, 393–448.

WEISS, P. (1945). Experiments on cell and axon orientation *in vitro:* The role of colloidal exudates in tissue organization. *J. Exptl. Zool.* **100**, 353–386.

WEISS, P. (1961). Guiding principles in cell locomotion and cell aggregation. *Exptl. Cell Res. Suppl.* **8**, 260–281.

WEISS, P., AND GARBER, B. (1952). Shape and movement of mesenchyme cells as functions of the physical structure of the medium. Contributions to quantitative morphology. *Proc. Natl. Acad. Sci. U.S.* **38**, 264–280.

WEISS, P., AND TAYLOR, A. C. (1960). Reconstitution of complete organs from single-cell suspensions of chick embryos in advanced stages of differentiation. *Proc. Natl. Acad. Sci. U.S.* **46**, 1177–1185.

WESTON, J. A. (1963). A radioautographic analysis of the migration and localization of trunk neural crest cells in the chick. *Develop. Biol.* **6**, 279–310.

WESTON, J. A., AND ABERCROMBIE, M. (1967). Cell motility in fused homo- and heteronomic tissue fragments. *J. Exp. Zool.* (in press).

WETZEL, R. (1929). Untersuchungen am Hühnchen. Die entwicklung des Keims Während der Ertsen Beiden Bruttage. *Arch. Entwicklungsmech. Organ.* **119**, 188–321.

WILSON, H. V. (1907). On some phenomena of coalescence and regeneration in sponges. *J. Exptl. Zool.* **5**, 245–258.

The Formation of
Patterns in Development

HEINRICH URSPRUNG

Department of Biology, The Johns Hopkins University, Baltimore, Maryland

I. Introduction

The vast majority of investigators in developmental biology have in the recent past directed their efforts toward the problem of cellular differentiation. Consequently, the differentiated states of many cell types have been described very accurately in structural and chemical terms, and in addition considerable insight has been gained into some of the mechanisms that are important in the control of differentiation.

A related, though possibly more complex problem, patterning, has drawn comparatively little attention recently. The word pattern is defined as an arrangement of parts that suggests a design or orderly distribution. In developmental biology, the term pattern denotes the nonrandom occurrence of given cell types, or their products, in the organism. A wide spectrum of embryological investigations is relevant to this problem, from cell- and tissue-specific synthesis of macromolecules to regional inductive processes in cell and tissue interactions. I have chosen in this brief review not to force these well-known and often reviewed contemporary findings into the pattern problem, however. Instead, I have selected a few examples of patterns that have been analyzed strictly at the cell and tissue level in the past. Occasionally, I shall make a suggestion as to how these problems might benefit from knowledge accumulated in related areas.

II. Patterns in Bird Feathers

Among the most striking patterns observed in nature are those of bird feathers. Figure 1 shows the simple dark-light banding pattern of the Barred Plymouth Rock variety of fowl. For an understanding of the ontogeny of this pattern it is necessary to be familiar with the em-

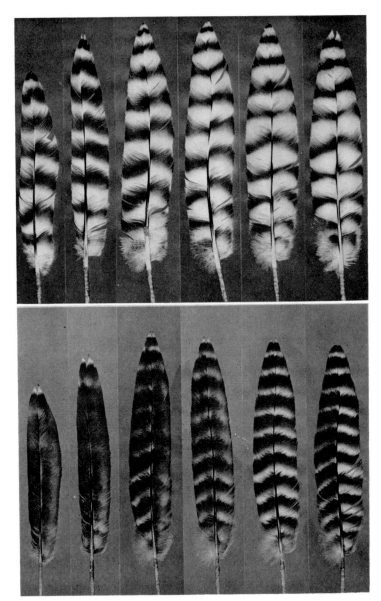

F<small>IG</small>. 1. Juvenile contour feathers of male (upper row) and female (lower row) Barred Plymouth Rock chickens. (Modified from Willier and Rawles, 1944b.)

bryology of feather formation. Our knowledge of feather morphogenesis is largely due to the efforts of Lillie and his school (see Hamilton, 1952, for review). In normal development or in regeneration, the feather forms in the feather follicle which consists of a dermal papilla surrounded by epidermis. The actual formation of a new feather takes place at the collar of the papilla; this collar is a ring of epidermal cells and melanoblasts (Fig. 2). From the dorsal side of the collar, the shaft (rachis) is produced by continuous addition of cells which eventually keratinize.

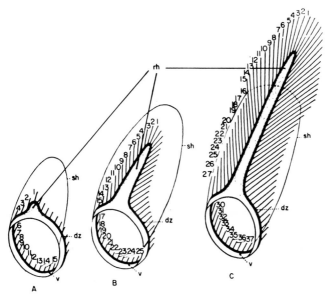

Fig. 2a.   Three stages (A, B, C) of feather development. From the collar (ring), barb ridges arise (straight lines with numbers). Their bases are carried along by the growing rachis (rh). dz: differentiation zone (see text); sh: sheath; it arises from the collar and eventually ruptures apically (C); v: ventral locus of collar. (From Hamilton, 1952.)

From the ventral side of the collar, so-called barb ridges are formed, mostly from the two zones on either side of the midventral line. Each barb ridge represents a large number of cells that later become keratinized. The barb starts forming at its tip. Progressively more basal components are then added to the barb as it grows in length. At the same time, the rachis increases in size, and the bases of the barbs shift toward it. Two kinds of cells are contributed to the growing rachis and barbs by the collar: epidermal cells and melanoblasts. The latter are known to be derived from the neural crest of the embryo. Neural crest, but no other tissue, if grafted from a pigmented breed to a non-pigmented variety of fowl will lead to pigmentation of feathers that develop in the area of the graft (see Willier, 1948, for review). Recent autoradiographic analysis of the migratory behavior of neural crest cells confirms the earlier findings that melanoblasts migrate from the neural crest into the epidermis (Weston, 1963).

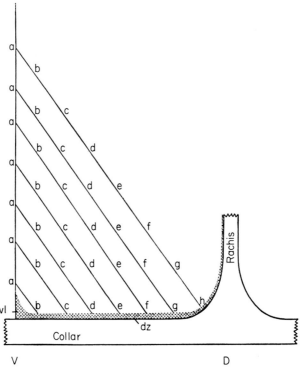

Fig. 2b. A portion of a feather cylinder, cut open, showing seven successive positions of a single barb during its growth. The barb originates at the ventral locus (vl) and then increases in length by the addition of cells from the differentiation zone (dz) of the collar. a: The oldest part of the barb; b–h: progressively younger portions. (From Hamilton, 1952.)

The melanoblasts are largely responsible for the patterning. Once they have invaded the collar, they multiply and are then released, together with epidermal cells, into the growing barbs. They do not differentiate into melanin-producing melanocytes until they have reached the so-called differentiation zone, somewhat apical to the collar. In Fig. 2b this zone is indicated by stippling. In it, melanoblasts are first transformed into melanocytes, that is, typical branched pigment cells. Their dendritic processes establish contact with epidermal cells, and release globules containing melanin granules which are engulfed by the epidermal cells. The melanocytes then die.

The presence or absence of melanoblasts in the feather follicle at the time of feather formation is, of course, decisive for pigmentation. In the Black Minorca strain, for example, the down feathers on the wing tips and on the ventral surface are white, while all other feathers are black. Watterson (1942) explains this pattern by the observation that melanoblasts have not reached the areas of wing tip and ventral surface at the time these feathers form.

This "presence or absence scheme" of pattern formation in the Minorca strain is by no means the mechanism by which the black-white banding pattern of the Barred Plymouth Rock is formed, however. From all the evidence accumulated, primarily through the work of Willier and Rawles (e.g., 1944a,b), it appears that in most varieties of fowl, melanoblasts are always and continuously present in the collar and growing barbs of the feather, no matter whether a banded, an all-black, or even an all-white feather results. The strongest support for this assumption comes from the work of Nickerson (1944), who isolated various parts of the developing feather, including prospective white and prospective black barb ridges from Barred Plymouth Rock and implanted them into the coelom of White Leghorn embryos. He found that both prospective white and prospective black areas contained cells that produced melanin under these experimental conditions, although in normal development only the melanoblasts contained in the black band produce pigment. I have not found conclusive reports stating whether these cells with the potential of pigment formation in the white bands exist as melanocytes, with dendritic processes, or as undifferentiated melanoblasts. In the former case, lack of pigment production under normal conditions would very likely be due to a block of melanin synthesis; in the latter, a more profound block preventing differentiation into melanocytes would have to be postulated.

The formation of an all-black feather is explained easily on the basis that melanoblasts enter the growing barbs at equal rates and deposit melanin into the epidermal cells at equal rates. The former seems to be true in Barred varieties also. The banding would thus most likely be controlled either at the level of synthesis or of release of melanin by the melanocytes. This hypothesis attributes the pattern trait to the activity of the melanocytes themselves. There is strong evidence that this is in fact the case. In an elegantly designed experiment, Willier and Rawles (1944a) isolated melanoblasts from a hybrid produced by crossing a female Barred Plymouth Rock to a male Rhode Island Red. The isolated tissue was grafted to White Leghorn hosts. For the understanding of the experiment it is important to know that the gene responsible for banding, B, is sex-linked. Thus a male hybrid is genetically hybrid Bb, whereas a female hybrid is hemizygous b. The results obtained in this grafting experiment showed clearly that the pattern—that is, barred or not barred—is a function of the genotype of the transplanted melanoblasts. Male tissue led to the formation, in the host, of barred feathers, whereas nonbarred feathers developed from female grafts, quite irrespective of the sex of the host.

The autonomy of the melanocytes goes even farther. Not only is a barred or nonbarred pattern produced according to the genotype of the grafted melanoblasts, but the relative extension of black and white portions of a bar are reproduced, and the rhythm at which a bar forms is maintained. This was shown by Nickerson (1944), who grafted melanoblasts from different strains into White Leghorn. In a normal Barred Plymouth Rock, the barring period ranges from about 5 to 6 days, depending on the feather tract. When barred melanoblasts were grafted to White Leghorn, the same barring period was observed. A different donor, Silver Campine, with a barring period from $2\frac{1}{2}$ to $4\frac{1}{2}$ days, also maintained its rhythm when grafted to White Leghorn.

However, the melanocytes are not entirely autonomous in their patterning activity. The relative width of white and black bands in a bar is modified by the feather papilla. In a normal Barred Plymouth Rock chicken, the relative band widths differ from one location in the body to another (Fig. 1). Such differences are also observed when melanoblasts are grafted to White Leghorn, and probably account for the fact that barring periods are not precisely the same for all feathers, but cover a range of from 5 to 6 days.

The reason for these differences in band widths in various parts of the plumage is not known. Although in several cases there seemed to exist a correlation between growth rate of the feather and periodicity of banding, in other cases this correlation did not hold (see Willier and Rawles, 1944b, for discussion).

For a while it appeared that hormones, particularly sex hormones, might be responsible for variations in band widths and possibly for barring as such. In the Barred Plymouth Rock the assumption is ruled out clearly, as we have already seen, by the fact that banding is quite independent of the sex of the host. Also, administration of female sex hormones to a normal male Barred Plymouth Rock does not render the barring patterns of regenerating feathers female, although the overall size and structure of the feathers in this experiment assume female characters.

In summary, we may state that the only consistently observed parameter responsible for the production of barring is the genotype of the melanoblast. Understanding the barred phenotype apparently requires an understanding of the rhythmical production and/or release of melanin by melanocytes that reach the zone immediately above the pigment-free zone. The following scheme, proposed in various forms by different workers in the field (see Willier and Rawles, 1944b, for review) might serve as working hypothesis. Let us assume that melanoblasts have terminated the differentiation into melanocytes as soon as a barb is several cells long, that is, as soon as it has reached the differentiation zone. Now melanin is synthesized (and released) at a rapid rate, which leads to a depletion, in adjacent epidermal cells and melanoblasts, of substrates for melanin production, such as tyrosine, or dopa (dihydroxyphenylalanine). Consequently, the next series of melanoblasts reaching the horizontal line, although differentiating into melanocytes, is not able to form melanin. Only still younger cells, reaching the critical zone later, would find substrate levels high enough for the production of the pigment. This scheme is purely speculative, and to my knowledge there is no experimental evidence available for its support. It appears to be testable, however, although the current understanding of melanin biosynthesis is limited. It is known that the enzyme tyrosinase is involved in its synthesis. This enzyme catalyses the oxidation of tyrosine into dopa and to dopa orthoquinone, which is then converted nonenzymically to 5,6-dihydroxy-dihydroindole-α-carbonic acid, which is oxidized nonenzymically to "dopachrome." A decarboxylation and oxidation lead to the corresponding orthoquinone, considered the immediate precursor of melanin which forms from its precursor by oxidation and polymerization (Leuthardt, 1959). Testing the proposed scheme would involve assaying these intermediates in various areas of the regenerating feather.

III. Pigment Patterns in Amphibians

The barred pattern in feathers apparently is a consequence of periodic activity of melanocytes that are ubiquitous in the primordium of the feather. Quite obviously, there is an alternative solution for patterned production of melanin, that is, presence or absence of melanin-producing cells. This seems to be the way in which amphibian pigment patterns are produced.

As in birds, melanocytes in amphibians are derived from the neural crest. Patterns of melanin in the skin reflect the grouping of differentiated melanocytes. This pattern could be brought about in at least

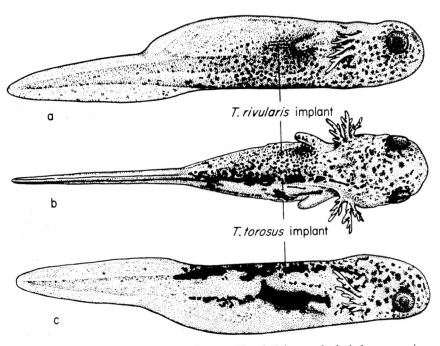

FIG. 3.   Left (a), top (b), and right (c) side of *Triturus rivularis* larva carrying grafted neural crest of *T. rivularis* on its left side, of *T. torosus* on its right side. Note that the pattern is donor-specific: diffuse (*rivularis*-type) on the left flank, striped (*torosus*-type) on the right flank. (From Kuehn, 1965; after Twitty, 1945.)

two ways. It could be that neural crest-derived melanoblasts populate the skin uniformly, but differentiate into melanin-producing melanocytes only in restricted areas. Alternatively, it could be that melanoblasts populate only those restricted areas initially.

In a classic paper, Twitty (1945) used two newts, *Triturus rivularis* and *Triturus torosus* to approach this problem. *Triturus rivularis* is characterized by a diffuse arrangement of melanocytes, whereas in *T. torosus* two longitudinal stripes of pigment are seen. Twitty removed neural crest material of a *rivularis* embryo bilaterally, and grafted into its place a piece of *rivularis* neural crest (on the left) and *torosus* neural crest (on the right). Figure 3 shows the results of this experiment. The chimera carries a *torosus* pattern on its right flank, but a *rivularis* pattern on its left. Thus the melanoblasts of the donor tissue led to the formation, in host skin, of a donor-specific pattern. This striking autonomy of melanoblasts is strong support for the second alternative, which makes population of restricted areas responsible for patterning, since the two sources of melanoblasts, *rivularis* and *torosus,* are compared on the same target skin. If local induction of differentiation—the first alternative—were operating, why would *torosus* melanoblasts not react with formation of a diffuse pattern?

The experiment does not uncover the guiding principle responsible for the population of restricted areas, however. Twitty (1945) carried the experiment further in his search for the guiding principle. He removed neural crest in a *torosus* embryo. He then prepared a piece of tissue comprising neural crestless neural tube and somites, and grafted this piece to a host in place of its somites. Figure 4 shows the scheme of the operation and the result. The host melanocytes populate the graft and come to a halt wherever they find dorsal edges of somites. Twitty explains the formation of stripes in *T. torosus* by assuming that the dorsal edge of somites is the "trap" over which melanocytes are coming to a halt after moving about. The *rivularis* embryos likewise have such a trap. *Rivularis* cells, however, are unable to respond to it and remain scattered. As we shall discuss in more detail and for different examples later (p. 188) this concept is very close to the prepattern concept formulated by Stern (1954a,b) for bristle patterns on insect integuments.

Twitty (1945) substantiates his view from other observations on *T. torosus.* During development of this organism he actually observed migration of melanocytes. They are almost uniformly distributed over the dorsolateral flank of the larvae and only secondarily become grouped into the band formed at the dorsal edge of the somites, and into a second band following the dorsal edge of the yolk.

This scheme of pattern formation does not hold for all species analyzed, however. Rosin (1940) reports a case in which neural crest material of the axolotl was grafted onto a *Triturus palmatus* host. The resulting pattern was entirely of host type. In this case, the individual melanocytes are easily identified, which enabled Rosin to discover that axolotl melanocytes participated in the formation of *Triturus* stripes. If we were to draw conclusions analogous to those drawn for the

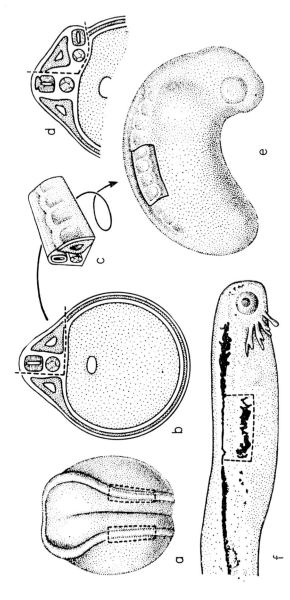

Fig. 4. Twitty's (1945) experiment revealing the dorsal edge of the somites as the guiding principle in stripe formation. a: The dotted outline indicates neural crest material removed. b: Cross-section of the resulting neural crestless embryo, from which a short piece of neural tube, notochord, and somites was then removed (c) and grafted onto a host larva in place of its own somites (d,e). f: The resulting larva bears stripes following the dorsal edge of its own somites and of the grafted somites. (From Kuehn, 1965; after Twitty, 1945.)

rivularis-torosus case, we would have to state that both axolotl and *palmatus* melanocytes can respond to the guiding principle, but that only *palmatus* possesses the particular guiding principle.

A large number of experiments of this nature have appeared in the literature, some resulting in host-specific, some in donor-specific development of patterns in chimeras. The reader is referred to comprehensive reviews by Twitty (1949), Lehman and Young (1959), and Wilde (1961), which contain ample references on the subject. Thus far no common denominator has been found. It may well be that application of methods designed to test the adhesive properties of cells, such as those devised by Steinberg (review, 1964), may prove fruitful in finding the common denominator. The importance of Steinberg's view for the patterning problem, in our mind, is that in his model, cells are not either adhesive or repulsive as such, but their surface properties lead them to assume final positions depending on the surface properties of all the other cells involved.

At the same time, future investigators may want to take advantage of tritiated thymidine for labeling cells. With the use of this label, latent melanoblasts will be detected more easily, and the experimenter will not have to rely on the presence of melanin granules in order to recognize a neural crest-derived cell.

IV.   Bristle Patterns in Insects

The bristle pattern in insects, like the pigment pattern in amphibians, is a pattern in space, that is, it is a pattern that reflects the arrangement of cells in space. In the case of insect bristles, however, evidence for or against cell migration during normal pattern formation is lacking. Insect bristles have been favorite objects of study because they are very obvious and clearly defined cell markers. The bristle as we observe it under the microscope is a part of a more complicated bristle apparatus consisting of several cells. The bristle cell (with its bristle) and the socket cell (which forms the socket surrounding the base of the bristle) are derived from a single stem cell, which undergoes an unequal division (see Stern, 1954b). We shall return to unequal divisions in more detail later in our discussion of scale patterns in butterfly wings and the arrangement of stomates on plant leaves.

For our discussion it is important to know that bristles on the body surface of *Drosophila*, to choose an example, occur in very rigid patterns (Fig. 5). During metamorphosis, the new adult epidermis which replaces the larval epidermis, consists of a sheet of cytologically undistinguishable cells derived from imaginal disks (cf. Hadorn, 1966). In some parts of this sheet, but not in others, a cell enlarges and undergoes the two divisions just described (cf. Fig. 11). The pattern of these stem cells is identical with the pattern of bristles on the body surface of the adult.

How then is the machinery for the biosynthesis and the structural organization of bristle materials initiated in certain cells, but not in others? The geneticist Curt Stern (1954a,b, 1956) offered a concept which is reminiscent of similar concepts formulated throughout the history of developmental biology by embryologists—a concept of organized distribution, in this sheet of cells, of chemical and physical conditions leading to the observed nonrandom initiation of bristle differentiation. For simplicity, he terms this nonrandom distribution of chemical and physical conditions a prepattern, because the conditions must be present in the tissue before differentiation of the observed trait occurs.

Together with this new formulation of a developmental concept, Stern (1954a,b, 1956) and his collaborator Tokunaga (1961) have offered a novel approach. *Drosophila* mutants were found that differed in their pattern of bristles. One such mutant, *engrailed,* is characterized by the presence, on the tarsus of the male foreleg, of two sex combs, rather than one as in wild type (Fig. 5). Stern's and Tokunaga's problem was to determine how the mutant allele led to the change in the bristle pattern. The prediction, clearly expressed, was that the mutation would lead to the formation of a different prepattern.

The experimental analysis, beautifully carried out for the *engrailed* trait and a number of other pattern mutants in Stern's laboratory, involved the production of mosaic flies consisting of wild-type and mutant tissues. Microsurgically, this is hardly feasible. However, somatic crossing-over, a cytogenetic process increased in frequency by X-ray treatment of larvae, produces chromosomal rearrangements that may lead to genetic mosaicism. Figure 6 describes somatic crossing-over for the *engrailed* case diagrammatically. As can be seen, somatic crossing-over occurring between *engrailed* and the centromere of the second chromosome leads to two cells of different genotype, one wild type both with regard to body color and bristle pattern, the other, hemizygous for the body color mutation *yellow* (*y*), and homozygous for the pattern mutant *engrailed*. Phenotypically, the two cells thus are wild type/wild

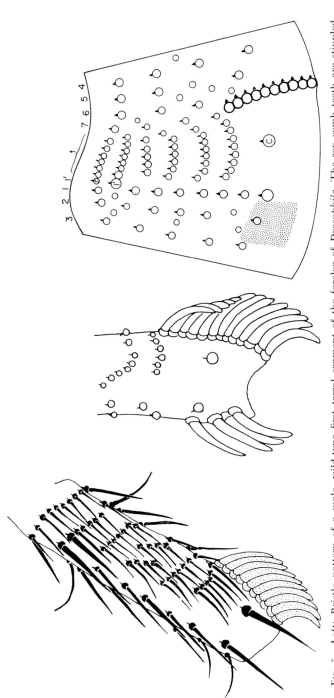

FIG. 5. Left: Bristle pattern of a male, wild-type first tarsal segment of the foreleg of *Drosophila*. The sex comb teeth are stippled. Center: A part of the same region in a fly homozygous for the pattern mutation *engrailed*. Note two mirror-image sex combs (white teeth). Right: Schematic representation of the bristle pattern. The stippled area indicates the location of the secondary sex comb in *engrailed* flies. t: Transverse rows; numbers: longitudinal rows. C: Central bristle. (After Tokunaga, 1961.)

type, and *yellow/engrailed,* respectively. It is important at this point to recognize the necessity for using the factor *yellow.* A cell carrying a pattern mutation cannot by definition itself be recognized as mutant in a mosaic unless it also carries a marker that is independent of the

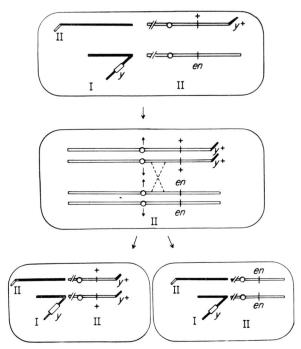

FIG. 6. Genetic constitution of the first (I) and second (II) chromosomes in heterozygous *en* larvae before (top) and after (center and bottom) X-irradiation. Somatic crossing-over (dotted line) between the centromere (open circles) and the *en* locus leads to two genetically different cells (bottom). One (left) is homozygous wild type for both body color $(y^+/y^+/y)$ and pattern $(+/+)$. The other (right) is hemizygous for body color (y) and homozygous mutant for the pattern trait (en/en). (From data of Tokunaga, 1961.)

location of the cell; *yellow* is such a marker. When a yellow bristle is found among black bristles, the investigator immediately knows that the cell forming that bristle is genetically also mutant with respect to pattern, that is, *engrailed.*

When the two genetically different cells of Fig. 6 divide, their progeny cells will of course retain the parental genotype. Thus, within the originally irradiated, heterozygous larva, two patches of homozygous tissues develop. One of them is phenotypically discernible from the larva as a whole. Depending on when the somatic crossing-over first occurred in development, the resulting homozygous patches will be small or large, and depending on where it occurred in the larva, the patches will or will not include those regions of the tarsus of the foreleg that are of interest for the analysis.

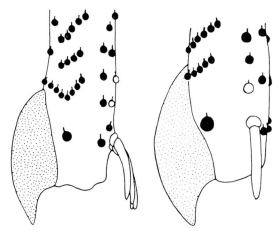

Fig. 7. Two cases of genetic mosaics in the sex comb region of the male foreleg. Stippled: outline of normal, primary, wild-type sex comb. Solid symbols: bristles of the genetic constitution wild type (body color) and wild type (pattern). Open symbols: bristles of the genetic constitution mutant (body color) and mutant (pattern). Left: A small portion of the tarsus is mutant; where this portion covers the region of the secondary sex comb, four sex comb teeth are formed. Right: A very small portion is mutant, giving rise to a bristle and, in the proper region, a single tooth of the secondary sex comb. (After Tokunaga, 1961.)

What were the results of microscopic analysis of mosaic tarsi? Two specific cases are shown in Fig. 7. Generally, a secondary sex comb (or parts thereof) always formed when *yellow* cells were present in the secondary sex comb area (stippled area in Fig. 5, right). *Yellow* cells found outside this area did form bristles, but not sex comb teeth, unless they were located in the primary sex comb region. When black, wild-type cells happened to occupy the secondary sex comb region, no sex comb teeth were formed by these cells. In other words, the mutant pattern trait showed up cell-autonomously. In fact it showed up cell-autonomously no matter what the relative sizes of the two areas of a mosaic were. "What, then, was the verdict which mosaics . . . pronounced on the hypothesis that the two different patterns of bristle differentiation were founded upon different patterns in the predifferentiated tissues? [patterns in predifferentiated tissues = prepatterns, author]. The verdict was: not valid!" (Stern, 1954b, for a similar case, *achaete*).

According to Stern's interpretation, the mutant does not lead to the formation of a new pattern by virtue of changing the prepattern. Or in other words, the prepatterns of both wild type and mutant are identical. What the mutation does, according to Stern, is alter the competence of cells to respond to this invariant prepattern. In the case of *engrailed*, homozygous mutant cells are competent to respond to the prepattern with the formation of sex comb teeth in the secondary sex comb area. In wild-type tissue, this prepattern for the formation of secondary sex comb teeth is present also, but wild-type cells are not competent to respond.

We must have a close look at definitions at this point. Pattern, in the case of bristles, refers to the nonrandom initiation of bristle stem cells. Prepattern, as originally conceived by Stern (1954a,b) denotes the invisible physical and/or chemical conditions preceding the formation of a visible pattern. If this definition is applied to any mutant—without experimentation—then the prepatterns of wild type and mutant must be different by definition. The observations of autonomy of pattern traits in mosaics then cannot prove identity of prepatterns of mutant and wild type. Identity of the two prepatterns from the observations of pattern autonomy in mosaics can only be concluded if prepattern is defined in a broader sense as the distribution, in space, of *any* physical or chemical condition permitting the formation of *any* pattern, provided appropriate competence of cells exists. Stern (1954b) has furnished such a broader definition stating that "a prepattern is a descriptive term for any kind of spatial differentness in development." With the use of this definition it is indeed logical to postulate that the prepattern is identical for both wild type and mutant, and that the mutation merely alters the competence of cells to respond to the invariant prepattern. The search for the basis of a prepattern becomes operationally difficult with this general definition, however, since an observed pattern might reflect only a small part of a potentially much broader prepattern, if the competence of the responding cells is considered limiting.

So far we have been assuming that the type of differentiation studied, that is, bristle formation, is initiated locally, in the absence of cell migration. We have been thinking of imaginal disks essentially as monolayers of undifferentiated epithelial cells not distinguishable from one another. Within this monolayer of cells, we thought, bristle apparatus stem cells would arise at specific locations. An alternative mode of formation of patterns would involve migration of determined cells. We could imagine, for example, that the stem cells for sex comb teeth would be manufactured at some location in the imaginal disk, and migrate, much the same as neural crest cells, into the epithelium. There they might come to a halt at specific sites, and differentiate bristles. The argument against this view is that cell migration has not been observed in imaginal disks. But we should hasten to say that it has not been looked for, either.

Under experimental circumstances, cell migration does occur. A number of years ago, a series of experiments were started in Hadorn's laboratory, for the purpose of studying pattern formation in dissociated and reaggregating cells (Hadorn *et al.,* 1959; Ursprung and Hadorn (1962). We were interested in the pattern of marginal bristles of the wing of *Drosophila.* As Fig. 8 shows, this pattern in some areas of the wing is characterized by three rows of bristles. One row consists of long, slender bristles spaced at short intervals, another, of shorter, heavier teeth also spaced at short intervals, and the third, of long, slender bristles between which large gaps free of bristles are seen. To the left and right of the marginal pattern, the wing lamella is covered with great numbers of short hairs.

The embryology of imaginal disks as a whole and of areas responsible for the formation of individual organs is well known (see Hadorn, 1966; Ursprung, 1963, for reviews). In our experiments, wing disks were dissected from third instar larvae, dissociated into single cells and cell groups of up to 100 cells by trypsin, washed, and the clump of dissociated cells injected into the body cavity of a host of the same age. There the cells undergo metamorphosis and differentiation in synchrony with the host organism. After metamorphosis, the implant can be recovered from the host's abdomen and analyzed microscopically. To our surprise, many of the implants contained rows of wing bristles arranged in precisely the same way as in a normal, untreated fly (Fig. 9). These normal patterns are not artifacts of selective survival of undissociated cell groups, but represent normal patterns formed by cells originating in different imaginal disks. We may make this statement with confidence, because in the experiment genetically labeled cells were used, each of which could be identified positively with respect to its origin in the

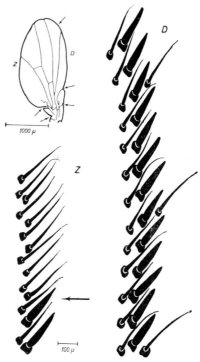

FIG. 8. Marginal bristle pattern of *Drosophila* wing. The small arrows point to the beginning and the end of different patterns, such as double rows (*Z*) or triple rows (*D*). The heavy arrow points to the transition zone between double and triple rows. (From Hadorn *et al.*, 1959.)

metamorphosed tissue. As Fig. 9 shows, the mosaic patterns formed consist of wild-type and mutant cells. The mutants used as genetic markers are *yellow* (bristle color) and *multiple wing hair* (morphology of wing hairs).

This case of formation of mosaic structures by dissociated cells is not unique for the wing disk. Noethiger (1964), using a similar procedure, has found mosaics for dissociated and reaggregated genital disks. He focused his attention on the development of a few characteristically patterned structures within the genital apparatus, particularly, anal plates and median plates (claspers). When male genital disks of two body color markers were mixed and permitted to reaggregate in the body cavity of a larval host, they formed mosaic claspers and mosaic anal plates. The normal pattern in these cases was not as truly reformed as in our original experiments on wing cells, perhaps due to a some-what different dissociation procedure, but it is clear that cells from two independent sources cooperated in forming the observed mosaics.

Fig. 9.   Reaggregating cells from dissociated wild type (black) and yellow; multiple wing hair (white) wing imaginal disk. Note that a normal triple-row bristle pattern is formed by cells originating from different imaginal disks. (From Ursprung, 1963; after data of Ursprung and Hadorn, 1962.)

Interestingly enough, when male and female genital disks were mixed and reaggregated, mosaic anal plates were observed, but no mosaic claspers. More interestingly yet, no mosaic tissues at all were formed when cells obtained from wing disks were mixed with genital disk cells, although there was no reason to believe that mixing was not just as thorough.

Noethiger (1964) interprets these findings to mean that cells of homologous structures—such as anal plates of the male and anal plates of the female—will form mosaics, whereas cells of nonhomologous struc-tures—such as anal plates and wings—will not. Most recently, Garcia-Bellido (1966) has extended this finding to the wing disk itself. The fate map of this disk has been worked out by Hadorn and Buck (1962). Garcia-Bellido combined, in a typical dissociation reaggregation experi-ment, wing disk areas that contained the bristle-forming zone and those that did not, using different genetic color markers for labeling the two areas. The results showed very clearly that mosaics in the wing patterns occurred only if material containing bristle anlage was mixed with other material that also contained bristle anlage.

These findings of Noethiger and Garcia-Bellido are best explained on the assumption that sorting-out occurs, which involves cell migration. It is tempting to make sorting-out responsible not only for this demonstrated separation of, e.g., wing material from genital material during aggregation but also for the restitution of normal bristle patterns in the reaggregation experiment. According to this scheme, cells in the imaginal disk are rigidly determined at the time of the experiment. During reaggregation they move about freely, and those cells with the potential to become bristle stem cells are lined up in the proper order and spacing. During metamorphosis, they differentiate. We must realize, however, that thus far sorting-out has been demonstrated only at the level of entire imaginal disks or areas that do or do not contain bristle-forming cells. Direct demonstration of sorting-out of bristle stem cells requires actual observation of labeled stem cells during reaggregation.

The question now arises as to how the patterns are formed in the course of normal development. In a typical imaginal disk, cell multiplication occurs throughout the larval development at a steady pace. Upon onset of metamorphosis, cell multiplication temporarily comes to a halt. During this postmitotic phase, here and there in the tissue large cells become apparent, some of which become bristle stem cells, as we have already mentioned. No direct evidence has been reported on cell migration in this phase. On the other hand, it is known that bristle-forming cells of the wing are confined to a rather limited area of third instart wing disk (Hadorn and Buck, 1962). When the future wing lamella is formed, considerable movement of tissue occurs (Auerbach, 1936). In this process, groups of cells could easily be moved. There is also indirect evidence for such group movements during normal formation of the male sex comb (Tokunaga, 1962).

Thus, it is conceivable that pattern formation is not caused by the local initiation of given types of differentiation as formulated in Stern's prepattern concept, but by passive (by tissue dislocations) or active (autonomous) migration of determined cells. Cell lineage alone, as shown for the compound eye by Becker (1957), or combined with polarized adhesive properties of the determined cells, could thus lead to proper orientation.

V. Stomatal Patterns in Plant Leaves, with a Note on *Drosophila* Ocelli and Turing's Model

After discussing an example of pattern formation involving cell migration, pigmentation in amphibians—and one in which cell migration cannot be ruled out—bristle patterns in insects, I now want to turn to a case in which cell migration does not occur in pattern formation. The rigid framework of cellulose walls of plant cells prevents cell migration effectively. Yet in leaves, certain cell types such as hairs and stomata occur in patterns (Fig. 10).

Work on patterns in plants has been dormant in the recent past. The most up-to-date accounts that I have found are those of Buenning (1965), Bloch (1965) and Stebbins (1965). An earlier review has appeared by Geitler (1954). English versions of this work, much of which was originally published in German, will be found in the forthcoming translation of Kuehn's masterful text on developmental biology (Kuehn, 1965).

The epidermis of young plant leaves consists of small, polygonal cells in rapid division. In the maturing leaf, when cell divisions have essentially ceased, a few cells become conspicuous from among the otherwise homogeneous tissue by virtue of their size and density of cytoplasm. They are stoma stem cells, each of which has originated from ordinary epidermal cells by an unequal division which resulted in the formation of a stem cell and another ordinary epidermal cell. In monocotyledons and dicotyledons, each stem cell then divides with the spindle at right angle to the previous division, giving rise to two guard cells. In dicotyledons, the two epidermal cells directly adjoining either side of the stem cell also undergo an unequal division, each giving rise to an auxiliary cell of the stoma and another ordinary epidermal cell.

How are the unequal divisions that lead to the formation of stem cells initiated? We mentioned that they occur after mitosis in the rest of the leaf has come to a halt. This seems to be a prerequisite for the onset of unequal divisions, for when mitoses in the leaf are stimulated experimentally by wounding, or by applying leaf homogenates locally, unequal divisions do not occur in that part of the leaf.

If such an experimental disturbance is not produced, unequal divisions do occur, but they do not occur simultaneously on the entire leaf. Stem cells appear here and there, and at roughly equal distances from these stem cells, new stem cells appear. Each stem cell is surrounded by a constant area within which, as a rule, no other stem cells appear (Fig. 10). There are exceptions, particularly in monocotyledons, in that sometimes two stem cells appear simultaneously side by side. In these cases, however, one of the stem cells invariably dedifferentiates into an ordinary epidermis cell, and only the other stem cell divides to give rise to a stoma.

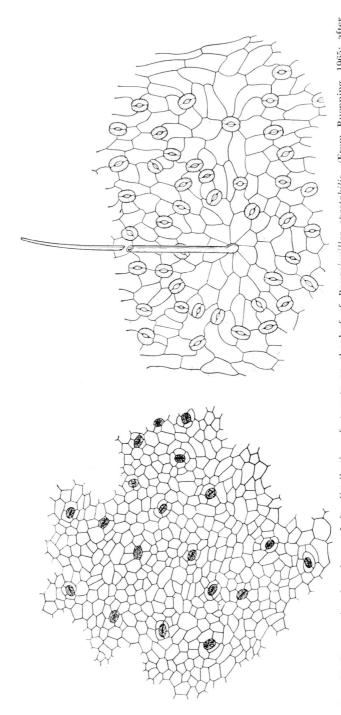

FIG. 10. Patterns in plant leaves. Left: distribution of stomata on the leaf of *Bougainvillea spectabilis*. (From Buenning, 1965; after Buenning and Sagromsky, 1948) . Right: Hair on a leaf of *Pulsatilla*. Note the stoma-free zone surrounding the hair. (From Buenning, 1965; after Zimmerman *et al.*, 1953.)

198

Thus far, the patterned initiation of stem cell formation may be explained on the assumption that a stem cell, once formed, creates an area around itself that is inhibitory to the production of another stem cell. In this connection an observation by Buenning and Sagromsky (1948) and Leick (1955) is interesting. These authors noticed independently that within a fixed pattern of stomata new stomata appear if the leaf undergoes growth in area, during which existing stomata become separated from one another secondarily.

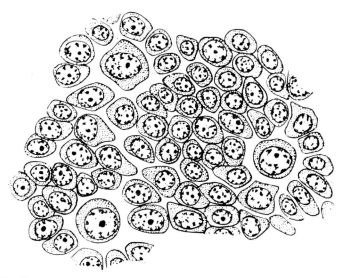

FIG. 11.   Tangential section through a pupal wing of *Ephestia*. Note the large stem cells of scales. (From Kuehn, 1965; after Koehler, 1932.)

Similar inhibitory areas, for hairs, have been observed by Zimmerman *et al.* (1953). Apparently, inhibitory areas surrounding a hair may interfere with those surrounding stomata (Fig. 10, right). Very little is known of the properties of such inhibitory areas. The only cytological observation available is that cell nuclei in the inhibitory area are located in the parts of the epidermal cells closest to the stem cell of the stoma. The meaning of this peculiar arrangement of nuclei is not known.

Concentric zones of inhibition, as postulated for stoma-forming areas, are conceptually similar to concentric zones of precursor concentrations as postulated for equidistant spacing of ocelli and other chitinous structures of insect integument by Maynard-Smith (1960) and Maynard-Smith and Sondhi (1960). Their concept is essentially based on a mathematical model developed by Turing (1952) and is directly applicable to the spacing of stomata. Turing's model, which is discussed in more detail in a comprehensive review on patterns by Sondhi (1963), starts out with a homogeneous distribution of "morphogens" in a tissue. The morphogens are assumed to be unrestricted in their diffusion through the tissue. According to Turing, a random disturbance of the original distribution of morphogens may give rise to standing waves of concentration of the morphogens. Of course this model has been exploited in support of the prepattern concept (Sondhi, 1963). A physical and/or chemical demonstration of concentration peaks remains to be made, however. Plant leaves would appear to be ideal material for the search for such conditions, simply because a given type of differentiation in the case of stomata is actually initiated at specific sites. The process of patterning, if it is at all related to the cases discussed for amphibians and insects, appears much simpler in leaves because the complication of cell migration can be excluded.

VI. Scales, Color Patterns, and Hinges of Butterfly Wings

The embryology of scales on butterfly wings has been worked out in great detail by Henke's school (e.g., Henke, 1933, 1946; see Sondhi, 1963, for additional references). The individual scale apparatus is homologous to the bristle apparatus as described above (p. 187), and is formed in a very similar way through a series of unequal divisions leading to a patterned distribution of stem cells (Fig. 11). The cytology of these divisions has been worked out in considerable detail. Thus it is known, for example, that the scale stem cell of the first order divides with a spindle at right angles to the wing surface, whereas the spindle is shifted to an angle of 30° when the scale stem cell of the second order divides (Fig. 12). Cell lineage can thus be followed very precisely, and its study has led to an understanding of the reasons for the rigid grouping in which scales are arranged. These observations have been reviewed recently (Sondhi, 1963; Kuehn, 1965) and will not be reported here especially since one of the most exciting conclusions, the so-called complementation principle, is the object of ardent debate in view of more recent findings (Esser, 1961; Lipp, 1966). Furthermore, one aspect

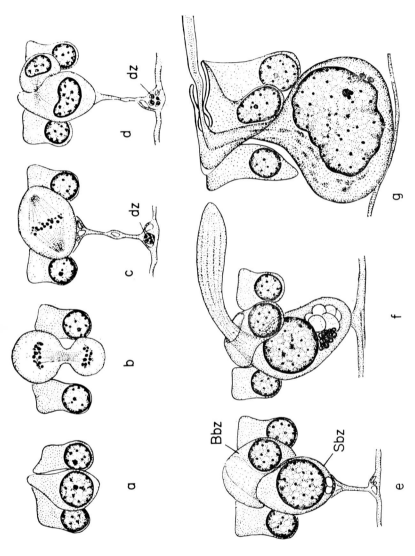

Fig. 12. Development of scales in *Ephestia*. A first order scale stem cell (a) undergoes its first unequal division (b). One of the resulting cells degenerates (dz); the other undergoes a second unequal division (c). The two resulting cells differentiate into scale and socket, respectively (d–g). Bbz: scale-forming cell; Sbz: socket-forming cell. (From Kuehn, 1965; after Stossberg, 1938.)

of patterning, that is, the initiation of scale stem cells, poses identical problems to those discussed above for insect bristles.

Lepidotera wings, however, show additional patterns that apparently are formed quite independently of the grouping of scales. The forewings of *Ephestia,* e.g., carry a very characteristic dark-light banding pattern, which has been analyzed experimentally by Kuehn and Henke (1932)

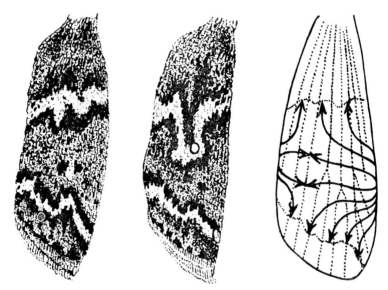

FIG. 13.   Banding pattern on the forewing of *Ephestia.* Left: Control wing. Center: Wing developing after thermocautherization (hole); note that the white band has not moved to the proximal end of the wing all the way across its surface, but is "retarded" at the site of the injury. Right: Interpretation of a large number of similar experiments. The arrows indicate the direction of a "determination stream." (From Kuehn, 1965; after Kuehn and von Engelhardt, 1933.)

and Kuehn and von Engelhardt (1933) (Fig. 13). These authors damaged pupal wing primordia by microthermocauterization of various small areas at various times of development and then observed the color patterns on the differentiated wing. They observed deformation of bands which were interpreted to be caused by a block, established by the wound, against centrifugal diffusion of agents responsible for the deposition of pigments. From the nature of these deformations, Kuehn and von Engelhardt (1933) postulated two centers in the wing from which a "determination stream" normally originated. They pictured this determination stream as proceeding over the wing surface essentially in a centrifugal direction toward the proximal and distal end of the wing (Fig. 13). Local heat treatment is thought to act as a diffusion barrier.

Since the banding pattern on these moth wings most likely represents localized melanin synthesis and deposition, it is conceivable that the dark bands reflect concentration peaks of melanin precursors. These concentration peaks could arise from point sources of production according to Turing's (1952) model; their establishment would be interrupted by local heat damage. This model is also purely speculative, but testable.

The spreading of a "determination wave" has also been postulated by Kroeger (1958). This author studied the development of wing hinges, which are composed of sclerites of very elaborate morphology. If a wing imaginal disk of *Ephestia* is dissected out from a larva and implanted back into the body cavity of a host larva, a mirror image disk grows from the wound edge of the implant, and during metamorphosis a symmetrical adult structure is formed, having an overall size that depends on the length of time elapsed between the implantation and the onset of metamorphosis. Interestingly enough, this hinge is always symmetrical, even in cases in which it reaches only a small size. A normal hinge may be classified into more centrally and more laterally located sclerites. In the experimental hinges, Kroeger observed that whenever a given pair of symmetrical structures was missing, all of the normally more centrally located structures were also missing, whereas the more lateral structures were differentiated. He interpreted this finding as an indication that a "determination wave" is initiated in the center, at the axis of symmetry, and travels distally toward either side, thereby sequentially determining sclerites of the hinges, lateral ones first, central ones last.

In keeping with Stern's concept, Kroeger suggested that what is laid down by the determination stream is a prepattern for hinge formation. He was led to this conclusion by a different experiment, reported in 1959. The hinges of fore- and hindwing of *Ephestia* differ in coloration and structural detail of sclerites (Fig. 14). Kroeger dissected fore- and hindwing imaginal disks and by an ingenious microsurgical technique sewed the disks together in pairs of two. The pairs were then implanted into host larvae where they regenerated and underwent metamorphosis. The structures that formed were symmetrical, integrated wing hinges, as was to be expected. Surprisingly, however, there existed a rigid negative correlation between the amount of forewing and hindwing material contributing to the integrated hinge. This is a very interesting and at the same time puzzling observation. Kroeger (1959) explained it on the assumption that upon fusion of the two primordia, a new prepattern for hinge is laid down in the regenerated portion which assigns hinge properties to whatever cells come under its influence. Here again, however, as in the bristle mosaics, a very broad definition of the prepattern term is required. In fact, in this example one has to postulate that both forewing and hindwing have identical prepatterns, but that fore- and hindwing cells react differentially. Since they are genetically alike, the difference in their competence must lie in their developmental history. Taken to this extreme, the prepattern concept, although logically still sound, again loses much value operationally.

VII. Appendix

A. *The Current Status of the Pattern Problem*

The pattern problem today is in a state in which far more factual information is needed. In the case of bird feather patterns: does the prospective white zone contain melanoblasts that never differentiate dendritic processes? Or do these cells form dendrites, but fail to synthesize melanin? Do they fail to synthesize melanin because of lack of tyrosine, or tyrosinase? Electron microscopy and radioautography could help enormously in answering these questions, as could histochemistry. In amphibian pigmentation patterns: do adhesive properties of melanocytes in their interaction with cells of the skin and the somites explain the patterned distribution of pigment cells? Competitive sorting-out experiments *in vitro* could contribute here. In insect bristle patterns: does cell migration occur during normal development of patterns or during their restitution under experimental conditions? The use of radioactively labeled cell, color markers, and time-lapse cinematography would be fruitful for answering these questions by direct observation; a reliable tissue culture method would also be valuable for such investigations. In the case of banding patterns on the wings of Lepidoptera: is there in fact a directed flow of any material through the wing anlage? Are there local concentration peaks of melanin precursors?

It is intriguing to search for a common denominator of a set of problems. I doubt that there is one in the area of pattern formation today. Patterns can arise in many different ways, of which we have presented only a few. The fact that some of them have unequal division in common is probably a sampling error.

Of course one could carry the *concept of differential gene function* further and say that patterns are initiated by a nonrandom distribution of those conditions that regulate the occurrence of a particular type of

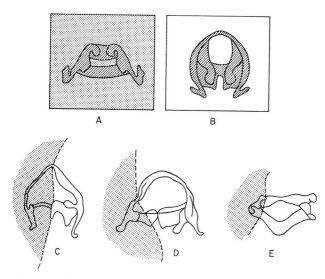

Fig. 14. Doubled hindwing (stippled, A) and forewing (white, B) hinge region of *Ephestia*. C–E: Three cases of mosaic forewing-hindwing hinges. (From Ursprung, 1963; after Kroeger, 1959.)

cell differentiation. It is immediately obvious that we gain little from this stepped-up concept, since we know little about these conditions even in the simplest case of differentiation.

On the other hand, when formulated at the right time, unifying concepts may have an enormous heuristic value. The current dogma on gene action is having a great impact on other branches of biology, including developmental biology (see Ursprung, 1965, for review). In this sense, biologists interested in patterns may want to familiarize themselves with the work of physically oriented chemists working on the properties of large molecules. Can large molecules assume various shapes autonomously or by interacting with their environment? Can larger molecules become grouped into larger entities autonomously? Furthermore, biologists interested in pattern formation may want to follow the exciting work of biochemists on metabolic oscillations. Are there in fact known cases of metabolites being produced rhythmically?

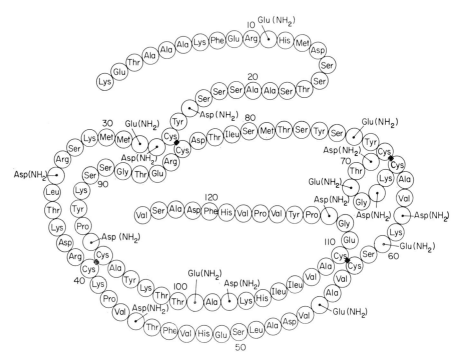

FIG. 15.   The covalent structure of bovine pancreatic ribonuclease. Disulfide bridges are indicated by black squares. (From Anfinsen, 1964.)

In this Appendix we shall now briefly mention a few examples illustrating these two major phenomena that might bear on the pattern problem: autonomous production of shape by constituent molecules, and antonomous rhythms in metabolic pathways.

B.   *Ribonuclease*

Does the primary structure of a protein determine its higher orders of structure? Of several proteins that have been analyzed with respect to this question, ribonuclease is particularly worth mentioning. Conditions for denaturing and renaturing this enzyme have been worked out by Anfinsen and his collaborators (Anfinsen, 1964; Haber and Anfinsen, 1962; White, 1961).

Disruption of the four disulfide bridges of this molecule (Fig. 15) by incubation in 8 M urea in the presence of mercaptoethanol leads to molecules devoid of demonstrable tertiary and secondary structure, and devoid of enzymic activity. This reduced ribonuclease contains eight sulfhydryl groups and consequently could form 105 possible arrangements with four disulfide bridges upon oxidation. If reduced RNAse is oxidized, by exposure of dilute solutions to molecular oxygen, full enzymic activity is regained, and physico-chemical evidence such as optical rotation, rotatory dispersion, viscosity, trypsin digestibility, and ultraviolet absorption suggest that only native RNAse is formed during oxidation under these conditions, with a recovery of close to 100%.

If oxidation is carried out under conditions adverse to correct sulf-hydryl pairing, such as in 8 M urea or in 4 M guanidinum chloride, inactive derivatives are produced which are susceptible to trypsin digestion, have a modified ultraviolet spectrum, and have a viscosity intermediate between reduced and native RNAse. Other physico-chemical measurements support the assumption that these derivatives are molecules formed by random disulfide pairing. As soon as they are exposed to high pH and mercaptoethanol, disulfide interchange occurs and the native form of RNAse is assumed.

Taken as a whole the evidence suggests strongly that the native secondary and tertiary structure of ribonuclease are the thermodynamically most stable configuration. On the other hand, it is also evident that there can be conditions under which this configuration is not realized.

Reversible denaturation of enzymes is not unique to ribonuclease (see Anfinsen, 1964, for review). A number of other proteins, with or without disulfide bridges, have been studied recently with results generally pointing to the same conclusions that were drawn for ribonuclease (e.g., Deal *et al.*, 1963; see Anfinsen, 1964, for additional references). Proteins, it seems, tend to assume the thermodynamically most stable shape in solution quite autonomously after having been disrupted. Thus, the primary amino acid sequence alone contains information at least for the formation of tertiary structure.

C. *Ribosomes*

Reversible disruption of structure has not only been demonstrated for several proteins, but recently also for organelles. Lerman *et al.*

(1966) report that they succeeded in disrupting *Escherichia coli* ribosomes into a series of smaller particles, and that these smaller particles
could spontaneously reaggregate with the formation of intact ribosomes.
In their experiments, they dissociated ordinary 70 S ribosomes into 50 S
and 30 S subunits by low magnesium, and then subjected these subunits
to a high concentration of CsCl. Upon incubation in 5 M CsCl and
$2 \times 10^{-3} M$ MgCl$_2$, protein-deficient particles (43 S and 28 S, or 36 S and
23 S) are formed. The protein that is removed from the particles forms
an equilibrium mixture with the particles. If it is removed from the
particles by flotation, two new ribonucleoprotein types form which are
even more deficient in protein, with values of 28 S and 22 S, respectively. Thus, a series

$$[70\ S] \rightarrow \begin{bmatrix} 50\ S \\ 30\ S \end{bmatrix} \rightarrow \begin{bmatrix} 43\ or\ 36\ S \\ 28\ or\ 23\ S \end{bmatrix} \rightarrow \begin{bmatrix} 28\ S \\ 22\ S \end{bmatrix}$$

is formed.

When these last particles were exposed to dilute buffer in the presence of magnesium and dissociated protein original 70 S ribosomes were
found with increasing magnesium concentration, whereby the sequence
of intermediary particles was again encountered, in reverse. The resti-
tuted 70 S particles were indistinguishable from native ribosomes with
regard to protein content and density.

The stepwise production of altered particles suggests that protein is
lost in discontinuous aliquots. The successful reaggregation is strong
support for the assumption that groups of molecules can interact on
their own with the formation of progressively more complex structures
in cell-free systems—again provided that the conditions permit this
reaggregation.

D. *Bacterial Flagella*

Autonomous assembly of groups of molecules into organelles is also
apparent in the reconstruction of bacterial flagella, as reported by Abram
and Koffler (1964), and by Asakura *et al.* (1966). Flagella can be isolated from bacteria by vibration and centrifugation. At low pH, a
preparation of flagellin is obtained which is a protein of a molecular
weight between 20,000 and 45,000 containing small amounts of carbohydrate. At acid pH it exists in the form of individual molecules and
small aggregates.

If this preparation is reaggregated by dialysis against water or dilute
buffer (0.02–0.1 M phosphate), heavier material is formed and can be

recovered from suspension by centrifugation. Electron microscope analysis of the material shows that it consists of one or two components, depending on the conditions during the reaggregation. At pH values at or below 4.7, rodlike bundles of fibers are formed. The individual fiber of these aggregates measures 30–40 Å in diameter. The bundles may have diameters of 1000 Å or more, and measure up to 20 μ in length (Fig. 16). These structures have not been seen in native flagella material. However, if the pH is raised to 5.4, flagellalike material is formed that is indistinguishable from native flagella both in electron microscope appearance (Fig. 16) and in some physico-chemical properties such as kinetics of heat denaturation. The same flagellalike material can be obtained from the rodlike structures under appropriate pH conditions.

The reaggregation of flagellin into flagellalike material is a slow process. Although some reaggregated material can be recovered within less than an hour of incubation, the reaction requires about 10 hours for completion. Apparently the restitution is nonenzymic; it occurs at 2° C and even in the frozen state.

Although the fine structure of flagella is little known, the results thus far obtained suggest that flagella can form autonomously from their component molecules under appropriate conditions, a conclusion similar to the one drawn from the results of *in vitro* ribosome assembly.

E. *Cytoplasmic Membranes*

Whaley *et al.* (1964) in an earlier symposium of the Society, showed exciting electron micrographs (Figs. 36 and 37 of that paper) of cytoplasmic membranes induced experimentally in plant root cap cells. At the level of electron microscope analysis, these induced membranes are not distinguishable from native ER; even RNP particles may appear to be attached to the surface of these membranes. Conditions leading to the formation of such structures include lowering oxygen tension, administering colchicine, high intensity radiation, and mechanical effects. The induced membranes may be formed within only a few seconds.

The findings are interpreted by Whaley as an indication that the cytoplasm contains a reservoir of membrane components that under appropriate conditions become zipped into organelle configuration. Again, it is apparent that molecular components contain information for the creation of higher orders of structure, and that the realization of such higher orders of structure may be controlled by environmental conditions.

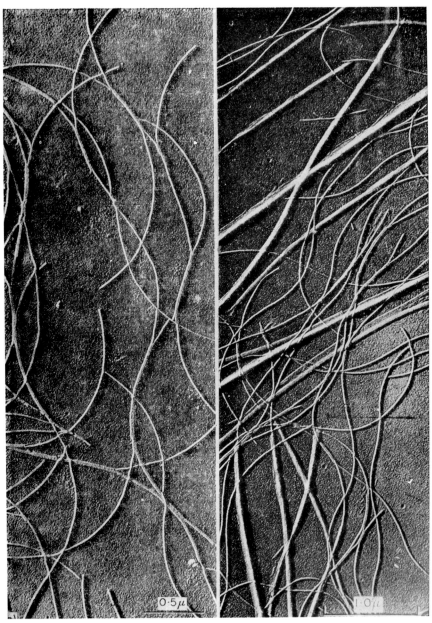

FIG. 16. Native (left) and reconstituted (right) bacterial flagella. In the electron micrograph on the right note the slender flagella that are indistinguishable from native flagella, in addition to thicker bundles, from which the slender material may also be obtained under appropriate conditions. (From Abram and Koffler, 1964.)

F.   *A Biological Oscillator*

One of the mechanisms postulated for pattern formation is periodicity in time. We have encountered it in the case of barred feathers in birds, in which periodic biosynthetic activity of melanoblasts was held responsible for the formation of pigment bands. In modified form, we have again encountered it in the assumed "determination streams" occurring on the butterfly wing.

Recent observations primarily by Chance and associates (see Chance *et al.,* 1965; Pye and Chance, 1966; for references) may be relevant to this phenomenon. These authors observed oscillations of reduced pyridine nucleotide in yeast suspensions as well as in cell-free extracts after the addition of metabolites of the glycolytic pathway to starved cells. Figure 17 shows a short train of damped oscillations observed when glucose was added to a suspension of baker's yeast that had been starved for 24 hours. Using a cell-free extract of *Saccharomyces carlsbergensis,* Pye and Chance (1966) have now been able to induce much longer trains of as many as 90 undamped oscillations; in these experiments, a single addition of trehalose was used instead of glucose. The authors propose that in this case sustained rather than damped oscillations are observed because trehalose, through trehalase, provides a continuous supply of glucose to glycolysis. It may well be, as the authors point out, that these oscillations are the basis for biological clocks. For our present discussion, it should merely be added that such metabolic oscillations may be eminently relevant for the rhythmical production and release of agents that, in space, might be responsible for patterned differentiations.

VIII.   Conclusions

At the Embryological Conference sponsored by the *Journal of Experimental Embryology and Morphology,* and held in the fall of 1965 in London, S. Brenner (unpublished) gave what he called the "Molecular Biology Sermon." In his conclusions, he stated that before long it would be possible to compute a mouse. There was a roar of protest in the audience.

However, others are also optimistic. John Kendrew (1962) wrote: "In the long run it may be that a knowledge of amino acid sequence . . . will be enough for all our purposes. This is a distant goal which will perhaps not be attained in our generation; nevertheless our recognition of it will serve to define the direction of our studies and to focus them on fruitful problems."

IX.   Summary

A brief survey of some major ways of pattern formation at the cellular level has been given, including barred patterns in bird feathers, pigment

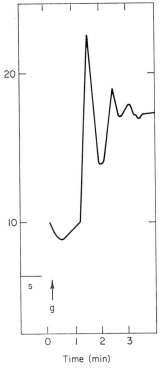

Fig. 17. Fluorescence (ordinate) of a suspension of starved yeast cells at various times (abscissa) after addition of glucose (g) ; s: fluorescence level of starved suspension. (Modified from Duysens and Amesz, 1957.)

patterns in amphibians, patterns of bristles, scales, sclerites, and pigments in insects, and arrangements of stomata in leaves. A number of unsolved, but testable questions have been asked with regard to these patterns. The question of autonomy of the creation of shape was discussed, using spontaneous restitution of large molecules and organelles as examples. Recent biochemical evidence for metabolic oscillations was presented.

ACKNOWLEDGMENTS

I am indebted to Drs. B. H. Willier and M. E. Rawles for help in learning much about feathers; to graduate students in this department, particularly Henry Wehman and Herbert Phillips, for thoughtful discussions of the prepattern concept; to Dr. Ludwig Brand for directing my attention to metabolic oscillations; and to Charles Weber for the art work. I am grateful to Drs. C. Stern and C. Tokunaga for their critical comments.

REFERENCES

ABRAM, D., AND KOFFLER, H. (1964). *In vitro* formation of flagella-like filaments and other structures from flagellin. *J. Mol. Biol.* **9,** 168–185.

ANFINSEN, C. B. (1964). On the possibility of predicting tertiary structure from primary sequence. *In* "New Perspectives in Biology" (M. Sela, ed.), pp. 42–50. Elsevier, Amsterdam.

ASAKURA, S., EGUCHI, G., AND IINS, T. (1966). *Salmonella* flagella: *in vitro* reconstruction and over all shapes of flagellar filaments. *J. Mol. Biol.* **16,** 302–316.

AUERBACH, C. (1936). The development of the legs, wings, and halteres in wild-type and some mutant strains of *Drosophila melanogaster. Trans. Roy. Soc. Edinburgh* **58,** 787–819.

BECKER, H. J. (1957). Ueber Roentgenmosaikflecken und Defektmutationen am Auge von Drosophila und die Entwicklungsphysiologie des Auges. *Z. Vererbungslehre* **88,** 333–373.

BLOCH, R. (1965). Histological foundations of differentiation and development in plants. *In* "Encyclopedia of Plant Physiology" (W. Ruhland, ed.), Vol. **15,** pp. 146–188. Springer, Berlin.

BUENNING, E. (1965). Die Entstehung von Mustern in der Entwicklung von Pflanzen. *In* "Encyclopedia of Plant Physiology" (W. Ruhland, ed.), Vol. **15,** pp. 383–402. Springer, Berlin.

BUENNING, E., AND SAGROMSKY, H. (1948). Die Bildung des Spaltoeffnungsmusters in der Blatt-epidermis (Mit Anmerkungen ueber weitere Musterbildungen). *Z. Naturforsch.* **3**b, 203–216.

CHANCE, B., SCHOENER, B., AND ELSAESSER, S. (1965). Metabolic control phenomena involved in damped sinusoidal oscillations of reduced diphosphopyridine nucleotide in a cell-free extract of *Saccharomyces carlsbergensis. J. Biol. Chem.* **240,** 3170–3181.

DEAL, W. C., RUTTER, W. J., MASSEY, V., AND VAN HOLDE, K. E. (1963). Reversible alteration of the structure of enzymes in acidic solution. *Biochem. Biophys. Res. Commun.* **10,** 49–54.

DUYSENS, L. N. M., AND AMESZ, J. (1957). Fluorescence spectophotometry of reduced phosphopyridine nucleotide in intact cells in the near-ultraviolet and visible region. *Biochim. Biophys. Acta* **24,** 19–26.

ESSER, H. (1961). Untersuchungen zur Entwicklung des Puppenfluegels von *Ephestia kuehniella. Arch. Entwicklungsmech. Organ.* **153,** 176–212.

GARCIA-BELLIDO, A. (1966). Pattern reconstruction by dissociated imaginal disc cells of *Drosophila melanogaster*. *Devel. Biol.* (in press).

GEITLER, L. (1954). Morphologie und Entwicklungsgeschichte der Zelle. *In* "Fortschritte der Botanik" (E. Gaeumann and O. Renner, eds.), pp. 1–15. Springer, Berlin.

HABER, E., AND ANFINSEN, C. B. (1962). Side-chain interactions governing the pairing of half-cystine residues in ribonuclease. *J. Biol. Chem.* **237,** 1839–1844.

HADORN, E. (1966). Dynamics of determination. *In* "Major Problems in Developmental Biology" (M. Locke, ed.), pp. 85–104. Academic Press, New York.

HADORN, E., AND BUCK, D. (1962). Ueber Entwicklungsleistungen transplantierter Teilstuecke von Fluegel-Imaginalscheiben von *Drosophila melanogaster*. *Rev. Suisse Zool.* **69,** 302–310.

HADORN, E., ANDERS, G., AND URSPRUNG, H. (1959). Kombinate aus teilweise dissoziierten Imaginalscheiben verschiedener Mutanten und Arten von *Drosophila*. *J. Exptl. Zool.* **142,** 159–175.

HAMILTON, H. L. (1952). "Lillie's Development of the Chick," 3rd Ed., 624 pp. Holt, New York.

HENKE, K. (1933). Untersuchungen an *Philosamia cynthia* drury zur Entwicklungsphysiologie des Zeichnungsmusters auf dem Schmetterlingsfluegel. *Wilhelm Roux Arch. Entwicklungsmech. Organ.* **128,** 15–107.

HENKE, K. (1946). Ueber die verschiedenen Zellteilungsvorgaenge in der Entwicklung des beschuppten Fluegelepithels der Mehlmotte *Ephestia kuehniella*. *Biol. Zentr.* **65,** 120–135.

KENDREW, J. (1962). *Pontif. Acad. Sci. Scripta Varia* **22,** 449 (cited in Anfinsen, 1964).

KOEHLER, W. (1932). Die Entwicklung der Fluegel bei der Mehlmotte *Ephestia kuehniella*, mit besonderer Beruecksichtigung des Zeichnungsmusters. *Z. Morphol. Oekol. Tiere* **24,** 582–681.

KROEGER, H. (1958). Ueber Doppelbildungen in die Leibeshoehle verpflanzter Fluegel-Imaginalscheiben von *Ephestia kuehniella*. *Arch. Entwicklungsmech. Organ.* **151,** 301–332.

KROEGER, H. (1959). Determinationsmosaike aus kombiniert implantierten Imaginalscheiben von *Ephestia kuehniella*. *Arch. Entwicklungsmech. Organ.* **151,** 113–135.

KUEHN, A. (1965). "Vorlesungen ueber Entwicklungsphysiologie," 2nd Ed. Springer, Berlin. (English transl. to be published by Springer.)

KUEHN, A., AND VON ENGELHARDT, M. (1933). Ueber die Determination des Symmetriesystems auf dem Vorderfluegel von *Ephestia kuehniella*. *Wilhelm Roux Arch. Entwicklungsmech. Organ.* **130,** 660–703.

KUEHN, A., AND HENKE, K. (1932). Genetische und Entwicklungsphysiologische Untersuchungen an der Mehlmotte *Espestia Kuehniella*. *Abhandl. Akad. Wiss. Goettingen, Math.-Physik Kl.* **15,** 7–12.

LEHMAN, H. E., AND YOUNG, L. M. (1959). Extrinsic and intrinsic factors influencing amphibian pigment pattern formation. *In* "Pigment Cell Biology" (M. Gordon, ed.), pp. 1–36. Academic Press, New York.

LEICK, E. (1955). Periodische Neuanlage von Blatt-Stomata. *Flora (Jena)* **142,** 45–64.

LERMAN, M. C., SPIRIN, A. S., GAVRILOVA, L. P., AND GOLOV, V. F. (1966). Studies on the structure of ribosomes. II. Stepwise dissociation of protein from ribosomes by cesium chloride and the reassembly of ribosome-like particles. *J. Mol. Biol.* **15,** 268–281.

LEUTHARDT, F. (1959). "Lehrbuch der Physiologischen Chemie," 14th Ed., 917 pp. Gruyter, Berlin.

LIPP, C. (1966). Zur Discussion ueber die Schuppen-Epithelverbaende von *Ephestia kuehniella. Biol. Zentr.* **85,** 231–235.

MAYNARD-SMITH, T. (1960). Continuous, quantized, and modal variation. *Proc. Roy. Soc. (London)* **B152,** 397–409.

MAYNARD-SMITH, T., AND SONDHI, K. C. (1960). The genetics of a pattern. *Genetics* **45,** 1039–1050.

NICKERSON, M. (1944). An experimental analysis of barred pattern formation in feathers. *J. Exptl. Zool.* **95,** 361–397.

NOETHIGER, R. (1964). Differenzierungsleistungen in Kombinaten, hergestellt aus Imaginalscheiben verschiedener Arten, Geschlechter und Koerpersegmente von Drosophila. *Entwicklungsmech. Organ. Arch.* **155,** 269–301.

PYE, K., AND CHANCE, B. (1966). Sustained sinusoidal oscillations of reduced pyridine nucleotide in a cell-free extract of *Saccharomyces carlsbergensis. Proc. Natl. Acad. Sci. U.S.* **55,** 888–894.

ROSIN, S. (1940). Zur Frage der Pigmentmusterbildung bei Urodelen. *Rev. Suisse Zool.* **47.**

SONDHI, K. C. (1963). The biological foundations of animal patterns. *Quart. Rev. Biol.* **38,** 289–327.

STEBBINS, G. L. (1965). Some relationships between mitotic rhythm, nucleic acid synthesis, and morphogenesis in higher plants. Brookhaven Symp. in Biology **18,** 204–221.

STEINBERG, M. S. (1964). The problem of adhesive selectivity in cellular interaction. *In* "Cellular Membranes in Development" (M. Locke, ed.), pp. 321–365. Academic Press, New York.

STERN, C. (1954a). Genes and developmental patterns. *Caryologia* **6,** Suppl., 355–368.

STERN, C. (1954b). Two or three bristles. *In* "Science in Progress" (G. A. Baistell, ed.), 9th Ser., pp. 41–84. Yale Univ. Press, New Haven, Connecticut.

STERN, C. (1956). Genetic mechanisms in the localized initiation of differentiation. *Cold Spring Harbor Symp. Quant. Biol.* **21,** 375–392.

STOSSBERG, M. (1938). Die Zellvorgaenge bei der Entwicklung der Fluegelschuppen von *Ephestia kuehniella. Z. Morphol. Oekol. Tiere* **34.**

TOKUNAGA, C. (1961). The differentiation of a secondary sex comb under the influence of the gene *engrailed* in *Drosophila melanogaster. Genetics* **46,** 157–176.

TOKUNAGA, C. (1962). Cell lineage and differentiation of the male foreleg of *Drosophila melanogaster. Develop. Biol.* **4,** 489–516.

TURING, A. M. (1952). The chemical basis of morphogenesis. *Phil. Trans. Roy. Soc. London* **B237,** 37–72.

TWITTY, V. C. (1945). The developmental analysis of specific pigment patterns. *J. Exptl. Zool.* **100,** 141–178.

TWITTY, V. C. (1949). Developmental analysis of amphibian pigmentation. *Growth* **13,** Suppl., 133–162.

URSPRUNG, H. (1963). Development and genetics of patterns. *Am. Zool.* **3,** 71–86.

URSPRUNG, H. (1965). Genes and development. In "Organogenesis" (R. L. DeHaan and H. Ursprung, eds.), pp. 1-27. Holt, New York.

URSPRUNG, H., AND HADORN, E. (1962). Weitere Untersuchungen über Musterbildung in Kombinaten aus teilweise dissoziierten Flügel-Imaginalscheiben von Drosophila melanogaster. Develop. Biol. **4,** 40-66.

WATTERSON, R. L. (1942). The morphogenesis of down feathers with special reference to the developmental history of melanophores. Physiol. Zool. **15,** 234-259.

WESTON, J. A. (1963). A radioautographic analysis of the migration and localization of trunk neural crest cells in the chick. Develop. Biol. **6,** 279-310.

WHALEY, W. G., KEPHARDT, T. E., AND MOLLENHAUER, H. H. (1964). The dynamics of cytoplasmic membranes during development. In "Cellular Membranes in Development" (M. Locke, ed.), pp. 135-174. Academic Press, New York.

WHITE, F. H., JR. (1961). Regeneration of native secondary and tertiary structures by air oxidation of reduced ribonuclease. J. Biol. Chem. **236,** 1353-1358.

WILDE, C. E. (1961). The differentiation of vertebrate pigment cells. Advan. Morphogenesis **1,** 267-298.

WILLIER, B. H. (1948). Hormonal regeneration of feather pigmentation in the fowl. Spec. Publ. N.Y. Acad. Sci. **IV,** 321-340.

WILLIER, B. H., AND RAWLES, M. E. (1944a). Genotypic control of feather color pattern as demonstrated by the effects of a sex-linked gene upon the melanophores. Genetics **29,** 309-330.

WILLIER, B. H., AND RAWLES, M. E. (1944b). Melanophore control of the sexual dimorphism of feather pigmentation pattern in the Barred Plymouth Rock fowl. Yale J. Biol. Med. **17,** 319-340.

ZIMMERMAN, W., WOERNLE, D., AND WARTH, L. (1953). Genetische Untersuchungen an Pulsatilla. V. Die Entwicklung von Haaren und Spaetöffnungen bei Pulsatilla. Z. Botan. **41,** 227-246.

Protein Structure
in Relation to Cell Dynamics
and Differentiation

D. E. KOSHLAND, JR. AND M. E. KIRTLEY

Department of Biochemistry, University of California, Berkeley, California

Our knowledge of enzymes, those key catalytic units that direct essentially all the dynamic processes of living systems, is progressing at an enormous rate. The recent International Commission on Enzyme Nomenclature was able to list over 800 clearly distinct reactions catalyzed by specific enzymes, and more are being discovered every day. Many of these enzymes have been crystallized, and most of them have been isolated in a high state of purity. The complete primary structure, i.e., the position of each amino acid in the polypeptide, has been determined for at least a dozen proteins, and the complete three-dimensional structure, as determined by X-ray crystallography, has recently been obtained for one enzyme, lysozyme (Blake *et al.*, 1965).

Because enzymes play such a key role in the living system, they touch on almost every aspect of biology. It would be clearly impossible in the time allotted to cover all the correlations between structure and function of proteins. We have therefore chosen to concentrate only on a few aspects, but they are the aspects which we believe will be central to problems of differentiation and growth.

Three-Dimensional Structure of Proteins

Let us begin by considering the forces responsible for the three-dimensional structures of proteins and their location in the cell. In Fig. 1 the steps in the synthesis and the morphological positioning of polypeptide chains are outlined. The sequence of nucleotides in the deoxyribonucleic acid is "transcribed" to give a messenger ribonucleic acid molecule which is in turn "translated" to give the polypeptide chain. The position of each amino acid in this polypeptide chain is

thus derived directly from the code in the original nucleic acid molecule and is referred to as the primary structure of the protein. During
completion of the chain, or following release from the template, the
polypeptide folds into the three-dimensional structure characteristic of
that protein. Sela *et al.* (1957) first showed that the peptide chain of
native ribonuclease can be unfolded and that under appropriate conditions the unfolded protein spontaneously refolds to give the correct
tertiary structure with full catalytic activity. Other enzymes have now

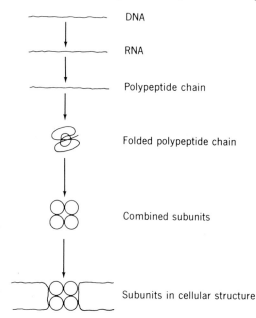

Fig. 1. The formation of complex protein structure from the information in DNA.
Information stored in DNA as a sequence of nucleotide bases is transcribed into RNA
and translated into a sequence of amino acids. Noncovalent side chain interactions
lead to folding followed by association of subunits. The polymerized subunits may then
associate into more complex structures. Active protein may be observed in any of the
last three stages.

been shown to refold spontaneously after they have been unfolded. In
some of these cases disulfide bridges are formed within the folded
molecule, but it is clear that the noncovalent forces between the amino
acid side chains determine the three-dimensional structure. The disulfide bridges provide further stability for the molecule but are not essential for the folding process. Myoglobin contains no disulfide bonds and

yet a precise three-dimensional structure accurately reproducible to a fraction of an angstrom has been ascertained by X-ray crystallography. Thus, the folding of a polypeptide to a three-dimensional array having biological activity is predetermined by the linear sequence of amino acids as specified by the DNA code. The mechanism for achieving a precise three-dimensional structure for the linear polypeptide chain operates through the noncovalent interactions of side chains following the laws of physical chemistry.

Many functional proteins, however, are composed of more than a single polypeptide and it appears that association of peptide chains occurs via the same physical forces which lead to the initial folding of the molecule. The same kind of protein perturbants, e.g., urea, detergents, pH, various ions, etc., which cause unfolding and folding of individual chains also cause dissociation and association of subunits.

Finally, it is increasingly evident that these same noncovalent forces lead to the formation of complexes of several enzymes which are needed to carry out sequential reactions, e.g., the α-ketoglutarate dehydrogenase complex (Mukherjee *et al.*, 1965), and also to form complexes of proteins in layer structures such as in viruses and membranes. Thus, a reasonable extrapolation from existing data is that the folding of the individual polypeptide chain and the positioning of this chain in the cell is determined by the amino acid sequence and the physical chemistry of noncovalent interactions.

It seems statistically improbable that an intact cell could be disaggregated, completely unfolded, and then be reconstituted in the test tube by physical forces alone. It does appear likely, however, that individual subunits are made in a sufficiently localized environment so that they do not have too many alternatives. Thus, the α chains of hemoglobin may preferentially encounter the β chains and the dimers so formed associate with other α-β dimers to give the tetrameric hemoglobin molecule (Rossi-Fanelli *et al.*, 1964). Proteins in the mitochondria are perhaps separated from other proteins by membranes and by the location of their syntheses so that they are likely to agglomerate and precipitate only with proteins in their immediate vicinity. Thus, some geographical factors undoubtedly enter to limit the possible interactions to a reasonable number. The general conclusion reached from the formation of the three-dimensional structure of each polypeptide, however, can hold for the more complex associations of peptide chains, i.e., that physical chemistry plays a major role in the position and the neighbors of the individual protein molecule.

Before considering the relation of these conclusions to differentiation we might ask how this physical chemistry is thought to operate. An illustration of a linear peptide chain containing some hydrophobic groups, a + charge, and a — charge, is shown in Fig. 2. Hydrophobic or oily groups associate with each other in the same way that oil droplets coalesce in an aqueous environment. Water-water interactions and oil-oil interactions are more favorable than oil-water interactions, and there is thus a free energy which drives amino acid groups into the neighborhood of like groups. This force will lead to the association shown in the lower part of the figure in which the hydrophobic groups are aligned with each other. The + and — groups provide an electrostatic attraction which further stabilizes the molecule. The main force leading

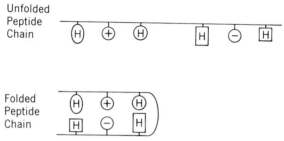

Fɪɢ. 2. The forces leading to peptide folding. In this example, the linear peptide chain folds so that hydrophobic groups (H) have the greatest degree of interaction with each other, and charged groups of opposite polarity are matched. Hydrogen-bonding groups would also play a role but are not included because the principle is the same.

to the three-dimensional structure of a protein appears to come from the hydrophobic interactions. The electrostatic interactions contribute to the final stability, but in actuality most + and — charges on a peptide in water are associated with small counterions such as Na^+ and Cl^-, and the net free energy of a change in partners is not very great. They will provide added stability to the molecule as indicated, however. Moreover, electrostatic or hydrogen bonds are stronger when embedded in a hydrophobic environment.

A mutation which would substitute a positive group, e.g., lysine, for the negative group, e.g., aspartic acid, would convert the attractive +— to a repulsive ++ in the structure shown in Fig. 2. Similarly, the fit of the hydrophobic groups in the figure is critical for this structure. If the hydrophobic group shown as the small circle were to be replaced by a large square, obviously this would also cause a bulge leading to a new shape for the protein chains. Thus the forces causing folding are the noncovalent hydrophobic, electrostatic, and hydrogen bonds, and the specificity of the individual interactions determines the particular protein structure. Evidence from chemical studies and from amino acid changes in the course of evolution can be explained by this type of reasoning, and therefore, although the detailed mechanism of the folding is unknown, known physical chemical principles apparently can explain its basic features.

A new question now arises. How many alternative types of structures in terms of monomers, dimers, trimers, etc., exist? The answer appears to be "a great number." In Table I are summarized a few representative

TABLE I

NUMBER AND TYPES OF PEPTIDE CHAINS IN SOME PROTEINS

Protein	Molecular weight	Total number of peptide chains	Number of different peptide chains
Ribonuclease	13,700	1	1
Lysozyme	14,400	1	1
Myoglobin	17,000	1	1
Liver alcohol dehydrogenase	83,000	2	1
Glyceraldehyde-3-phosphate dehydrogenase	140,000	4	1
Hemoglobin	68,000	4	2
Lactic dehydrogenase	140,000	4	2

examples of proteins having compositions that are well established. Some proteins are fully effective as a single polypeptide chain of rather low molecular weight. Others exist as dimers, tetramers, or polymers of large size. Furthermore, the subunits are not always identical. In hemoglobin two similar chains, α and β, have been identified (Rossi-Fanelli *et al.,* 1964); in aspartyl transcarbamylase two chains of totally different functions, one containing the catalytic site and the other the regulatory site, have been identified (Gerhart and Schachman, 1965). In lactic dehydrogenase the permutations in the combination of subunits are probably used by the organism to advantage in designing the specific functional proteins (Markert, 1963).

Another question which is important in relation to the properties we shall discuss shortly is the following. Are proteins always made in the thermodynamically most stable form? This question must be answered carefully. The folding process leads to a molecule which under the conditions of folding is formed initially in its thermodynamically stable form. Thus, we can say in the case of ribonuclease that the structure of refolded ribonuclease is the same as the native enzyme. It should be emphasized however, that this does not mean that an enzyme always maintains the same structure. The pH of the environment may change, new metal ions may be present, or subsequent physiological events may modify the structure. In fact, the reason for formation of disulfide bonds after the molecule has folded may very well be to "fix" the protein so that a change to a different environment will not cause too large a change in the structure of the molecule. Thus the disulfide bonds in ribonuclease and lysozyme are unnecessary for the correct initial folding of these molecules; they are formed after this folding. Since the active molecules may then migrate to other locales, however, the disulfide bonds may be needed to maintain the initial structure in diverse media.

A correlative question might also be asked, i.e., can we improve on the activity of an enzyme? The answer to this is yes. Enzymes operate with different efficiencies on different substrates and frequently they do not operate at optimum pH. Metal ions other than the native metal ions can increase the velocity of an enzymic reaction and recently we have been able to show (Weiner *et al.*, 1966) that the modification of a methionine residue of chymotrypsin not directly involved in catalytic activity actually improved the efficiency of that enzyme toward hydrolysis of acetyl tyrosine ethyl ester. Furthermore, the modification increased the ability of the enzyme to discriminate between acetyl tyrosine ethyl ester and acetyl tyrosine amide. This change from the nonpolar methionine group to the polar methionine sulfoxide is the kind of change that could be produced in nature by a mutation from methionine to aspartic acid. Thus, we have an example in the laboratory of the improvement of a protein with respect to its activity and specificity. If acetyl tyrosine ethyl ester were a substrate on an important metabolic pathway, this might be a highly favorable mutation. Thus, enzymes have reached a high standard of catalytic efficiency in the process of evolution, but it is not true that they have always reached their optimum activity. Moreover, this change in the activity and specificity in chymotrypsin is caused by the change in a single amino acid which apparently perturbs the three-dimensional structure of the molecule. As we shall see, a change in structure may occur by noncovalent alterations as well as by covalent ones.

In assessing this knowledge of protein structure in the light of the existing knowledge of differentiation and growth, it seems quite possible that we have a very important tool for the achievement of biological diversity. Although the primary structure is fixed by the sequence in the chromosome, the three-dimensional structure depends in part on the environment during the folding. Moreover, the aggregation of subunits into more complex structures can be influenced by the environment. Changes in the environment during the formation or even after the formation of such structures could (a) change the folding of the individual polypeptide chain, e.g., producing an altered protein (b) change the subunits associating with each other, and (c) change the location of the protein in the cell. If the enzyme on a membrane were itself involved in further sequential actions such as the deposition of collagen, it is easy to see how a change in the milieu which causes a change in associations could be further amplified to cause major morphological changes in the cell.

Protein Flexibility in Relation to Enzyme Action

We may now turn to a second property of enzymes and proteins which has come under increasing study in recent years and which is probably more directly related to their role in differentiation than any other single property. This is the evidence that the function of a protein is related to its flexibility.

The specificity of an enzyme is a *sine qua non* for its biological effectiveness. Each enzyme is tailored for a specific reaction. If all the metabolites of one type, e.g., carboxylic acids, could indiscriminately interact with all the enzymes acting on carboxyl groups, complete chaos would result. But just as one lock can be designed to accept only one specific key, so an individual enzyme appears to be tailored to accept a particular substrate. The classic key-lock or template mechanism as an explanation of enzyme specificity, which was enunciated by Emil Fischer in 1894 (Fischer, 1894), postulated that the surface of the enzyme has a catalytic group which must come into juxtaposition with the reacting bond on the substrate molecule for reaction to occur. Molecules may lack necessary binding groups and hence will not be attracted to the active site or may be too big and hence will not fit. Several years ago we were studying isotope effects and examining the role of water in enzymic reactions. We observed phenomena which were extremely difficult to explain based on the template theory of enzyme action (Koshland, 1958, 1963). Once this seed of doubt had been planted, examination of the literature indi-

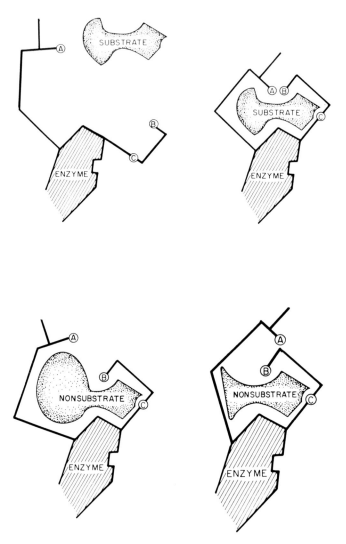

Fig. 3a. Formation of an active site induced by the binding of substrate. In order for catalysis to occur the catalytic groups (A and B) must be properly aligned. When the nonsubstrates are bound, the alignment of the catalytic groups is not correct and no reaction occurs.

cated that there were other examples which did not fit the template theory either, but which had been, so to speak, "swept under the rug" and obscured by the manifold successes of the theory in explaining most enzyme action. It appeared that a new theory must retain the fit idea of the template theory, but the postulates in relation to the structure of the protein and the nature of the small molecule-protein forces had to be modified. The theory which evolved is shown schematically in Fig. 3a. When the substrate molecule approaches the enzyme, it induces a change in the alignment of the protein in such a way that the catalytic groups (A and B) become aligned, and this alignment is essential in order for the reaction to ensue. If a different molecule which is either larger or smaller than the substrate approaches the site, binding may still occur, but the catalytic groups will not be aligned in proper positions for the catalysis to occur and hence these molecules, which may be

TABLE II
Comparison of Template and Induced Fit Theories

Template	Induced fit
Protein exists in solution as "negative" of substrate	Protein not present as "negative" of substrate
Atoms in protein do not change positions on formation of ES complex	Atoms in protein undergo significant shifts in position as substrate bound
"Substrate analogs" fail to react because of nonbinding	"Substrate analogs" may fail to react because of inadequate conformational change or nonbinding
Distant parts of molecule do not change when ES forms	Distant parts of molecule undergo changes when ES forms
Catalytic groups oriented before S adsorbed	Catalytic groups oriented after S adsorbed

very similar to the substrate, fail to react. We shall define as substrate analogs those molecules which are similar to the substrate, have bonds which are capable of reacting, but do not react because of their structure.

The differences between such a theory and the template theory are outlined in Table II. The template theory does not state that the protein is entirely rigid; atomic vibrations certainly occur. It does state, however, that the active site exists essentially as a negative of the substrate. No significant changes in atomic position occur when the substrate is bound. On the other hand, according to the induced fit theory the enzyme does not exist in the beginning as a negative of the substrate but is induced into this alignment. The former theory, therefore, postulates the fit of a jigsaw puzzle of relatively rigid pieces. The latter is the fit of the hand in the glove. The glove is not in the three-dimensional shape of the hand but it becomes so as the fingers are inserted.

The last three entries in Table II are predictions based on the two theories which can be tested. For example, substrate analogs in the template theory will fail to bind; substrate analogs may bind but may not react in the induced fit theory. We can also test whether or not different parts of the enzyme molecule change in shape when the substrate absorbs. The template theory predicts that they will not. The induced fit theory predicts that the atoms will change positions.

An example of the type of evidence that can be obtained for a flexible enzyme hypothesis comes from the work on phosphoglucomutase. This enzyme is found in muscle and catalyzes a key step in the metabolism of glucose. Through the work of Jagannathan and Luck (1949) and Najjar and Pullman (1954), it was established that this enzyme is phosphorylated in its native state and that this phosphate group is transferred to a sugar molecule during the enzyme action. In the absence of sugar, the site previously occupied by the sugar must be filled with water. We now come to one of the anomalies which led to the requirement of a flexible enzyme. The water molecule is as nucleophilic as sugar, at least within an order of magnitude. Since the enzyme can transfer phosphate to sugar in a thousandth of a second, isolated phosphoglucomutase, with its reactive phosphate group, should transfer the phosphate to water if the template hypothesis were correct. Although we might explain the lack of reactivity of a smaller molecule such as ethanol by the fact that it is not absorbed to the active site, we cannot use this explanation for water, since in an aqueous medium the water molecule is ubiquitous and is so small it can clearly occupy the site previously occupied by glucose. Hence, we would expect the phosphoryl enzyme to lose its phosphate in the absence of substrate. In fact, it does not. This stability, however, can be explained by the induced fit hypothesis as shown in Fig. 3b. It is postulated here that the binding of the sugar molecule is necessary to induce a conformational change leading to an unfolding of the protein. In this case, the previously buried phosphate group is now exposed to the hydroxyl group of the sugar, leading to reaction and phosphorylation of this oxygen. The small water molecule which lacks the R group is incapable of causing this unfolding, and hence it cannot gain access to the phosphate group.

Thus, the induced fit theory can explain the stability of a phosphoryl enzyme. More importantly, this mechanism leads to certain predictions, i.e., that the folding of the protein occurs on exposure to the substrate, and this can be demonstrated in a number of ways (Yankeelov and Koshland, 1965). As the phosphate group is exposed to the substrate, a previously buried sulfhydryl group is also exposed. This newly exposed group can be reacted with iodoacetate and the modified group can then be measured on the amino acid analyzer. At the same time, methionine and lysine residues far from the active site can be folded into the interior of the molecule so that they are no longer exposed. Again this can be demonstrated by chemical techniques. Fluorescence and absorption spectra were also used to confirm these conclusions.

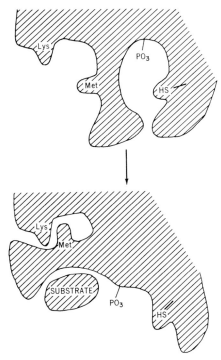

Fig. 3b. Schematic illustration of conformational changes in phosphoglucomutase on binding of substrate. In the native enzyme the phosphate and sulfhydryl groups are masked and the lysine and methionine groups are exposed. When substrate binds, the conformation of the protein changes so that the phosphate group is adjacent to the substrate, the sulfhydryl group becomes exposed, and the lysine and methionine groups become masked.

Other enzymes in many laboratories have also been studied in similar ways. For example, Theorell (1965) and Brändén (1965) have used X-ray crystallography, optical rotatory dispersion, and thermal lability to show that the enzyme alcohol dehydrogenase undergoes conformational changes on binding substrate.

Protein Flexibility in Relation to Activation Processes

Another consequence of the induced fit theory is that it provides an explanation for the action of activators. If a potential substrate fails to react because it is too small, a modifier molecule of the right shape might be able to complement the structure of the inadequate smaller molecule and induce a proper conformation (cf. Fig. 4). This has been demonstrated in a number of cases, a particularly clear example being the work of Inagami and Murachi (1964). One of the substrates of

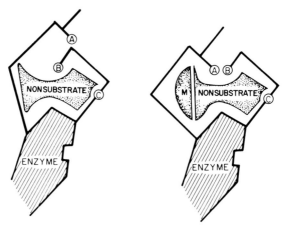

Fig. 4. A schematic illustration of the way in which a small molecule can activate the reaction of a second   molecule by contributing to the proper conformational change. The nonsubstrate shown on the left is inadequate because it lacks the full structure of a substrate (cf. Fig. 3a), but the addition of the nonmetabolized modifier (M) supplies the absent structural feature and allows reaction of the nonsubstrate. In the trypsin example in the text, acetyl lysine ethyl ester is the substrate, acetyl glycine ethyl ester the nonsubstrate, and ethylamine the modifier (M).

trypsin is an ester of lysine which contains an amino acid side chain with a positive charge. Glycine ethyl ester does not contain this positive side chain and reacts only at extremely slow rates. The induced fit theory would say that the glycine ethyl ester lacks sufficient structure, either because of size or charge or both, to induce a proper conformational change. The template theory would state that glycine ethyl ester lacks the necessary binding groups. Inagami and Murachi, however, added ethylamine as well as glycine ethyl ester, supplementing the structure of the glycine ethyl ester, so that the protein would be induced into the same shape as if lysine were there (Fig. 4). When they did this, the reaction of the glycine ethyl ester was enormously enhanced, not quite up to that of normal lysine ester, but significantly closer than the glycine ethyl ester itself. Moreover, it was established in this catalysis that the ethylamine did not change the binding strength of the glycine ethyl ester at all. Thus, the predictions of the induced fit theory were followed precisely and there is a direct conflict with the template theory.

Protein Flexibility in Relation to Inhibition Processes

Another example of enzyme flexibility is in the area of feedback inhibition. This work has developed so elegantly from the work of Umbarger (1956), Gerhart and Pardee (1962), Monod *et al.* (1963),

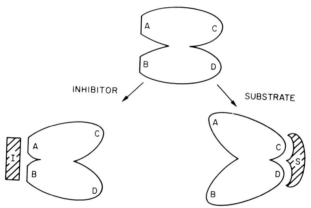

FIG. 5. Binding of substrate and inhibitor at different sites. In this case binding of S induces a conformational change preventing binding of I and vice versa, resulting in competitive inhibition even though I and S are structurally dissimilar.

and others that it perhaps needs little development to a modern biological audience, but it will be mentioned briefly since no talk on flexible enzymes would be complete without it. In the synthesis of cytidine triphosphate (CTP) from aspartic acid, the product of the last reaction is quite different in size and shape from the substrates of the first reaction. Yet it is found that the final product, cytidine triphosphate, can inhibit the first enzyme in the sequence. This is clearly a great advantage to the microorganism. When it obtains enough CTP it simply switches off the steps leading to CTP synthesis. Yet how can this happen? The CTP does not look like the substrates of the initial enzyme in the sequence and according to the template theory it would not be expected to absorb to its active site.

Inhibition by a flexible enzyme is illustrated in Fig. 5. The binding of the inhibitor to its site induces a conformational change in the protein. If this change affects the alignment of a catalytic group C at the active site, then substrate may still be able to bind at site D but will fail to react. The observed effect then will be a noncompetitive inhibition. If on the other hand the proper alignment of both C and D is required for binding of the substrate, then the inhibitor will prevent

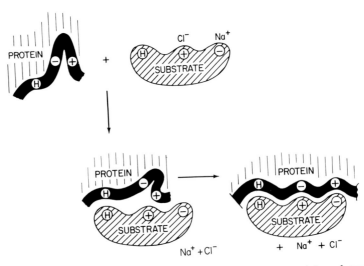

Fig. 6. The induced conformational change in a protein caused by substrate. The initial pairing of hydrophobic regions (H) of substrate and protein results in a realignment of charged groups on the protein. In this way the net formation of one bond, in this case the hydrophobic bond, and the interchange of several other bonds, in this case electrostatic bonds, can lead to an extensive conformational change. On dissociation the process will reverse.

both binding and catalysis and the effect will be competitive inhibition. Examples of both types of inhibition by end product have now been observed in this important control mechanism for metabolism.

A Mechanism for Protein Conformational Changes

At this stage you might ask, how can this flexibility come about? Gloves and templates are all right as mechanical models for events occurring with dimensions of inches but we are dealing with chemicals at the level of angstroms. How can a small molecule cause unfolding of a protein? Figure 6 shows one illustrative model for such a conformational change. The protein is initially held together by an electrostatic attraction between a positive and negative charge and has a hydrophobic site (H) exposed to the solvent. The substrate in this case also has a hydrophobic region and also a positive and negative charge which are neutralized, for example, by sodium and chloride ions. As the two hydrophobic groups interact, the net repulsions and attractions lead to an unfolding of the protein as shown, so that finally a stable arrangement is achieved with the protein in a different shape than it had initially. Note that the number of electrostatic attractions stays the same. The net force of attraction, therefore, is only the formation of one hydrophobic bond. The positive and negative charges on protein, sodium chloride, and substrate have therefore changed partners with no net change in energy but this molecular minuet has also led to the alignment of catalytic groups and therefore the reaction will ensue. Three points are worthy of emphasis here. First, the enzyme initially has a precise structure. Second, the thermodynamic forces required for a very significant change in shape may be small, in this case one hydrophobic bond. As long as the other groups are involved in exchange reactions, a small net energy need be supplied for a considerable change in the shape of a protein. Third, the substrate essentially catalyzes the unfolding of the enzyme and the enzyme, of course, later catalyzes the reaction of the substrate.

What properties of these flexible molecules may be helpful in explaining other biological phenomena? No one can predict the full range, but we should like to discuss some recent findings which may be helpful in some of the areas which are advancing in molecular biology and are helping to account for the phenomena of classic biology.

Cooperative Effects

The isolation in the pure state of enzymes involved in feedback control has revealed that these molecules are made up of subunits and that many of them exhibit cooperative effects of the type shown in Fig. 7. This figure plots the fractional saturation of binding sites as a function of the substrate concentration. The dotted line is the classic Michaelis–Menten curve typical of the saturation of a monomer or of a polymer in which the binding sites are independent. The solid line shows a sigmoid curve in which cooperative effects occur. Such a curve can be explained by an interaction of two molecules in such a way that the binding of the first molecule aids in the binding of the second. Although such sigmoid curves have been known for a long time, the nature of the cooperation has been a mystery. Flexible proteins may provide the clue.

The type of model which we have used to explain these effects is shown very schematically in Fig. 8. For illustrative purposes a protein containing four subunits is shown since this is a frequently observed structure for proteins, many of which show cooperative effects. The circles represent the subunits in the conformation observed in the native protein in the absence of substrate. On binding of substrate the conformation of the subunit is changed and this new conformation is designated by the square. As successive molecules of substrate are bound, more and more subunits are converted from the "circle" conformation to the "square" conformation. If adjacent square conformations are unusually attractive to each other, i.e., more than to adjacent circles, it can be seen that the binding of the second molecule of substrate will be easier than the second, and so forth. Thus, the cooperative effect of one substrate increasing the ease of binding of the next substrate molecule is qualitatively explained. If the interaction between favorable square conformations is unusually attractive, i.e., a juxtaposition of two square subunits is more stable than that of two circles or a circle and a square, it might even happen that the first binding of substrate will not only convert one of the subunits to the square conformation but may even convert adjacent subunits not containing substrate to the square conformation as shown in the second, third, and fourth rows of the figure.

In this model (Koshland et al., 1966) we are assuming for each subunit exactly the type of conformational changes induced by substrate which we have been discussing, but are adding a contribution of subunit interactions because of the known polymeric nature of so many enzymes. This model not only explains the qualitative effects observed but can be fitted to quantitative data. By the use of computers and various diagnostic procedures, we have been able to devise simple nomograms for fitting experimental data to theoretical models and the results of fitting the theoretical models to the binding of oxygen by hemoglobin are shown in Fig. 9. Simply by measuring three points, the points at 90% saturation, 50% saturation, and 10% saturation, in the oxygen binding curves, the fit of theory and data obtained with several hemoglobins is found to be excellent. It should be emphasized that this is not the only model which may fit these data. Other models have been de-

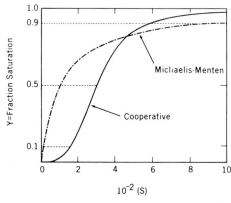

$S_{0.9}, S_{0.5}, S_{0.1},$ Substrate Concentration at Y=0.9, 0.5, and 0.1 Respectively.

$$R_S = \frac{S_{0.9}}{S_{0.1}}$$

FIG. 7.   Representative curves for the binding of substrate to a protein which has more than one binding site. The Michaelis–Menten curve (dotted line) is obtained when the binding sites are completely independent; the sigmoid curve (solid line) is obtained when cooperative interactions occur. The quantities $S_{0.1}$, $S_{0.5}$ and $S_{0.9}$ are used to compare theory and experiment.

signed by Monod *et al.* (1965), Klingenberg *et al.* (1965), Atkinson *et al.* (1965), and indeed by us (Koshland *et al.*, 1966), which are capable of fitting cooperative binding curves of hemoglobin and control enzymes to various degrees. The model shown in Fig. 8 is quite general and can be simplified to the other models with relatively minor assump-

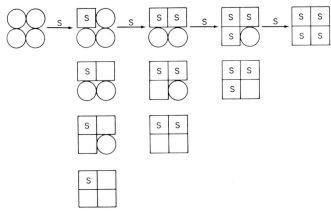

FIG. 8.   Model for ligand-induced conformational changes in a protein composed of four subunits. In the native enzyme all the subunits are in one conformation (circle). Binding of ligand (S) to one of the subunits causes a change to a new conformation (square) which has a different interaction with its neighbors.

tions in regard to the size of the interaction constants. The basic feature of this model is the application of the flexibility we have been discussing plus the added feature of subunit interactions. Since the detailed justifications and methods of the models have been and are being published elsewhere (Koshland *et al.*, 1966; Kirtley and Koshland, 1966), we shall not repeat them here but will apply them to a number of situations which may be important in growth and differentiation.

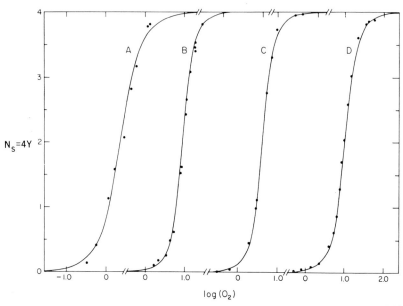

FIG. 9.   Application of the model to the oxygen-binding equilibrium of hemoglobin. The experimental points are taken from the work of Rossi-Fanelli *et al.* (1961), (A, human Hb, low μ, and B, human Hb, high μ), Roughton *et al.* (1955) (C, sheep Hb), and Lyster (quoted in Monod *et al.*, 1965) (D, horse Hb), and the lines are the theoretical curves calculated from the model.

The binding curves of hemoglobin which occur during the metamorphosis of a frog are shown in Fig. 10 (Frieden, 1961). These changes can at least be rationalized as being beneficial to the frog in its transition from an aquatic to a land environment. This shift in the curves can be duplicated on the computer by changes in the interaction constants between subunits. Until a detailed analysis has been made of the purified proteins of the frog hemoglobin, it cannot be said whether or not this effect is responsible for the change in these curves, but it would be logical to guess that this is so. The very fact that the properties can be changed by subunit interactions alone illustrates that there is an added permutation which nature can use to its advantage in controlling metabolism.

There is a further important feature of this model which may have significance in differentiation. Due to the cooperative action of several subunits, the steepness in the rise in activity with increased substrate concentrations is much greater than the usual Michaelis–Menten curve.

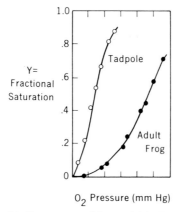

FIG. 10.   Oxygen-binding curves of hemoglobin in tadpole and frog.

For example, any enzyme obeying Michaelis–Menten kinetics requires an 81-fold increase in ligand concentration to increase from 10% to 90% of maximal activity. In some of the cooperative cases a ratio of only 1.5 in substrate concentration is sufficient to cause the same increase in activity. The same could be true of a modifier molecule which promoted enzyme activity or some analogous property of the molecule.

Protein Flexibility in Relation to Other Biological Processes

Protein flexibility may also play an important role in membrane phenomena. Figure 11, for example, shows schematically a possible situation in which two molecules containing two subunits each are found on the interface of a cell connected on both sides by a membrane. If a modifier molecule (M) is adsorbed to the subunits, a conformational change might occur leading to a shrinkage in the total volume occupied by these protein molecules. As a result, an opening could be formed leading to the passage of material through the membrane, or an opening could be enlarged to permit passage of larger molecules than in the absence of the modifier. The permeability change might then cause further changes in the cell.

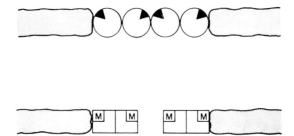

FIG. 11. A mechanism by which specific conformational changes of a protein can affect the permeability of a membrane.

A second possibility of the same type is shown in Fig. 12. Here the binding of a modifier to an external site induces a conformational change which activates the active site. In the absence of this modifier the enzyme could be in contact with a substrate inside the cell but the substrate would not react because the enzyme was present in an inert form. In the presence of modifier, however, the molecule has been converted to the active conformation and now substrate is converted to product inside the cell. The production, of course, of the first molecule of product could be amplified rapidly by this process since the enzyme in its active conformation can convert many molecules of substrate to product and this indeed could be further amplified if these products are themselves modifiers of other enzymic reactions and so forth. Thus, a mechanism has been devised in which a modifier molecule which is not consumed in the reaction and is morphologically separated from the substrate may initiate a reaction. It seems apparent that this type of

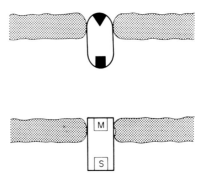

FIG. 12. A mechanism by which a molecule absorbed on one side of a membrane can affect enzymic activity on the other side of the membrane.

mechanism could also apply to such phenomena as taste, smell, and nerve conduction.

It seems clear, moreover, that the modifier need not necessarily be small. The conformational changes might occur by mechanical stress or by attachment to a surface or to another cell; the deformations produced by these interactions could turn off enzymes as well as turn them on. Thus an enzyme might exist in an active conformation in a single cell but be induced into an unfavorable conformation when the cell adheres to other cells or to another surface.

Protein Flexibility in the Control of Protein Synthesis

With this brief outline of the importance of protein flexibility in protein function we can consider the means by which flexibility might play a role in the control of the synthesis of proteins, i.e., in induction and repression of protein synthesis. The importance of this area to differentiation and growth has encouraged us to examine this field from the viewpoint of a protein chemist. Before suggesting a model it might be worthwhile to summarize certain conclusions which are prevalent. The illustration in Fig. 13 taken from the book by Watson (1965) will serve as a point of reference.

(1) It appears that induction and repression operate at the level of transcription of DNA to messenger RNA (as shown in Fig. 13, Jacob and Monod, 1961), or at the level of translation of messenger RNA into protein molecules (Stent, 1964).

(2) Induction and repression of protein synthesis are triggered by the concentration of a specific metabolite, hormone, or structural analog of these.

(3) Genetic evidence suggests that some of the effects of regulation by induction and repression are related to genetic sites outside the structural genes of the proteins affected (Jacob and Monod, 1961; Ames and Martin, 1964). The concepts of a separate site for a regulatory gene and a new site for an operator outside the structural genes of the proteins have been postulated to account for this evidence.

(4) In cases in which there is evidence for an i-type regulatory gene the function of this gene results in the formation of a product which participates in repression.

Considered separately these facts have led to various suggestions for the nature of repressor substances and for the mechanism by which inducers and corepressors act. Arguments have been advanced that re-

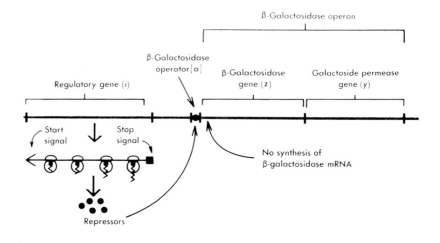

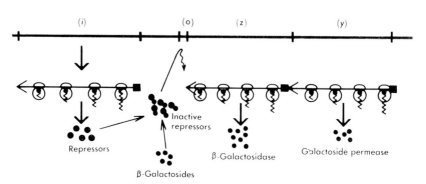

FIG. 13. The current ideas of how the synthesis of β-galactosidase and β-galactosidase permease is controlled by the interaction of repressor, inducer, and operation in *Escherichia coli* (taken from Watson, 1965).

pression is mediated by a protein (Monod *et al.*, 1963), or a nucleic acid (Jacob and Monod, 1961), or a combination of nucleic acid and protein (Sadler and Novick, 1965; Miller and Sobell, 1966).

Certainly the specificity observed in induction and repression is the type of specificity usually associated with protein molecules (cf. Ames and Martin, 1964). Thus, histidine represses the histidine operon and α-methyl histidine derepresses. Lactose induces the lactose operon and o-phenylgalactosides do not. Other than the case of complementary base pairing of polynucleotides, this discrimination between closely similar molecules has so far only been found associated with proteins. And, as we have seen, the specificity of interactions between proteins and substrates or other molecules can be determined by the flexibility of the protein.

Let us first consider the possibility that inhibition of protein synthesis occurs at the level of transcription of DNA and is mediated by a repressor molecule. If the repressor is a protein, it must bind specifically to a specific operator region of DNA. There is precedent for the idea that a protein can attract a nucleic acid: amino acid-activating enzymes certainly are able to recognize the large soluble RNA, ribonucleases and DNase cleave specific bonds of nucleic acids, DNA and RNA polymerases are known. Nevertheless a closer examination of this proposal makes it appear unlikely. Almost all the reactions in which enzymes act on large polymeric materials occur because of a recognition of a small part of that structure. Thus, proteolytic enzymes act at a few specific bonds which they recognize in the total protein. The same is true for nucleases and for polysaccharide-degrading enzymes. The most likely reason for the specificity of amino acid-activating enzymes is that small parts of the soluble RNA are recognized by the enzyme. On the other hand, if a protein is to act as a repressor, it must recognize a specific sequence of deoxyribonucleotides in order to bind to a specific region of the chromosome. Since there appear to be a fairly large number of repressors and since it is important that the repressor not be "confused" by similar sequences in other operators or structural genes, it appears likely that the repressor molecule recognizes stretches of DNA of ten or more nucleotides. Not only would this be geometrically improbable considering the dimensions of a protein of reasonable size but it would have no precedent in known properties of existing enzymes *in vitro*.

The difficulties of recognition of a specific site on DNA by protein have led some investigators to suggest that the repressor molecule is a nucleic acid. This makes the problem of recognition of a section of DNA easy since complementary base pairing occurs in DNA replication, transcription, and translation. Here, however, the dilemma of the specific interactions of a small molecule such as histidine with a polynucleotide seems insurmountable since no test tube analogs have been observed.

The dilemmas of these two alternatives naturally lead to the suggestion that a nucleoprotein is the functional repressor: one part is composed of a nucleic acid which can associate with and is complementary to a region of the DNA, and the other part is composed of a protein which can interact with the inducer or corepressor molecule. Although this proposal appears to combine the best of two possible worlds, it still presents formidable difficulties. First, the idea of a long nucleic acid tail bound to a protein raises several questions. If the right protein and tail must be selected and matched, do we not have the same problem as the recognition of the DNA site by a protein? And what kind of conformational change in the protein could either facilitate or prevent the binding of a nucleic acid to DNA or destabilize the complex once it had formed?

The protein conformational changes that involve the exposure and burying of groups as detected by reaction with amino acid reagents, and the changes in structure observed by Perutz *et al.* (1966) on the binding of oxygen to hemoglobin involve significant changes in position. These changes involve movements of amino acid side chains by less than 8 Å, however. This is a very considerable change when one considers the requirements of an active site or the detailed structure of a molecule, but it is a very small change if one asks the new conformation to engulf a large nucleic acid in order to mask its ability to complex DNA.

Before attempting to resolve any of these dilemmas, let us consider the possibility that control of protein synthesis occurs at the level of translation. Attractive arguments have been presented in support of the idea that many experimental observations can be accounted for if control is imposed at this level. Halvorson (1960), for example, has proposed that a nascent polypeptide, while still bound to the ribosome, can interact with the effector molecules or with other polypeptides and so change its conformation that it will affect the rate of completion of its own chain.

Two questions immediately arise when considering such mechanisms. Is it likely that an incomplete polypeptide chain while attached covalently to a large sRNA molecule bound to a ribosome can fold in such a way that it will form a site specific for the right inducer or corepressor molecule? If such a site is possible, what conformational change of the polypeptide would be necessary in order to affect the complex machinery of protein synthesis?

Experiments on the unfolding and refolding of ribonuclease and other proteins certainly suggest that the folding of a polypeptide chain can occur spontaneously and it is not unreasonable to suspect that the folding process starts soon after the synthesis of the polypeptide begins. The conformation of a polypeptide which is only a portion of the completed protein, however, will not necessarily be the same as that of the same polypeptide in the completed molecule since the interactions of groups near the end of the chain can affect the conformation of the whole molecule. Could one of these conformations produce a specific site for the right effector molecule to bind and cause a conformational change which affects the completion of the chain, and is it reasonable to say that for each protein molecule with controlled synthesis the right site is constructed for the right effector molecule?

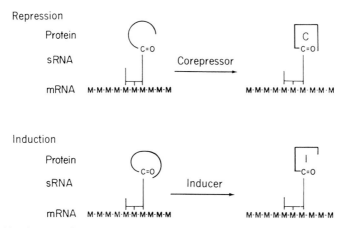

Fig. 14. A model for the action of a translation repressor. The partially completed polypeptide chain while still covalently bound to sRNA on the ribosome folds into a conformation similar to that of the native protein. In folding it can construct sites similar to the binding sites of the native protein. Binding of the proper small molecule to the site causes a conformational change of the polypeptide which either blocks access to the activated carbonyl group or removes a block to this group which must be exposed if the protein molecule is to be completed.

Weighing the many pieces of evidence, some of it fragmentary and some of it conflicting, we have devised a model for repression which may take a step in the direction of resolving these dilemmas. The postulates of the model are as follows:

(1) The receptor which recognizes the small molecule (the inducer or the corepressor) is a protein which in many cases is the enzyme (or one of its subunits) for which the inducer or corepressor is a substrate or feedback inhibitor.

There is a striking correspondence between the molecules which act as feedback inhibitors or are substrates for specific enzymes and the molecules which serve as corepressors or inducers for the same enzymes.

242   D. E. KOSHLAND, JR. AND M. E. KIRTLEY

(2) The recognition of any significant portion of DNA occurs through interaction with a complementary ribonucleic acid which is a fragment of a messenger RNA for that region.

(3) Two types of control occur, one at transcription and one at translation, and two types of repressor molecules exist, both of which are nucleoproteins.

(4) One type of repression is at the level of translation on the ribosome (Fig. 14). This occurs by interaction of the nascent polypeptide

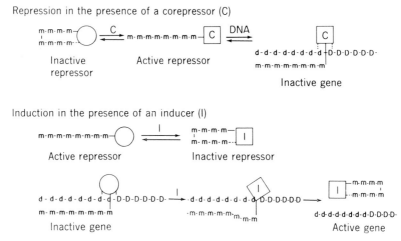

FIG. 15. A model for the action of a transcription repressor. The repressor molecule is a protein covalently bound to an RNA fragment (m-m-m-) having a base sequence complementary to a specific operator sequence of DNA (d-d-d-). In one conformation the protein interacts with a small portion of the RNA in such a way that the formation of a complex of the repressor with DNA is inhibited. In a second conformation the binding of the repressor to DNA is facilitated and stabilized by interaction of the protein with DNA. The conformation of the protein can be influenced by the binding of a corepressor (C) or an inducer (I).

chain covalently bound to sRNA with the translation mechanism in its own ribosome. The site for the binding of inducer or corepressor is the same as the site for these molecules when they act as substrate or inhibitor, and the conformational changes induced are probably the same. Since the formation of a specific site requires the participation of a number of groups from different parts of the molecule, protein synthesis is affected at a point at which synthesis of most of the primary structure of the enzyme has been completed.

(5) A second type of repression occurs at the transcription level and involves a nucleoprotein in which a polynucleotide complementary to an operator segment of DNA is covalently bonded to a protein containing the appropriate binding site for the small molecules (Fig. 15).

The repressor is formed from the portion of messenger RNA comple-

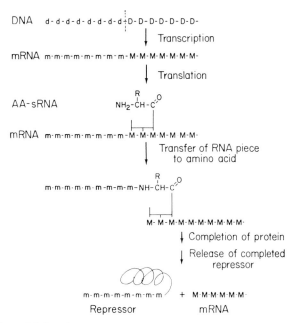

Fɪɢ. 16. A model for the synthesis of the repressor molecule. Transcription of an operon of DNA with its operator (d-d-d-) into messenger RNA forms a molecule with an operator section (m-m-m-) having a base sequence complementary to the operator of DNA. When an aminoacyl-sRNA is bound to the first site of the first protein messenger (M-M-M), the operator RNA is transferred from the messenger to the amino acid where it is covalently bound. After completion of the polypeptide chain, the repressor is released. Subsequent reading of the same messenger RNA produced only the normal protein since the operator RNA section has been removed.

mentary to the operator and the protein having a structural gene adjacent to the operator.

(6) In each case the protein chain interacts with only a small part of the nucleic acid. In the case of the translation repressor a portion of the protein blocks the activated carbonyl group which must react with the adjacent amino acid in order that translation can continue. In the case of the transcription repressor the protein interacts with the DNA

by means of a few electrostatic interactions to stabilize the binding of RNA to the operator site of DNA.

(7) Corepressors in either case induce a conformation which inhibits transcription or translation. Inducers in either case induce a conformation which permits transcription or translation (cf. Figs. 14 and 15). The conformational change required for the translation repressor is one which affects the activated carbonyl. The conformational change required for the transcription repressor is one which changes the interaction of the protein with DNA or with part of the RNA.

(8) The nucleoprotein repressor of transcription is formed on the ribosome in a transfer-type mechanism (e.g., a transphosphorylation) in which a portion of the messenger RNA corresponding to the DNA operator becomes attached to an amino acid of the nascent polypeptide chain being synthesized (cf. Fig. 16). Reasonable mechanisms can be written and enzyme analogies exist for the formation of a phosphoramide bond, a Schiff base, an ester bond, or a phosphate ester bond between nucleotides and amino acids.

(9) A system which is repressible or inducible at the transcription level is not necessarily also repressible or inducible at the translation level and vice versa.

Let us consider some of the reasons for and consequences of this model. First, there is an economy in regard to production of protein. The repressors are seen to contain some or all of the subunits of the enzyme which already have sites to bind the inducer or corepressor molecules. This accounts, of course, for the coincidence observed between those enzymes which are inhibited by feedback control mechanisms and the fact that these same enzymes are also involved in repression.

In the transcription repressor the formation of a covalent link between the "operator" portion of messenger RNA and the nascent protein appears to be the greatest extrapolation from existing data. There appears to be no insurmountable handicap to finding an enzyme which could catalyze such a process as the formation of nucleoprotein when the nucleic acid is bound to the N-terminal or C-terminal amino acid. Amino acid activation is accomplished by reaction of sRNA at the carboxyl group of the amino acid. During protein synthesis the amino group of the amino acid to be added is acylated before the ribosome moves on to the next position. In fact the discharge of the positively charged α-ammonium group may be the signal for the ribosome to translate the next position in the messenger. Perhaps the requirement for this signal is the reason for the occurrence of formyl or acetyl groups at the N-terminal end of many proteins. There are a few analogies for the specific cleavage and formation of new bonds in nucleic acid polymers. Repair mechanisms exist for the replacement of bases in DNA. Specific mechanisms for cutting nucleic acids appear to operate in the replication of circular DNA and in the crossing-over phenomenon. It seems possible therefore that some cutting machinery can occur at the translation level. Possibly a combination of codons, such as UAGUAG, would signal that a transfer of a part of a nucleic acid messenger to the first amino group of the new peptide chain or to the ribosome and then to the terminal carboxyl group should occur.

An *i*-type regulatory gene might arise from translocation of DNA material as is thought to have occurred in the structural genes for the α and β chains of hemoglobin. Thus a translocation which results in a repetition of the operator and first structural gene region of an operon in another position could explain the presence of *i*-genes without requiring a special new repressor protein. This would provide two potential sites for synthesis of repressor and allow for the possibility of independent mutations of the regulatory gene and the operon. Alternatively, of course, the protein produced by the regulatory gene could be different from the enzyme.

The notable elusiveness of the repressors to isolation can be accounted for if the transcription repressor is a normal protein bound by a relatively unstable link, such as the phosphoramide bond, to a small molecule of RNA. Hydrolysis of such a repressor would give products indistinguishable from the normal cell constituents. The repressor would itself be unstable unless additional stabilization was acquired by its binding to other molecules in the cell. The concentration of a specific repressor would be a function of its rate of synthesis, rate of binding to DNA or other stabilizing molecules, and its rate of enzymic or nonenzymic hydrolysis. In addition, the rate of repressor synthesis could not exceed the rate of messenger production since each messenger can produce only one repressor molecule. After the RNA operator has been transferred to the first protein to form the repressor, subsequent translation of the same messenger produces only the normal proteins.

This voyage from the safe shores of protein structure into the turbulent seas of repressor theory was induced by the chairman's request to look into the future. Being realistic about such theories at our present stage of knowledge, it is unlikely that all the details of the mechanism will turn out to be true. Certain basic features, however, e.g., that the protein can only recognize a limited area of any substrate, that protein conformational changes must be limited to appropriate dimensions, that nucleic acid is the best substance to recognize long stretches of nucleic acid would seem to be required of any successful theory. The combination of the various components appears to be palatable to a modern protein chemist; whether or not they are palatable to the living system only time will tell.

Amplification of Biological Changes

In the preceding discussion we have outlined a number of ways in which a change in the cellular milieu can have dramatic effects on the

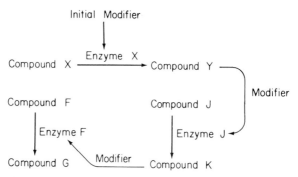

FIG. 17. Mechanism by which a small concentration change of a modifier can be amplified to produce large changes in the cell. The initial modifier affects the rate of conversion of X to Y. Y modifies the conversion of J to K either by a direct effect on enzyme J or by inducing the synthesis of enzyme J. In turn K modifies conversion of F to G by affecting the activity or synthesis of enzyme F.

properties of a given system. Great as some of these effects are, we are faced with the fact that an apparently subtle gradient can in some cases lead to large changes in the morphology, composition, and function of the cells in an organism. If some of the quantitative changes that occur in the differentiation of cells in vertebrates are considered, it seems probable that amplification of a small initial change is necessary and the systems discussed above lend themselves to such an amplification. In Fig. 17, a schematic diagram of such an amplification is given. A change in the concentration of a modifier could turn on (or greatly increase the velocity of) enzyme X. The product of this reaction could then influence the velocity of enzyme J. The product of this second reaction could in turn influence the velocity of enzyme F. Since the molecules influencing the enzyme activity are modifiers which are not consumed in the reaction, a few molecules absorbed on the enzyme surface can affect many hundreds or thousands of molecules which are consumed or produced in the enzymic reactions.

In Fig. 17, modifier M which changes the conformation of enzyme X could be a product which accumulates in a cellular mass but which diffuses rapidly away from a single cell. If the first enzyme is turned on, as suggested in Fig. 17, it might trigger events in enzymes J and F which could ultimately change the cellular morphology. For example, this change in metabolites might lead to the activation of an enzyme that would deposit structural material, or to the induction of an enzyme that synthesizes a membrane component.

The potential of amplification in sequential systems has been discussed previously (McFarlane, 1964; Wald, 1966). The schematic illustration (Fig. 17) shows that the availability of flexible proteins makes such amplification even more potent since it allows a molecule not directly consumed in a reaction to influence that reaction.

Suggestions for Mechanisms of Differentiation

In summary, therefore, we have seen that present knowledge of protein structure can at least lead to suggestions of ways in which the environment can affect the metabolism and morphology of a cell. Some of the more important of these individual effects are summarized below:

(a) The folding of an individual polypeptide chain, its association with other subunits, and its position in the cell may be affected by pH, ionic strength, or the presence or absence of metabolites.

(b) The flexibility of a protein makes it possible to control the activity of enzymes already present in a cell, perhaps leading to further changes in the cellular environment. This acceleration or inhibition of existing enzymes can be caused by molecules which are not produced or consumed in the reaction they affect and even by molecules which are morphologically separated from the active site of the enzyme.

(c) Physical stress may deform molecules leading to increase or decrease in activity.

(d) Modifiers could affect the permeability of a membrane by affecting the conformation of molecules on its surface.

(e) The interaction of subunits in a polymeric protein can lead to an enhanced sensitivity to small changes in concentration.

(f) The flexibility of proteins can be used to explain the induction or inhibition of protein synthesis at either the transcription or translation level by small molecules in the medium.

(g) The changes effected in one system can be transmitted to other systems by modifier molecules, thus leading to amplification of the initial event.

Whether any or all of these effects are involved in differentiation must await experimentation. We can only hope that these deductions based on the behavior of enzymes and proteins will be helpful in the elucidation of one of the most fascinating problems in modern biology.

ACKNOWLEDGMENTS

The authors would like to express their gratitude to the National Institutes of Health (Grant AM-9765) and the National Science Foundation (Grant GB-4186) for their support of this research.

REFERENCES

AMES, B. N., AND MARTIN, R. G. (1964). Biochemical aspects of genetics: the operon. Ann. Rev. Biochem. 33, 235–258.

ATKINSON, D. E., HATHAWAY, J. A., AND SMITH, E. C. (1965). Kinetics of regulatory enzymes. J. Biol. Chem. 240, 2682–2690.

BLAKE, C. C. F., KOENIG, D. F., MAIR, G. A., NORTH, A. C. T., PHILLIPS, D. C., AND SARMA, V. R. (1965). Structure of hen egg-white lysozyme. Nature 206, 757–761.

BRANDEN, C. I. (1965). Structure of horse liver alcohol dehydrogenase. I. Structural symmetry and conformational changes. Arch. Biochem. Biophys. 112, 215–217.

FISCHER, E. (1894). Einfluss der Configuration auf die Wirkung der Enzyme. Ber. Deut. Chem. Ges. 27, 2985–2993.

FRIEDEN, E. (1961). Biochemical adaptation and anuran metamorphosis. Am. Zoologist 1, 115–149.

GERHART, J. C., AND PARDEE, A. B. (1962). The enzymology of control by feedback inhibition. J. Biol. Chem. 237, 891–896.

GERHART, J. C., AND SCHACHMAN, H. K. (1965). Distinct subunits for the regulation of catalytic activity of aspartate transcarbamylase. Biochemistry 4, 1054–1062.

HALVORSON, H. (1960). The induced synthesis of proteins. Advan. Enzymol. 22, 99–156.

INAGAMI, T., AND MURACHI, T. (1964). The mechanism of the specificity of trypsin catalysis. J. Biol. Chem. 239, 1395–1401.

JACOB, F., AND MONOD, J. (1961). Genetic regulatory mechanisms in the synthesis of proteins. J. Mol. Biol. 3, 318–356.

JAGANNATHAN, V., AND LUCK, J. M. (1949). Phosphoglucomutase: I. Purification and properties. J. Biol. Chem. 179, 561–568.

KIRTLEY, M. E., AND KOSHLAND, D. E., JR. (1967). In preparation.

KLINGENBERG, M., GOEBELL, H., AND WENSKE, G. (1965). DPN-specific isocitrate dehydrogenase of mitochondria. II. pH dependence of the kinetics and the mechanism of activation. Biochem. Z. 341, 199–223.

KOSHLAND, D. E., JR. (1958). Application of a theory of enzyme specificity to protein synthesis. Proc. Natl. Acad. Sci. U.S. 44, 98–104.

KOSHLAND, D. E., JR. (1963). The role of flexibility in enzyme action. Cold Spring Harbor Symp. Quant. Biol. 28, 473–480.

KOSHLAND, D. E., JR., NEMETHY, G., AND FILMER, D. (1966). Comparison of experimental binding data and theoretical models in proteins containing subunits. *Biochemistry* **5**, 365–385.

MACFARLANE, R. G. (1964). An enzyme cascade in the blood clotting mechanism, and its function as a biochemical amplifier. *Nature* **202**, 498 (1964).

MARKERT, C. L. (1963). Epigenetic control of specific protein synthesis in differentiating cells. *In* "Cytodifferentiation and Macromolecular Synthesis" (M. Locke, ed.), pp. 65–84. Academic Press, New York.

MILLER, J. N., AND SOBELL, N. M. (1966). A molecular model for gene repression. *Proc. Natl. Acad. Sci. U.S.* **55**, 1201–1205.

MONOD, J., CHANGEUX, J.-P., AND JACOB, F. (1963). Allosteric proteins and cellular control systems. *J. Mol. Biol.* **6**, 306–329.

MONOD, J., WYMAN, J., AND CHANGEUX, J.-P. (1965). On the nature of allosteric transitions: a plausible model. *J. Mol. Biol.* **12**, 88–117.

MUKHERJEE, B. B., MATTHEWS, J., HORNEY, D. L., AND REED, L. J. (1965). Resolution and reconstitution of the *E. coli* α-ketoglutarate dehydrogenase complex. *J. Biol. Chem.* **240**, PC2268–2269.

NAJJAR, V. A., AND PULLMAN, M. E. (1954). The occurrence of a group transfer involving enzyme (phosphoglucomutase) and substrate. *Science* **119**, 631–634.

PERUTZ, M. F., KENDREW, J. C., AND WATSON, H. C. (1966). Structure and function of hemoglobin. *J. Mol. Biol.* **13**, 669–678.

ROSSI-FANELLI, A,. ANTONINI, E., AND CAPUTO, A. (1961). Studies on the relations between molecular and functional properties of hemoglobin. *J. Biol. Chem.* **236**, 397–400.

ROSSI-FANELLI, A., ANTONINI, E., AND CAPUTO, A. (1964). Hemoglobin and myoglobin. *Advan. Protein Chem.* **19**, 73–222.

ROUGHTON, F. J. W., OTIS, A. B., AND LYSTER, R. L. J. (1955). The determination of the individual equilibrium constants of the four intermediate reactions between oxygen and sheep hemoglobin. *Proc. Roy. Soc. (London)* **B144**, 29–54.

SADLER, J. R., AND NOVICK, A. (1965). The properties of repressor and the kinetics of its action. *J. Mol. Biol.* **12**, 305–327.

SELA, M., WHITE, F. H., JR., AND ANFINSEN, C. B. (1957). Reductive cleavage of disulfide bridges in ribonucleases. *Science* **125**, 691–692.

STENT, G. S. (1964). The operon: on its third anniversary. *Science* **144**, 816–820.

THEORELL, H. (1965). Die Alkoholdehydrogenase. Ihre Wirkungsweisen und Komplexverbindungen. *Experentia* **21**, 553–561.

UMBARGER, H. E. (1956). Evidence for a negative feedback mechanism in the biosynthesis of isoleucine. *Science* **123**, 848.

WALD, G. (1966). Visual excitation and blood clotting. *Science* **150**, 1028.

WATSON, J. D. (1965). "Molecular Biology of the Gene." Benjamin, New York.

WEINER, H., BATT, C. W., AND KOSHLAND, D. E., JR. (1966). A change in specificity of chymotrypsin caused by chemical modification of methionine residues. *J. Biol. Chem.* **241**, 2687.

YANKEELOV, J. A., JR., AND KOSHLAND, D. E., JR. (1965). Evidence for conformation changes induced by substrates of phosphoglucomutase. *J. Biol. Chem.* **240**, 1593–1602.

Intercellular Regulation in Plants

ANTON LANG

MSU/AEC Plant Research Laboratory, Michigan State University, East Lansing, Michigan

Pharmacological Aspects

The idea of chemical communication between different parts of the plant was clearly enunciated as early as 1880 and 1882, by J. Sachs in his concept of organ-forming substances, that is, substances arising in one organ of a plant and required for the development of another organ. Sachs' supporting evidence was indirect and open to other interpretations, however, and the notion of specific chemical messengers between plant cells and organs was rejected, remaining so even when animal endocrinology was undergoing its spectacular early development.

This situation changed in 1928 when F. W. Went succeeded in "isolating" the first plant hormone, by placing tips of the first leaves (the coleoptiles) of dark-grown oat seedlings on agar blocks and trapping the hormone in the agar. The hormone was soon after christened auxin.

Then botanists, who had been so hesitant in accepting the occurrence of hormones in plants, went to another extreme. They were so fascinated by auxin that they tried to interpret all phenomena of growth regulation in plants in terms of this hormone. Relatively little effort was diverted to the search for other hormones.

It must be admitted that there were good reasons for this single-mindedness. The animal hormones known at that time were characterized by well-defined, single, and specific functions, exerted in single, particular organs. Auxin did not fit this pattern at all.

In order to appreciate this we should recall, briefly, the developmental history of a typical plant cell. This history can be divided in three distinct (although often overlapping) stages. The first is a period of *cell division*. This is the process by which all cells constituting the body of the plant are produced. Plant cells, however, after having been produced, usually undergo a very substantial increase in size, based mainly, although not exclusively, upon uptake of water. This stage in cell development is called *cell enlargement* or, if it proceeds—as it does in many

plant organs—predominantly in one direction, *cell elongation*. The third
stage is the functional specialization of the cells, or *cell differentiation*.
Auxin had been discovered as a promoter of cell elongation, exerting
its effects in the growth of seedlings. It soon became apparent, however,
that it was also capable of affecting both cell division and cell differentiation, and that it was effective in many different organs of the
plant. Thus, it was found to promote the growth of fruits, a process
which involves both cell division and enlargement; the growth of calli
and of the vascular cambium—the tissue by means of which plants
grow in thickness—processes based mainly on cell division; and the
formation of roots in stems, a process involving both cell division and
cell differentiation. Auxin was also found to control the early growth
of lateral buds which, at least at this particular stage, is mainly a matter
of cell division; in this case, the effect of auxin was one of inhibition
rather than promotion. Auxin thus seemed capable of regulating all
three phases of plant cell development and the growth of many if not
all plant organs. As late as 1954, some authors were arguing that auxin
was the sole plant hormone.

In the middle 1950's, however, another major development in plant
hormone research took place. This was the almost simultaneous discovery of two new groups of plant hormones, the gibberellins and the
cytokinins (the latter first called kinins).

In the case of the gibberellins, the word "discovered" is not entirely
valid. The first gibberellin was isolated and chemically characterized at
about the same time Went isolated auxin. It was first described as an
agent involved in a disease of a particular plant, the "bakanae" disease
of rice, caused by the fungus *Fusarium moniliforme* and characterized
by excessive shoot growth. Unfortunately, the work was published in the
Japanese language and in journals little known outside Japan. The discovery thus remained unnoticed, even though the early Japanese work
had clearly shown that the growth-promoting effect of gibberellin was
by no means limited to the rice plant, but was equally evident in any
other plant to which gibberellin was applied (for a review of this
earlier work, see Stowe and Yamaki, 1957). It was only about 1955 that
investigations in Great Britain and in the United States, confirming and
extending the Japanese work, lead to the recognition of the general
nature of this gibberellin response (cf. Phinney and West, 1961).

The discovery of the first cytokinin was more straightforward. It grew
out of the finding that cell division in tobacco pith tissue was dependent,
apart from auxin, on another unknown factor which occurred naturally

in the vascular tissue of the tobacco stem. The natural factor in this tissue has remained unknown, but it could be replaced by a compound which was first obtained by degradation of deoxyribonucleic acid. The compound was named kinetin. It was identified as 6-aminofurfurylpurine and its structure confirmed by synthesis (Miller *et al.*, 1956).

However, when plant biologists began probing the full scope of action of gibberellins, as well as cytokinins, they encountered the same situation as with auxin. The response which lead to the discovery of gibberellin, the overgrowth of the shoot in rice, was based on increased cell elongation. Kinetin had been discovered as a promoter of cell division. Either substance, however, was soon found to be also able to influence

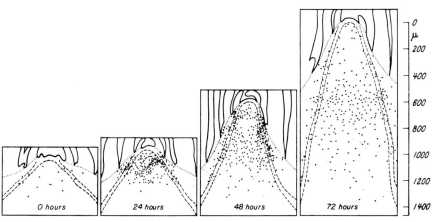

FIG. 1. Effect of gibberellin (gibberellic acid = gibberellin A_3) on cell division activity in the subapical region of the shoot meristem of the long-day rosette plant *Samolus parviflorus*, grown under short-day conditions. Each dot stands for a mitotic figure in a median tissue slice, 64 μ thick. The broken lines indicate the prevascular tissue, the dotted ones the position of the leaf bases. Mitotic figures in the uppermost region of the meristem (the eumeristem), the number of which is much less affected by gibberellin, are not shown. (From Sachs *et al.*, 1959.)

the two other fundamental stages of plant cell development. Among the effects of gibberellin on cell division is promotion of this process in the subapical region of the shoot meristem of rosette plants (plants which for part of their lives do not possess elongate stems); among its effects involving cell differentiation is the induction of flower formation in the same type of plants (Lang, 1957; Sachs *et al.*, 1959; see also Lang and Reinhard, 1961; Sachs, 1961, 1965; Lang, 1961, 1965b, pp. 1466–74; Figs. 1 and 2). In either case, gibberellin substitutes for the effect of certain

specific environmental conditions which normally control stem growth
and flower formation in these plants, namely, either a period of low
temperature, or long photoperiods. Kinetin promotes cell enlargement
in the stems of some plants and in sections of leaf tissue, and in conjunction with auxin controls bud and root formation in tobacco tissue
—processes clearly dependent on cell differentiation (Skoog and Miller,
1956; see Fig. 3).

A more comprehensive list of effects of auxin, gibberellin, and cytokinins on growth processes involving cell division, cell enlargement, or
cell differentiation is given in Table I.

Physiological Aspects

Except for some of the early auxin work which was done using
natural materials diffused from coleoptile or shoot tips, the work reviewed so far was done with synthetic substances, or substances derived
from organisms quite unrelated to those in which the response to the
substance was studied. The auxin most commonly used was 3-indole-
acetic acid which was considered a native auxin but was prepared syn-
thetically. Substances like indolebutyric and naphthaleneacetic acid
which have never been demonstrated to occur in higher plants, or
2,4-dichlorophenoxyacetic acid which is clearly a non-natural compound
for these plants, were also widely used. The most commonly used cytokinins, kinetin and benzyladenine, were synthetic products which so far
have not been found in plants; the most common gibberellin, gibberellic
acid or gibberellin A_3, was obtained from *F. moniliforme*. Thus, this
work was mostly pharmacological. Does it reflect something of the natural, endogenous regulation of the growth processes which are modified
by exogenous auxin, gibberellin, or cytokinin: does it have physiological
significance?

The first question to be asked is whether or not auxins, gibberellins,
and cytokinins are endogenous constituents of higher plants. Rigorous
chemical evidence is still limited. Indoleacetic acid, often considered the
sole native auxin of plants, has been demonstrated by chemically conclusive methods in only one plant (maize) and never in its free form.
In regard to gibberellin, the situation is somewhat better; chemically
identified gibberellins have so far been obtained from half a dozen plant
species. Substances producing typical auxin or gibberellin responses in
highly specific bioassays, however, have been obtained from numerous
plants. There is no doubt that auxins and gibberellins are of ubiquitous

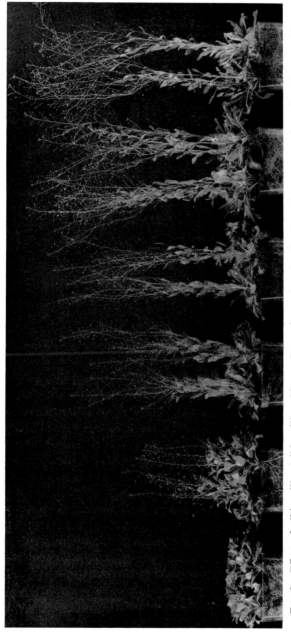

Fig. 2. Effect of gibberellin (gibberellic acid) on flower formation in the long-day rosette plant *Samolus parviflorus*, grown under short-day conditions. Left, controls; progressing to the right, plants treated with increasing levels of gibberellic acid. (From Lang, 1957.)

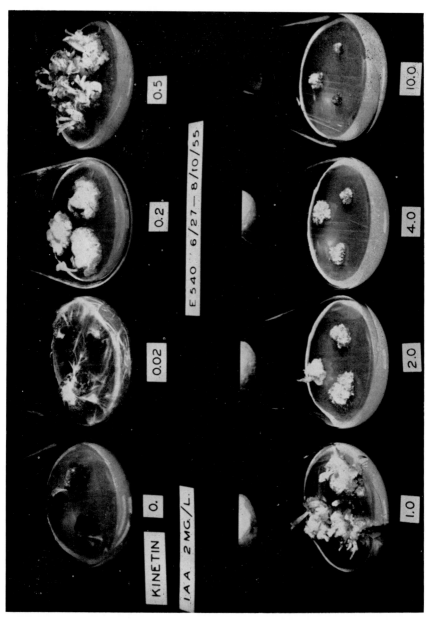

FIG. 3. Effect of kinetin and auxin (3-indoleacetic acid = IAA) on growth and organ formation in tobacco pith tissue cultured *in vitro*. Note lack of growth without kinetin; root formation at a relatively low kinetin/auxin ratio (0.02 mg/liter kinetin); undifferentiated growth at an intermediate ratio (0.2 mg/liter); and bud formation at relatively

TABLE I

Comparative Effects of Auxins, Gibberellins, and Cytokinins

Main process promoted	Auxins	Gibberellins	Cytokinins
Cell division	Callus growth Growth of many tissue cultures Cambial growth Growth of fruits Growth of lateral buds (*inhibition*)	Cell division activity in subapical region of shoot meristems Cambial growth Growth in some fruits Growth (termination of dormancy) in buds and seeds of certain plants	Cell division in certain excised tissues and tissue cultures Growth of lateral buds Growth of fruits Growth (termination of dormancy) in some buds
Cell enlargement	Growth of stems (including flower and fruit stalks) and coleoptiles Growth of flowers Growth of fruits	Growth of stems, and of leaves in some plants Growth of lateral buds Growth of petals Fruit growth Growth (termination of dormancy) in buds and seeds of certain plants	Stem growth in some plants Growth of leaf sections Growth (termination of dormancy) in some seeds
Cell differentiation	Root formation in cuttings and excised tissues Bud formation in some tissues Cambial differentiation Sex expression (formation of pistillate versus staminate flowers) in cucurbits	Flower formation in cold-, long-day- and long-short-day–requiring plants Bud formation (both promotions and inhibitions found) Root formation (*inhibition*) Sex expression (formation of staminate versus pistillate flowers) in cucurbits and other plants Transition between juvenile and adult phases (*promotion* or *inhibition*)	Root formation (low kinetin/auxin ratio) and bud formation (high kinetin/auxin ratio) in excised tobacco pith tissue Bud formation in other excised tissues and organs "Bud" formation in the protonema of mosses

TABLE I (*Continued*)

Main process promoted	Auxins	Gibberellins	Cytokinins
Subcellular and molecular effects	Promotion of proto-plasmic streaming	Antheridium formation in the prothallia of certain ferns "Bud" formation in certain mosses Synthesis of hydrolytic enzymes in cereal aleurone	Prevention of chlorophyll and protein loss in leaves; attraction and retention of metabolites and water

occurrence in higher plants.* The first cytokinin, kinetin, has—as already mentioned—not yet been found as a natural plant product, but another substituted adenine, zeatin, has, again in maize (Letham *et al.,* 1964), and substances with typical cytokinin activity, in at least some cases very probably identical with zeatin, have been demonstrated in several different plant species. It may be premature to claim that cytokinins are as ubiquitous in higher plants as are auxin and gibberellin, but it appears very probable. There is no doubt that they occur as native constituents of higher plants. Naturally occurring auxin, gibberellin, and cytokinin are shown in Fig. 4.

Thus, the work reviewed in the first section of this paper, while pharmacological in approach, was done with substances native to higher plants. The presence of a regulatory substance in a plant or plant organ, however, is not evidence that the substance has an active role in the regulation of growth in this plant or organ. To be certain of such a

* In the case of gibberellin, we are in fact faced with a certain embarrassment of riches. In higher plants, at least eight different gibberellins have been found, a single plant often containing two or more of these compounds. The total number of chemically identified gibberellins is presently 17, the actual number is undoubtedly still higher. Some of these gibberellins may be precursors of the active compounds. In other cases, however, there is no evidence for such an interpretation, and there are indications for at least a relative action specificity of different gibberellins, gibberellin I being more active in growth response A than in B, but gibberellin II showing the opposite order of activity in the same two responses (in the same plant). The physiological significance of the different gibberellins is a problem which requires a great deal more study.

function it must be shown to obey the following three principles, which paraphrase the principles of Robert Koch: Removal of the substance must alter the growth pattern of the plant or organ; exogenous application of the substance must restore the growth pattern to normal; and these effects must be specific for the substance in question.

In the case of auxin, more or less rigorous evidence of this kind is available for coleoptile, stem, and fruit growth, for cambial activity, and for lateral bud inhibition in some (although not all) plants. It may be noted that while auxin may control cell division in the cambium, and when applied exogenously, may promote cell division in various

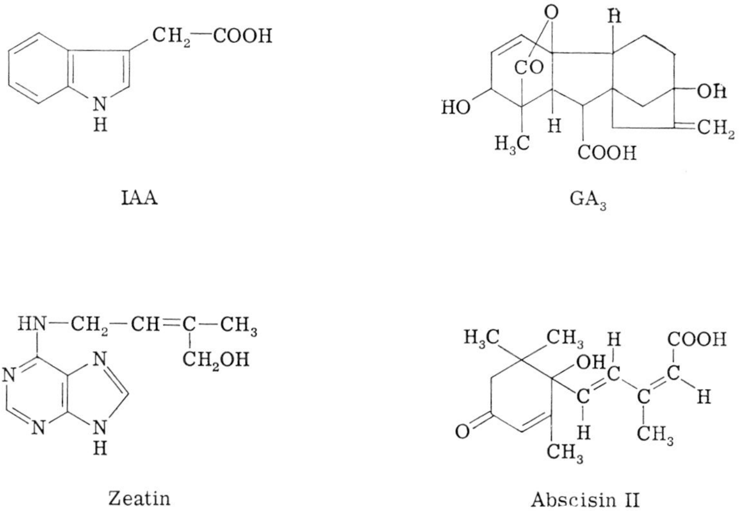

IAA   GA$_3$

Zeatin   Abscisin II

Fig. 4. Structure of native plant growth regulations; Auxin (3-indoleacetic acid = IAA); gibberellic acid or gibberellin A$_3$ (GA$_3$); cytokinin (zeatin); abscisin II.

other plant tissues, there is no positive evidence that it participates in the regulation of cell division in those tissues in which cell division is most prominent, namely, in the apical meristems of shoots and roots.

The usual procedure for removal of a regulatory substance is removal of the organ in which it is being produced. In the case of gibberellin, important evidence concerning its physiological functions has been obtained in a different manner, removal of the hormone by chemical means. This has been possible by the use of some of the so-called plant growth retardants.

The growth retardants (see Cathey, 1964), the first of which were described about the same time as the general significance of the gibberel-

lins began to be recognized, are a group of chemically unrelated compounds which, when applied to plants, cause reduction of stem growth.
Their effect is thus opposite to the most common effect of applied
gibberellin; moreover, it can be reversed by application of gibberellin.
The retardants were therefore sometimes called anti-gibberellins, but
their mode of action was at first unknown. More recently, it has been
shown that the retardants AMO-1618 and CCC (Fig. 5) suppress

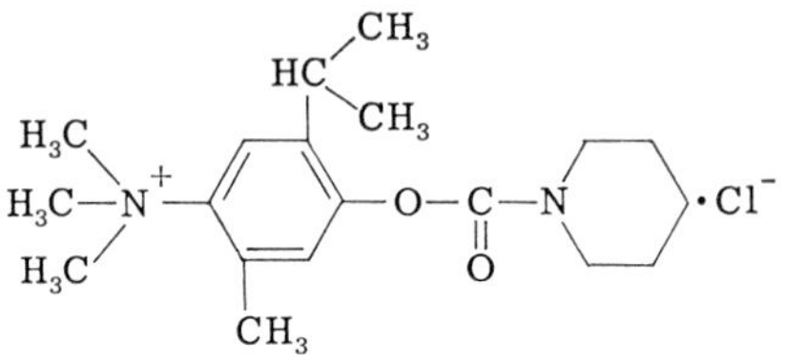

AMO-1618

2-Isopropyl-4-dimethylamino-5-methylphenyl-
1-piperidinecarboxylate methyl chloride

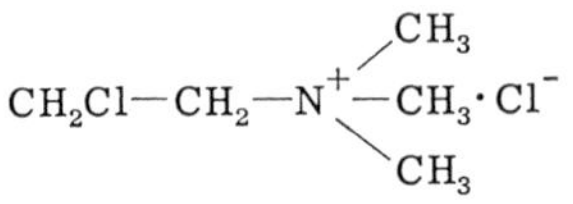

CCC (Cycocel)

(2-Chloroethyl) trimethylammonium
chloride

Fig. 5.   The plant growth retardants AMO-1618 and CCC.

gibberellin production in *F. moniliforme* without having an effect on
the growth of the organism (Kende *et al.*, 1963; Ninnemann *et al.*, 1964;
see Table II). The reduced gibberellin production was not based on
destruction of gibberellin after it had been synthesized, nor on other
secondary causes. It was evidently based on suppression of gibberellin
biosynthesis by the organism. Analogs of CCC which differed in their
growth-retarding action on higher plants exhibited exactly the same
differences in their action on gibberellin production in *Fusarium*
(Harada and Lang, 1965; Table III), providing indirect but strong
evidence that the effect on growth in higher plants was based on inhibition of gibberellin biosynthesis. Finally, AMO-1618 caused a substantial
reduction in the gibberellin content of pea seeds developing in pea pods

TABLE II

Inhibition of Gibberellin Production in *Fusarium moniliforme* by
Different Concentrations of CCC[a]

Concentration of CCC (mg/liter)	Dry weight of mycelium (mg)	Gibberellin-A_3 equivalents per culture (μg)	Relative gibberellin production (%)
0	150	320	100
0.1	165	165	52
0.3	168	81	25
1	166	20	6
3	165	7	2
10	162	4	1
300	—	<1	0

[a] During a culture period of 3 days (after Ninnemann et al., 1964).

grown *in vitro* without causing, at least at lower concentrations, a comparable reduction in the growth of the seeds (Baldev et al., 1965; Table IV).

AMO and CCC are thus selective inhibitors of gibberellin biosynthesis in plants. They can therefore be used in the same manner as, for example, inhibitors of nucleic acid or protein synthesis are widely used in

TABLE III

Comparative Effects of CCC and Several Analogs on Growth in Higher
Plants and on Gibberellin Production in *Fusarium moniliforme*[a]

Compound	Inhibitory effect[b] On growth of higher plants	On gibberellin production in *Fusarium*
2-Chloroethyltrimethylammonium chloride	++	++
Allyltrimethylammonium chloride	++	++
2-Chloroallyltrimethylammonium chloride	++	++
Choline chloride	0	0
Bromoethyltrimethylammonium bromide	++	++
Bromoethyldimethylamine hydrobromide	0	0
Bromoethyltriethylammonium bromide	0	0
Tetraethylammonium bromide	+	+

[a] After Harada and Lang, 1965.
[b] (++) present, strong; (+) present, but much less; (0) absent.

molecular biology, that is, to determine the physiological significance of the compound in question.

By means of this approach it was shown that flower formation in certain plants was selectively inhibited by application of AMO-1618 or CCC, and restored by application of gibberellin (Zeevaart and Lang, 1963; Baldev and Lang, 1965; see Fig. 6). Cell division activity in the subapical region of the shoot apex of chrysanthemum was suppressed by AMO-1618 and restored by gibberellin (Sachs et al., 1960; Fig. 7). Similar evidence is available for a number of other growth responses,

TABLE IV

EFFECT OF AMO-1618 ON GROWTH AND GIBBERELLIN CONTENT OF PEA SEEDS DEVELOPING IN EXCISED PODS[a]

Days of culture	AMO concentration in medium (mg/liter)	Fresh weight of seed (gm)	Fresh weight of seed (%)	Gibberellin content per seed Gibberellin A₃ equivalents (µg)	Gibberellin content per seed (%)
0 (start)	—	0.0027	—	0.0015	—
10	—	0.31	100	0.430	100
10	5	0.30	97	0.173	40
10	50	0.26	84	0.055	13
10	500	0.07	23	0.04	11

[a] After Baldev et al., 1965.

including the formation of male (staminate) versus female (pistillate) flowers in the cucumber (E. Galun and A. Lang, unpublished data). In all these cases, gibberellins are thus established as physiological agents of growth regulation. In the case of subapical cell division activity in shoots, it may be assumed that they function as limiting factors of this process in rosette plants (cf. Fig. 1), but not normally in nonrosette plants like chrysanthemum.

In the case of naturally occurring cytokinins, conclusive evidence for specific regulatory functions in the plant is still scarce. The best case is the anti-ageing effect of cytokinins on leaves, first observed in detached leaves (Richmond and Lang, 1957), which seems also to be exerted in the intact plant by cytokinins produced in the root (Kulaeva, 1962; see discussion in Kende and Sitton, 1966). In some growth responses which are markedly affected by applied kinetin, there was no indication for a comparable effect of endogenous cytokinins (Kende and Sitton, 1966). If we are permitted to extrapolate the experiences with auxin and with gibberellin, however, it appears quite probable that the native cytokinins of higher plants do function in the regulation of various activities of the plant.

Fig. 6. Effect of the plant growth retardant CCC and of gibberellin (gibberellic acid) on flower formation in *Bryophyllum daigremontianum*. Left, untreated control; second from left, plant treated with CCC; third from left and following, plants treated with CCC and increasing levels of gibberellic acid. (Zeevaart and Lang, original.)

Comparative Biochemical Aspects

The foregoing discussion establishes auxins and gibberellins unquestionably as genuine hormones playing important roles in the endogenous regulation of a number of distinct and important growth processes in higher plants. A similar assumption seems permissible for the cytokinins.

The next logical question is: How do these hormones exert their actions? This question has been approached in various different ways

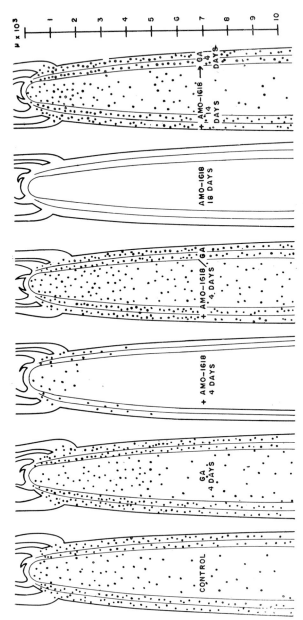

FIG. 7. Effect of the growth retardant AMO-1618 and of gibberellin (gibberellic acid) on cell division activity in the subapical region of the shoot meristem of chrysanthemum. Each dot represents a mitotic figure in a median tissue slice 64 μ in thickness. The light lines show the position of the prevascular and young vascular tissue. The older leaves are not shown. Not shown also are mitotic figures in the eumeristem the number of which is little affected by the treatments. (From Sachs et al., 1960.)

but is far from being answered. I shall discuss only one comparatively recent approach which establishes certain connections between the action of plant growth hormones and the synthesis of nucleic acids and proteins in plant cells, thus indicating relationships between hormone action, and the transcription and/or translation of genetic information in the cells during development.

The first demonstration of a relationship between the action of a plant hormone and nucleic acids was supplied by Masuda (1959), who showed that oat coleoptile sections treated with RNase lost their ability to respond to auxin. The loss was temporary, showing that it was not due to general injury to the tissue. Several years later it was shown, by Noodén and Thimann (1963) and Key (1964), that inhibitors of RNA and protein synthesis, for example, actinomycin D, puromycin, and p-fluorophenylalanine, reduced the growth of plant tissues, both in the absence and in the presence of auxin. An example is given in Table V. Key and Ingle (1964) showed that one particular RNA fraction, having

TABLE V

EFFECT OF ACTINOMYCIN D ON GROWTH, RNA CONTENT, AND RNA SYNTHESIS
IN SOYBEAN HYPOCOTYL SECTIONS[a]

Actinomycin D (mg/ml)	Growth[b] (%)	RNA (mg/gm fresh weight)	RNA synthesis[c] (counts/minute)
0	100	1.99	10,550
0.4	75	1.87	5,530
2.0	54	1.78	1,560
10.0	33	1.73	1,270
50.0	21	1.72	970

[a] After Key, 1964.
[b] Increase in fresh weight.
[c] Incorporation of ATP-8-C[14].

chemical and physical characteristics of a messenger RNA, was closely correlated with growth.

When similar experiments were undertaken on gibberellin-promoted growth it was found that this growth was also inhibited by inhibitors of protein and RNA synthesis. However, inhibitors of DNA synthesis or function, namely, 5-fluorodeoxyuridine (FUDR), amethopterin, mitomycin C, and phenethyl alcohol, were likewise very effective. The effect of FUDR was completely (and that of amethopterin partially) reversed by thymidine but not by uridine (Nitsan and Lang, 1965; see Fig. 8).

This finding would not be surprising, and would in fact be trivial, if this growth proceeded mainly by cell division. In one of the tissues used, however, the epicotyls (lowermost stem portions) of decapitated lentil seedlings, growth was exclusively, or very nearly so, by cell elongation; in another, the hypocotyls of lettuce seedlings, cell division accounted for only a relatively small fraction of total growth. Thus, synthesis of DNA appears to be a prerequisite for elongation growth in such plant cells in which this process can be promoted by gibberellin. The growth of the lentil epicotyls and lettuce hypocotyls was reduced

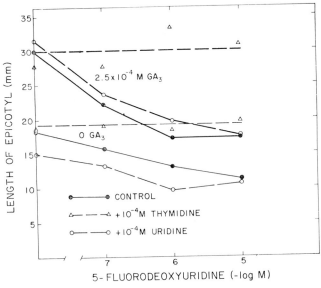

Fig. 8. Effects of 5-fluorodeoxyuridine, thymidine, and uridine on growth of the epicotyl of decapitated lentil seedlings in the absence and presence of gibberellin (gibberellic acid = GA₃). (From Nitsan and Lang, 1965.)

by FUDR and the other DNA antimetabolites in the absence of gibberellin. However, similar tissue is known to contain endogenous gibberellins. Thus, the inhibitory effect of FUDR, etc., on growth in the absence of exogenous gibberellin is probably a reflection of the need of DNA synthesis for the growth-regulating action of endogenous gibberellin.

If gibberellin-regulated cell elongation is dependent on synthesis of DNA it ought to be possible to detect DNA synthesis in the elongating cells. Furthermore, exogenous gibberellin ought to promote this process, and FUDR to inhibit both the DNA synthesis occurring in the absence of exogenous gibberellin and the increased synthesis caused by added gibberellin. Experiments with the lentil epicotyl showed that this is indeed the case (Nitsan and Lang, 1966).

Active DNA synthesis occurred, as measured by incorporation of labeled thymidine, during the elongation growth of this tissue, resulting in an increase of the DNA level in the tissue. The rate of synthesis and the increase in the DNA level were greater in the presence than in the absence of added gibberellin. The increase in DNA was reduced by FUDR. Some data illustrating these findings are shown in Tables VI and VII, and Fig. 9.

TABLE VI

DNA AND RNA CONTENT OF LENTIL EPICOTYLS AFTER INCUBATION WITH AND WITHOUT GIBBERELLIN (GA) IN THE PRESENCE AND ABSENCE OF FUDR[a]

		DNA		RNA	
	Length (mm)	(μg/ epicotyl)	($\mu\mu$g/ cell)	(μg/ epicotyl)	($\mu\mu$g/ cell)
Initial state					
	5.5	2.45	12.3	13.2	66.5
After 48 hours incubation					
Control	19.0	2.80	16.3	11.9	69.2
GA, 100 mg/liter	27.6	3.74	22.0	15.4	90.9
FUDR, $10^{-5} M$	10.9	2.20	12.2	11.2	62.1
GA + FUDR	16.9	2.96	17.7	11.9	71.3

[a] After Nitsan and Lang, 1966.

The findings of Noodén and Thimann and of Key, on the one hand, and those of Nitsan and Lang on the other, establish the following relationships: *Auxin—cell elongation—need for RNA and protein synthesis; Gibberellin—cell elongation—need for DNA synthesis.*

Do these findings reflect a general difference between auxin- and gibberellin-regulated cell elongation?

This question was approached in experiments with the uppermost portions (including cotyledons and shoot apex) of cucumber seedlings, and with coleoptiles of dark-grown wheat seedlings.

The cucumber tissue was chosen because it was known that cucumber seedlings are responsive to both auxin and gibberellin (Katsumi *et al.*, 1965); such simultaneous sensitivity is not too frequent in elongating

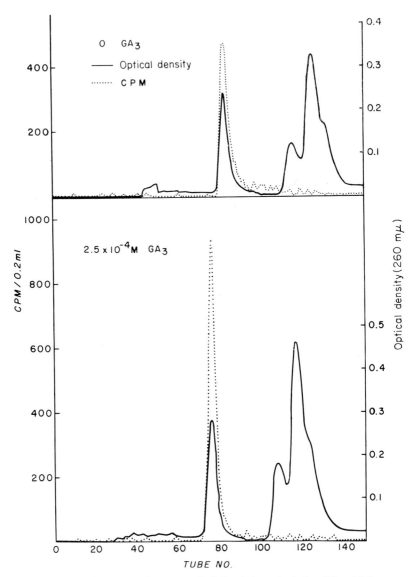

FIG. 9. Levels of nucleic acids (as optical density) and of thymidine-H³ incorporation (as counts per minute), appearing in a methylated albumin-kieselguhr (MAK)
column profile, in epicotyls of lentil seedlings incubated in the absence (above) and
presence (below) of gibberellin (gibberellic acid = GA₃). Note that the gibberellin-
treated tissue yields higher peaks in the positions characteristic of DNA and ribosomal
RNA, and shows higher counts corresponding to the DNA peak. (From Nitsan and
Lang, 1966.)

plant tissues. It was indeed found that the gibberellin-induced growth in this material was suppressed by FUDR, this effect being reversible by thymidine but not by uridine, whereas auxin-promoted growth was insensitive to this inhibitor (R. H. Groves, J. Nitsan, and A. Lang, unpublished data; see Table VIII).

The coleoptiles of dark-grown wheat seedling undergo striking changes in responsiveness to plant hormones during their growth. Early in growth they are strongly promoted by gibberellin but little if at all by auxin; at a later age, the sensitivity is the opposite (Wright, 1961). It was again found that the gibberellin-dependent growth was inhibited by FUDR and restored by thymidine while the auxin-dependent growth

TABLE VII

INCORPORATION OF THYMIDINE-C^{14} INTO DNA AND RNA OF LENTIL EPICOTYLS INCUBATED WITH AND WITHOUT GIBBERELLIN (GA₃) IN THE PRESENCE AND ABSENCE OF FUDR[a]

Treatment	Fresh weight[b] (mg)		Thymidine uptake into tissue[b] (counts/minute/mg)		Thymidine incorporation into DNA[b] (counts/minute/ epicotyl)	
	24 hr	48 hr	24 hr	48 hr	24 hr	48 hr
Control	14.4	21.8	65	114	436	851
GA₃, 100 mg/liter	19.0	31.0	77	110	925	1081
FUDR, $10^{-5} M$	13.4	19.8	100	123	716	1107
GA₃ + FUDR	16.4	40.6	117	147	1102	1890

[a] After Nitsan and Lang, 1966.
[b] Hours indicate length of incubation period.

was FUDR-insensitive (E. H. Liu, J. Nitsan, and A. Lang, unpublished data; Table IX).

Molecular Biological Aspects

The evidence reviewed in the last section establishes interrelations between the action of auxin and gibberellin on the one hand, and nucleic acid and protein synthesis on the other, in regulation of plant growth, especially cell elongation. In the case of gibberellin, synthesis of DNA is a premise for the action of the hormone; in the case of auxin, RNA and protein synthesis are required but DNA synthesis is not. The details of these interrelations are not known. The results of Key

TABLE VIII

EFFECT OF GIBBERELLIN (GA$_3$), AUXIN (IAA), FUDR, THYMIDINE, AND
URIDINE ON GROWTH IN CUCUMBER HYPOCOTYL SECTIONS[a]

	Control	FUDR $10^{-5} M$	FUDR $10^{-5} M +$ thymidine $10^{-4} M$	FUDR $10^{-5} M +$ uridine $10^{-4} M$
Control	32	30	31	29
10 mg/liter GA$_3$	41	32	42	32
Control	23	23	23	23
0.5 mg/liter IAA	29	29	29	29

[a] Eighteen mm long; in GA$_3$ experiment including cotyledons and shoot apex; in auxin experiment, decapitated. The figures indicate length in millimeters. (R. H. Groves, J. Nitsan, and A. Lang, unpublished data.)

TABLE IX

EFFECT OF GIBBERELLIN (GA), AUXIN (INDOLEACETIC ACID = IAA), FUDR, AND THYMIDINE ON THE GROWTH OF WHEAT COLEOPTILES IN DIFFERENT STATES OF DEVELOPMENT[a,b]

	2 Hours old			63 Hours old	
Treatment	Initial length (mm)	Final length (mm)	Increase (%)	Final length (mm)	Increase (%)
GA ($10^{-5} M$)	1.11	2.62	136	15.3	53
GA + FUDR ($10^{-5} M$)	1.04	1.89	81	14.8	48
GA + FUDR + thymidine ($10^{-4} M$)	1.18	2.50	112	14.1	41
Control	1.18	1.78	51	15.7	57
IAA ($10^{-5} M$)	1.04	1.18	13	22.0	120
IAA + FUDR	0.97	1.19	22	22.3	123
IAA + FUDR + thymidine	1.12	1.28	17	21.5	115
GA	1.01	2.89	153	—	—
Control	0.94	1.23	32	16.3	63

[a] Two hours old: whole embryos incubated, coleoptile measured; 63 hours old: 10 mm coleoptile sections incubated initially.
[b] E. C. Liu, J. Nitsan, and A. Lang, unpublished data.

and Ingle (1964) indicate, as already mentioned, that synthesis of a messengerlike RNA is a critical factor in cell growth. However, at present there is no conclusive evidence that auxin enhances the synthesis of this RNA. The results of Nitsan and Lang (1966) reveal a marked increase in DNA synthesis and content in elongating cells when gibberellin has been supplied. It is, however, by no means certain that all newly synthesized DNA is essential for cell elongation. In this connection, it is of interest that the presence of gibberellin resulted also in an increase in the level (Table VI) and in the synthesis (the latter measured as uridine incorporation) of RNA. The RNA resulting from this stimulated synthesis appeared on the methylated albumin-kieselguhr (MAK) column profile of nucleic acids in the position corresponding to that of ribosomal RNA (see Fig. 9). The increase in RNA was inhibited by FUDR (Table VI), that is, it was dependent on the synthesis of DNA. It is tempting to assume that the active DNA synthesis which is required for gibberellin-promoted cell elongation produces DNA needed for the synthesis of rRNA and that the latter is the factor actually limiting this type of growth. However, at present this is speculation.

In the case of the cytokinins, some intriguing relations with nucleic acid metabolism have also been demonstrated. On the one hand, it has recently been shown that an effect of kinetin, the promotion of "bud" formation in moss protonemata, is selectively inhibited by actinomycin D (Brandes and Bopp, 1965). On the other hand, zeatin has been found to occur in plants (developing maize kernels) not only in its free form but also in the form of the nucleotide and nucleoside (Letham, 1966; Miller, 1966). A closely related compound, 6-γ,γ-dimethylallylaminopurine, has been identified as a constituent of a transfer RNA for serine, being located next to the anticodon of this sRNA (Zachau et al., 1966). Dimethylallylaminopurine has so far not been found in higher plants, but has been in a Corynebacterium (Klämbt et al., 1966; Helgeson and Leonard, 1966). It is a highly active cytokinin.

The precise meaning of these findings, particularly the last-named ones, in relation to the growth-regulating function of cytokinins is not yet clear. As mentioned in another context, cytokinins retard the senescence of leaves. If part of a leaf is treated with kinetin, materials present in other parts are attracted to, and retained in the treated tissue. These materials include not only the precursors of proteins and nucleic acids (amino acids and purine and pyrimidine bases), but also carbohydrates, a nonproteinogenic amino acid such as α-aminoisobutyric acid, inorganic phosphate, and even water (see Mothes, 1960, 1961, 1964). This is difficult to interpret in terms of conventional nucleic acid synthesis or function. It suggests the possibility that cytokinins may regulate the condition and function of cell membranes which in turn may determine whether materials are retained in a cell or are moved out to another.

However, this is again becoming speculation. Rather than continuing with it I prefer to discuss a particular case of plant hormone action in which a relationship between the hormone and the synthesis of some *specific* proteins has been clearly established. This is the regulation of synthesis of α-amylase and, very probably, a number of other hydrolytic enzymes in the aleurone layer of the cereal grain by gibberellin.

It has been known since the 1890's that enzymes causing digestion of the storage tissue, the so-called endosperm, of cereal grains are produced and secreted by the outermost tissue of the endosperm, the aleurone, and that this enzyme production appeared to be controlled by a substance (or substances) coming from the germinating embryo. Yomo (1958, 1960b) showed that the embryo factor which causes increased amylase activity in barley endosperm was a gibberellin; later, it was shown that the nongrowing embryo does not contain measurable quantities of endogenous gibberellin, but that gibberellin synthesis by the embryo commences a short time after the seed has been allowed to start germination (Yomo and Iinuma, 1966). Yomo (1960a) and Paleg (1960) showed independently that gibberellic acid at concentrations as low as $10^{-10} M$ caused a dramatic increase in α-amylase activity in barley endosperm (Table X), and similar increases have been found for several other hydrolases, namely, β-glucanase (MacLeod and Millar, 1962), proteases (Briggs, unpublished data; J. V. Jacobsen and J. E. Varner, unpublished data; Yomo, unpublished data), and ribonuclease (M. J. Chrispeels and Varner, unpublished data; see also Varner and Chandra, 1964, and Chandra and Varner, 1965).

As in any other case of enzyme activity increasing under the influence of any external factor (substrate, another chemical agent, etc.) an essential question is whether this increase is based on "activation," that is, some change in already existing enzyme molecules, or on *de novo* synthesis. It should perhaps be borne in mind that, while *de novo* synthesis has been conclusively proved in several cases of induced enzyme activity in microorganisms, no comparable rigorous evidence has been available for similar cases in higher organisms. In the case of gibberellin-controlled increase in α-amylase activity in barley aleurone, such evidence has now been obtained by Filner and Varner (1966) who adopted a method which had first been used by Hu *et al.* (1962).

The conventional method of answering the question: *de novo* synthesis versus activation, has been to distinguish "old" and "new" protein by tagging one or the other with a radioactively labeled amino acid, then purifying the enzyme and determining whether it has the labeling characteristic of old or new protein. The method depends on purification of the enzyme and is inapplicable if the enzyme proves refractory to purification procedures. Even if it does not, the method is quite laborious; moreover, it often does not permit us to decide whether all of the enzyme, or only a part of it, has been synthesized *de novo*.

TABLE X
Effect of Gibberellin on α-Amylase Activity in Barley Endosperm[a]

Gibberellic acid (μg/ml)	Diastatic activity (units)
0	17
0.001	200
0.01	640
0.1	900
1	790
5	760
50	730

[a] After Yomo, 1960a.

The alternative method is based on a simple principle. If old protein can be distinguished from new by density-labeling one or the other with a heavy *stable* isotope such as O^{18}, N^{15}, C^{13} or H^2, then the density difference can serve as the physical basis for separating old protein from new. The necessary resolution can be achieved by density gradient equilibrium centrifugation which can detect a density difference of 0.2% whereas heavy isotopes can generate a density difference of 1% or more. Once the separation is achieved, it only remains to determine whether the enzyme activity corresponds to the density of old or new protein. Since the position of the enzyme in the density gradient can be determined by enzyme activity, impure enzyme preparations can be used.

α-Amylase and barley aleurone constitute a near ideal system for application of this method. α-Amylase is very stable, and easily measurable in crude preparations. Practically all synthesis of new protein in the aleurone proceeds from amino acids released by hydrolysis of old protein. Thus, if the aleurone tissue is incubated with gibberellin and with water containing heavy oxygen, H_2O^{18} (90A%XS), the carboxyl oxygens of the arising amino acids will become O^{18} labeled (45A%XS). If α-amylase is synthesized *de novo*, the peptide bond oxygens will be

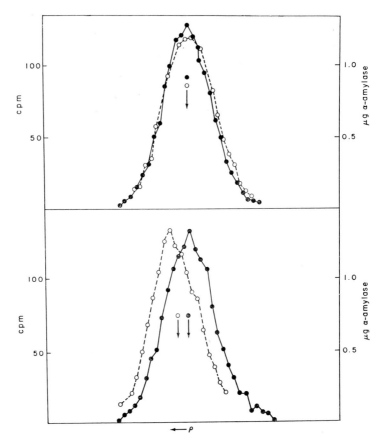

Fig. 10. Density gradient equilibrium centrifugation (CsCl) of α-amylase from barley aleurone, formed under the influence of gibberellin (gibberellic acid). Above, profile of highly purified, labeled (H^3) enzyme as measured by radioactivity, and of crude enzyme as measured by enzymic activity. Below, profile of enzyme formed in H_2O^{18} (90A%XS) and measured by activity in crude preparation, as compared with the purified, labeled enzyme formed in H_2O^{16}. The labeled enzyme was used at levels not detectable by biological activity. (From Filner and Varner, 1966.)

O^{18} labeled (45A%XS). This will increase the density of the protein by approximately 1%.

Figure 10 shows the results of such an experiment. In the upper part, it can be seen that highly purified α-amylase from barley aleurone, labeled with tritium, has the same density and band shape as crude

α-amylase assayed by enzyme activity. This control establishes the validity of locating an enzyme by enzyme activity in the density gradient of a crude protein preparation.

The lower part of Fig. 10 shows that when α-amylase is formed in barley aleurone, in the presence of gibberellin and in H_2O^{18} (90A%XS), the enzyme activity has exactly the same band shape as the highly purified $O^{16}H^3$ α-amylase, but that it has been displaced toward higher density. (Note in particular that both the heavy and the light edge of the O^{18} amylase are equally displaced from the marker curve.) The degree of displacement corresponds to a density increase of about 1%. Thus, the enzyme, and *all* of the enzyme, has been synthesized *de novo*.

After it had been established that the gibberellin-dependent increase in α-amylase activity in barley aleurone was *de novo* synthesis of the enzyme, Varner and co-workers (unpublished data) turned their attention to the possibility that this synthesis was under the control of an RNA, the synthesis of which was in turn dependent on gibberellin. In double labeling experiments it was found that there was increased incorporation of uridine into a peak in the MAK column nucleic acids profile that corresponded to the position of messenger RNA (G. R. Chandra and Varner, unpublished data). Actinomycin D was found to inhibit α-amylase synthesis by the aleurone layers, but mainly when it was present during the first few hours after gibberellic acid had been added.

The limitation in time of the susceptibility of α-amylase synthesis to actinomycin D inhibition could be interpreted as an indication that the hormone brings about the synthesis of an excess of the mRNA required for the synthesis of the enzyme, and that this mRNA is sufficiently stable to last for the entire period during which enzyme synthesis proceeds. If this were true, however, the requirement by the aleurone tissue for gibberellin itself should also be limited to the first few hours after addition of the hormone. This is not true. Removal of gibberellin after 12 hours greatly reduced the amount of enzyme synthesized.

Two explanations for this apparent disagreement may be suggested. First, it is possible that gibberellin is involved in the control of α-amylase synthesis at two different points, at the level of transcription *and* at the level of translation. Second, the specificity of actinomycin D as inhibitor of DNA-dependent RNA synthesis, while undoubtedly high, is not complete. It is conceivable that the effect of the inhibitor in barley aleurone is not, or not exclusively, on RNA synthesis but on some other phase of cell metabolism, and that it does not permit conclusions about the role of RNA synthesis in the gibberellin-dependent synthesis of α-amylase in this tissue.

For the other gibberellin-regulated enzymes of cereal aleurone— glucanase, protease, ribonuclease—*de novo* synthesis has not yet been directly proved. The increase in activity, the dependence on gibberellin concentration, and the kinetics of the activity rise, however, are all quite similar to those of α-amylase. Thus, it appears that gibberellin controls the synthesis of a group of functionally related enzymes in the aleurone cells. Varner (1966) proposes that the function of gibberellin in plant cells is, quite generally, the regulation of synthesis of exoenzymes.

A Look at the Past and Present

The objectives of the present discussion, so far, have been two-fold.

First, I have attempted to bring the present status of the plant hormone field into some perspective, as compared to its status at the time of the first Growth Symposium in 1939. At that time, auxin was the sole plant hormone generally recognized; most efforts were directed at understanding plant growth regulation in terms of this hormone only. It is clear that the discovery of two other major hormones has profoundly altered the situation in the entire field and has resulted in a much better understanding of the endogenous chemical regulation of plant growth and development. It has also posed, or re-emphasized, some problems which were already evident in connection with auxin. The main one is the apparent lack of functional specificity in any of the three major, well-established plant hormones. This is an aspect of general physiology in which plants and animals continue to exhibit a profound difference, although this difference, while striking, may be quantitative, rather than qualitative as it appeared to be at first.

Second, I wanted to indicate some of the most recent developments of research in the plant hormone field. The emphasis was on one particular direction, searches for relations between hormone action, and transcription and translation of the genetic information in cells. It may be appropriate to emphasize that other directions are possible and should be explored. Hormone action may be visualized not only at the transcription and translation levels, but also at the level of the protein molecule itself and at the level of subcellular structures. A hormone may be envisaged as modifying the configuration of an existing enzyme molecule, or perhaps controlling the addition of a small unit to an otherwise ready-made molecule. It may also be envisaged as modifying the structure of cell membranes which may control the access of necessary materials to enzymes, and thus exert a regulatory function. The possibility that cytokinins act at the cell membrane level has been suggested before. Braun and Wood (1962) have shown that the permeability of normal and tumorous plant cells to certain simple ions is very different, also indicating that differences in the type of growth may be based upon differences in membrane permeability or in ion transport systems. The experience of plant biologists with auxin is a warning against focusing all attention on a single factor, or now on a single level of action.

It is also evident that the study of interrelations between plant hormone action and nucleic acid and protein synthesis is at its beginning, and that very many questions are still unanswered. As indicated, the details of the relationship between auxin and gibberellin action, and the synthesis of RNA and DNA, respectively, which are needed for that action, are not understood. The relationship may be quite a direct one, that is, the hormones may act on the nucleic acids themselves. Their effect may also be indirect, however, based on some feedback mechanism. The connection between the work of Nitsan and Lang, showing the need for DNA synthesis for gibberellin action in cell elongation, and that of Varner and associates, showing the control of enzyme formation by gibberellin, perhaps at the mRNA level, is not clear. The barley aleurone is a strictly nongrowing tissue; can the gibberellin effects we observe in such a tissue account for the growth-regulating effects of the hormone?

Nevertheless, despite these and many other questions, the search for interrelations between plant hormone action and the synthesis of nucleic acids and proteins can already be called one of the most interesting developments in plant endocrinology. It has established the fact that the action of plant hormones is dependent on these fundamental processes of cell metabolism. It has supplied the first well-documented case of hormonal control of enzyme synthesis, and has narrowed down the molecular point of action of the hormone further than in any other existing case. No less important, it is an impressive demonstration of how useful the judicious exploitation of advances in another, younger field of biology can be for the progress of an older field.

The limitation of the discussion to auxin, gibberellin, and cytokinin is not to imply that there are no further hormones in plants, and that still more may not be found.

Apparently, a new hormone has been in fact discovered quite recently (Ohkuma *et al.*, 1965; Cornforth *et al.*, 1965a,b). It has been called abscisin II, and its structure is shown in Fig. 4. As may be seen the substance is a sesquiterpene. It has been found in a number of widely divergent plants and plant tissues (Addicott *et al.*, 1964; Cornforth *et al.*, 1966). Its main function appears to be in the induction of dormancy conditions (Wareing *et al.*, 1964) and perhaps of certain ageing phenomena in plants, namely, the shedding (abscission) of senescent leaves, of fruits, etc. (Addicott *et al.*, 1964). It is possible, however, that it also participates in the regulation of other growth processes by counteracting the effects of gibberellin, auxin, and perhaps cytokinin also (see Thomas *et al.*, 1965).

Several members of the vitamin B group and also some other substances, such as certain amino acids, are formed in some plants only in the shoot, but are also needed for the growth of the root (for a recent review, see Torrey, 1965, pp. 1264–66). In such plants, these materials can be considered root hormones. This function is not ubiquitous, however; other plant species are evidently capable of synthesizing the same compounds in the root itself. Moreover, at least some of these vitamins are cofactors of important enzymes of the general metabolism. They may thus be able, if present in limiting amounts, to determine the extent of root growth (although there is no evidence that they actually do this in the intact plant), but it is doubtful that they are suitable for more subtle, qualitative regulatory functions.

Other vitamins, particularly *my*oinositol (Pollard *et al.*, 1961), can promote the growth of certain plant tissue cultures. They usually show a synergistic interaction with the major plant hormones, particularly cytokinins. Their regulatory role in the intact plant is not understood, however.

Finally, there is substantial evidence for a true organ-forming hormone in plants, or possibly for two functionally interrelated hormones. This hormone, or these hormones, regulate the initiation of flowers in plants (see Lang, 1965b, pp. 1401–18 and 1489–92). However, the evidence rests on transplantation (grafting) experiments and other physiological approaches. An initial step toward isolation and chemical identification may have been made (Mayfield *et al.*, 1963), but at present the flower hormone is still essentially a physiological concept.

Intercellular Regulation in Plants: Short-Distance Effects

Rather than attempt a further discussion of other hormones, or possible hormones in plants, I wish in conclusion, to draw attention to another, different aspect of intercellular regulation in plants.

The major plant hormones—auxin, gibberellin, cytokinins—can exert their effects over considerable distances, both from one part of a plant organ to another part and from one organ to a different one. There is also evidence in plants of intercellular regulatory effects which seem to extend only over much shorter distances.

One such case has been presented in another paper in this volume by H. Ursprung. It is the nonrandom distribution of stomata in the epidermis of dicotyledonous leaves (see Fig. 10, p. 198). This kind of pattern is of course a case of a field effect, although plant biologists prefer to call it "mutual repulsion of differentiating sites." It is a very widespread type of pattern in plant tissues and organs (for a recent survey, see Bünning, 1965, pp. 395–404), and clearly based on intercellular regulation.

While mutual repulsion of differentiating sites is a common type of pattern formation involving cellular interaction in plants, it is not the only one. When the stem of a suitable plant is wounded by a horizontal incision or removal of a wedge of tissue, the xylem (the water-carrying part of the conductive tissue of plants) forms a bridge around the gap, thus restoring the continuity of the tissue. This regeneration of xylem involves dedifferentiation of cells already differentiated (pith cells) and redifferentiation to a widely differing cell type. The process progresses in a regular sequence, starting at the pre-existing, wounded xylem and moving from cell to cell around the wound (see Fig. 11). This is, as is mutual repulsion, a case of intercellular regulation and is a clear case of induction. Since the tissue which is being induced is similar to the inducing tissue we speak of "homeogenetic induction."

Another case, similar in essence but different in an important aspect, is illustrated in Fig. 12. The leaf epidermis of sugarcane, like that of many monocotyledons, exhibits a simple, basic pattern. The last cell division in the tissue is an unequal or differential division, producing a larger and a smaller daughter cell. The larger cell does not undergo extended further differentiation, becoming an ordinary epidermis cell,

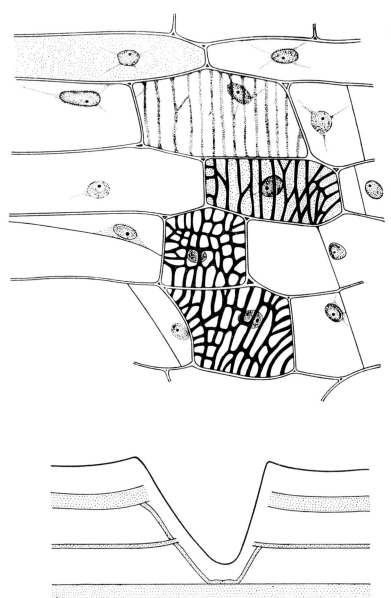

FIG. 11. Xylem regeneration in a wounded stem of *Coleus*. Left, overall diagram; right, progress of the differentiation (from left to right). Note that the wall thickenings (shown in black) in the newly formed xylem cells are matching one another in adjacent cells. (From Sinnott and Bloch, 1945.)

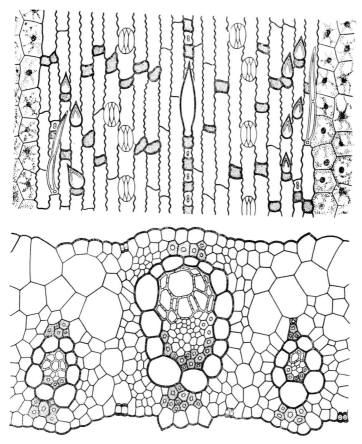

Fig. 12.   Cell differentiation in the upper epidermis of the leaf of sugarcane. Top, surface view of upper epidermis; bottom, corresponding cross-section of the leaf. (From Artschwager, 1940.)

but the smaller one does.* The kind of specialization which it undergoes, however, depends on the nature of the inner tissue of the leaf over which it happens to be situated. If it overlies a region between vascular bundles it becomes a stoma. If it overlies a major vascular bundle it develops either into a relatively large spine, or a so-called silica cell. If it is above a smaller bundle it may become either a similar but smaller spine, or a two-celled hair, or a silica cell. This is obviously

* This is another common type of origin of cellular patterns in plants (see Bloch, 1965, pp. 149–161), but does not call for the assumption of cellular interactions.

another case of induction, but since the induced tissue is different from the inducing one we call this type of induction "heterogenetic induction."

Homeo- and heterogenetic induction are no less common phenomena in plant differentiation than the repulsion of sites of differentiation (for a survey, see Lang, 1965a, pp. 411–417). It may be noted that the alternation of differing generations which is so common in the ontogenesis of plants is a case of heterogenetic induction.

While mutual repulsion of differentiating sites and homeo- and heterogenetic induction are such widespread phenomena in plant development, our understanding of their etiology is almost nonexistent. In xylem regeneration in wounded stems, auxin is an essential factor (Jacobs, 1952), but it probably has no other function than to enable the cells to resume growth and division activity. The character of the developing tissue is very likely determined by other factors acting from cell to cell over shorter distances. We have no knowledge whatever about these factors, as well as those involved in other cases of homeogenetic induction, in heterogenetic induction, and in mutual repulsion of differentiating sites. This whole area of cellular interaction can be called the forgotten dimension of plant development.

A step in the right direction has recently been taken by Wolk (1965, 1966) who has turned to a lower plant, the blue-green alga *Anabaena cylindrica*. This organism grows in the form of unbranched filaments, a single cell in thickness, and consists of three kinds of cells, vegetative cells, heterocysts, and spores.

The heterocysts (large, thick-walled cells with little content, the function of which is unknown) occur in the filament at nonrandom intervals. Spores arise generally by transformation of vegetative cells adjacent to a heterocyst, singly or in short strings.

Wolk (1965) was first able to obtain evidence suggesting that sporulation of a vegetative cell near a heterocyst depends on (1) a sequential process commencing adjacent to the heterocyst, and (2) abatement of a sporulation-inhibitory influence which acts on (or in) the vegetative cell.

In subsequent experiments he showed that disrupting the connection between heterocysts and adjacent vegetative cells prevented sporulation of the latter, apparently without impairment of their intrinsic capacity for sporulation. This result supports the hypothesis of a direct dependency of sporulation of vegetative cells on the heterocysts, that is, a genuine inductive relationship between the two cell types (Wolk, 1966).

The study of short-distance intercellular regulations in higher plants is faced with some serious difficulties. These processes usually take place at or near the apical meristems of roots and shoots, in a very limited area, and moreover in an area which is often hidden under older organs and thus not readily accessible to refined experimentation. The pattern of development may be a very complex one—as a look at Fig. 12 will show—with many different influences acting in the same tissue in close proximity and very probably interfering with one another.

Anabaena is obviously a much simpler organism, consisting of only three kinds of cells; in addition, it can be easily grown under controlled conditions. However, it exhibits at least two of the kinds of cell interactions in development which are common in higher plants. The relationship of heterocysts and spores is a case of heterogenetic induction, the arrangement of the heterocysts in the filament one of mutual repulsion of differentiating sites, or a simple field effect.

It may be expected that further work with this and similar relatively simple plants, will help us in understanding these and other kinds of short-distance intercellular regulation in plants, and may contribute to the understanding of induction and field phenomena in general.

ACKNOWLEDGMENTS

The author's personal research program, referred to in this paper, has been generously supported by grants from the National Science Foundation (G-16408, G-17483, GB-625, GB-3056) and the American Cancer Society (E-257, and institutional grant No. 39 to the California Institute of Technology), and is presently carried out under contract No. AT (11-1) 1338, United States Atomic Energy Commission.

REFERENCES

ADDICOTT, F. T., CARNS, H. R., LYON, J. L., SMITH, O. E., AND MCMEANS, J. L. (1964). On the physiology of abscisins. *In* "Régulateurs Naturels de la Croissance Végétale" (J. P. Nitsch, ed.), pp. 687–703. C.N.R.S., Paris.

ARTSCHWAGER, E. (1940). Morphology of the vegetative organs of the sugarcane. *J. Agr. Res.* **60,** 503–549.

BALDEV, B., AND LANG, A. (1965). Control of flower formation by growth retardants and gibberellin in *Samolus parviflorus,* a long-day plant. *Am. J. Botany* **52,** 408–417.

BALDEV, B., LANG, A., AND AGATEP, A. O. (1965). Gibberellin production in pea seeds developing in excised pods: effect of growth retardant AMO-1618. *Science* **147,** 155–157.

BLOCH, R. (1965). Histological foundations of differentiation and development in plants. *In* "Encyclopedia of Plant Physiology" (W. Ruhland, ed.), Vol. XV/1, pp. 146–188. Springer, Berlin.

BRANDES, H., AND BOPP, M. (1965). Spezifische Hemmung der Kinetin-Wirkung durch Actinomycin D. *Naturwissenschaften* **52,** 521.

BRAUN, A., AND WOOD, H. (1962). On the activation of certain essential metabolic systems in cells of *Vinca rosea* L. *Proc. Natl. Acad. Sci. U.S.* **48,** 1776–1782.

BÜNNING, E. (1965). Die Entstehung von Mustern in der Entwicklung von Pflanzen. *In* "Encyclopedia of Plant Physiology" (W. Ruhland, ed.), Vol. XV/1, pp. 383–408. Springer, Berlin.

CATHEY, H. M. (1964). Physiology of growth retarding chemicals. *Ann. Rev. Plant Physiol.* **15,** 271–302.

CHANDRA, G. R., AND VARNER, J. E. (1965). Gibberellic acid-controlled metabolism of RNA in aleurone cells of barley. *Biochim. Biophys. Acta* **108,** 583–592.

CORNFORTH, J. W., MILBORROW, B. V., RYBACK, G., AND WAREING, P. F. (1965a). Chemistry and physiology of "dormins" in sycamore. Identity of sycamore "dormin" with abscisin II. *Nature* **205,** 1269–1270.

CORNFORTH, J. W., MILBORROW, B. V., AND RYBACK, G. (1965b). Synthesis of (±)-abscisin II. *Nature* **206,** 715.

CORNFORTH, J. W., MILBORROW, B. V., AND RYBACK, G. (1966). Identification and estimation of (+)-abscisin II ("dormin") in plant extracts by spectropolarimetry. *Nature* **210,** 627–628.

FILNER, P., AND VARNER, J. E. (1966). Induced enzyme activity: *de novo* synthesis or activation? (in press).

HARADA, H., AND LANG, A. (1965). Effect of some 2-(chloroethyl)-trimethylammonium chloride analogs and other growth retardants on gibberellin biosynthesis in *Fusarium moniliforme. Plant Physiol.* **40,** 176–183.

HELGESON, J. P., AND LEONARD, N. J. (1966). Cytokinins: identification of compounds isolated from *Corynebacterium fascians. Proc. Natl. Acad. Sci. U.S.* **56,** 60–63.

HU, A. S., BOCK, R. M., AND HALVORSON, H. O. (1962). Separation of labeled from unlabeled proteins by equilibrium density gradient sedimentation. *Anal. Biochem.* **4,** 489–504.

JACOBS, W. P. (1952). The role of auxin in differentiation of xylem around a wound. *Am. J. Botany* **39,** 301–309.

KATSUMI, M., PHINNEY, B. O., AND PURVES, W. K. (1965). The roles of gibberellin and auxin in cucumber hypocotyl growth. *Physiol. Plantarum* **18,** 462–473.

KENDE, H., AND SITTON, D. (1966). Kinetin- and gibberellin-like root hormones and their physiological significance. *Ann. N. Y. Acad. Sci.* (in press).

KENDE, H., NINNEMANN, H., AND LANG, A. (1963). Inhibition of gibberellic acid biosynthesis by AMO-1618 and CCC in *Fusarium moniliforme. Naturwissenschaften* **50,** 599–600.

KEY, J. L. (1964). Ribonucleic acid and protein synthesis as essential processes for cell elongation. *Plant Physiol.* **39,** 365–370.

KEY, J. L., AND INGLE, J. (1964). Requirement for the synthesis of DNA-like RNA for growth of excised plant tissue. *Proc. Natl. Acad. Sci. U.S.* **52,** 1382–1388.

KLAMBT, H. D., THIES, G., AND SKOOG, F. (1966). Isolation of cytokinins from *Corynebacterium fascians. Proc. Natl. Acad. Sci. U.S.* **56,** 52–59.

KULAEVA, O. N. (1962). The effect of roots on leaf metabolism in relation to the action of kinetin on leaves. *Plant Physiol. (USSR)* **9,** 182–189.

LANG, A. (1957). The effect of gibberellin upon flower formation. *Proc. Natl. Acad. Sci. U.S.* **43,** 709–717.

LANG, A. (1961). Entwicklungsphysiologie. (Chemische Regulation der Entwicklung und verwandte Aspekte.) *Fortschr. Botan.* **23**, 312–345.

LANG, A. (1965a). Progressiveness and contagiousness in plant differentiation and development. *In* "Encyclopedia of Plant Physiology" (W. Ruhland, ed.), Vol. XV/1, pp. 409–423. Springer, Berlin.

LANG, A. (1965b). Physiology of flower initiation. *In* "Encyclopedia of Plant Physiology" (W. Ruhland, ed.), Vol. XV/1, pp. 1380–1536. Springer, Berlin.

LANG, A., AND REINHARD, E. (1961). Gibberellins and flower formation. *Advan. Chem. Ser.* **28**, 71–79.

LETHAM, D. S. (1966). Purification and probable identity of a new cytokinin in sweet corn extracts. *Life Sci.* **5**, 551–554.

LETHAM, D. S., SHANNON, J. S., AND MCDONALD, I. R. (1964). The structure of zeatin, a factor inducing cell division. *Proc. Chem. Soc.* **1964**, 230–231.

MACLEOD, A. M., AND MILLAR, A. S. (1962). Effect of gibberellic acid on barley endosperm. *J. Inst. Brewing* **68**, 322–332.

MASUDA, Y. (1959). Role of cellular RNA in the growth response of Avena coleoptiles to auxin. *Physiol. Plantarum* **12**, 324–335.

MAYFIELD, D. L., LINCOLN, R. G., HUTCHINS, R. Q., AND CUNNINGHAM, A. (1963). Concentration of a floral-inducing entity from plant extract. *J. Agr. Food Chem.* **11**, 35–38.

MILLER, C. O. (1966). The cytokinins of maize. *Ann. N. Y. Acad. Sci.* (in press).

MILLER, C. O., SKOOG, F., OKUMURA, F. S., VON SALTZA, M. H., AND STRONG, F. M. (1956). Isolation, structure and synthesis of kinetin, a substance producing cell division. *J. Am. Chem. Soc.* **78**, 1375–1380.

MOTHES, K. (1960). Über das Altern der Blätter und die Möglichkeit ihrer Verjüngung. *Naturwissenschaften* **47**, 337–351.

MOTHES, K. (1961). Der Beitrag der Kinetinforschung zum Verständnis pflanzlicher Korrelationen. *Ber. Deut. Botan. Ges.* **74**, 24–41.

MOTHES, K. (1964). Role of kinetin in plant regulation. *In* "Régulateurs Naturels de la Croissance Végétale" (J. P. Nitsch, ed.), pp. 131–140. C.N.R.S., Paris.

NINNEMANN, H., ZEEVAART, J. A. D., KENDE, H., AND LANG, A. (1964). The plant growth retardant CCC as inhibitor of gibberellin biosynthesis in *Fusarium moniliforme. Planta* **61**, 229–235.

NITSAN, J., AND LANG, A. (1965). Inhibition of cell division and cell elongation in higher plants by inhibitors of DNA synthesis. *Develop. Biol.* **12**, 358–376.

NITSAN, J., AND LANG, A. (1966). DNA synthesis in the elongating, non-dividing cells of the lentil epicotyl and its promotion by gibberellin. *Plant Physiol.* **41**, 965–970.

NOODÉN, L. D., AND THIMANN, K. V. (1963). Evidence for a requirement for protein synthesis for auxin-induced cell enlargement. *Proc. Natl. Acad. Sci. U.S.* **50**, 194–200.

OHKUMA, K., ADDICOTT, F. T., SMITH, O. E., AND THIESSEN, W. E. (1965). The structure of abscisin II. *Tetrahedron Letters* **1965**, 2529–2535.

PALEG, L. G. (1960). Physiological effects of gibberellic acid. I. On carbohydrate metabolism and amylase activity of barley endosperm. *Plant Physiol.* **35**, 293–299.

PHINNEY, B. O., AND WEST, C. A. (1961). Gibberellins and plant growth. *In* "Encyclopedia of Plant Physiology" (W. Ruhland, ed.), Vol. XIV, pp. 1185–1227. Springer, Berlin.

POLLARD, J. K., SHANTZ, E. M., AND STEWARD, F. C. (1961) . Hexitols in coconut milk: their role in nurture of dividing cells. *Plant Physiol.* **36,** 492–501.

RICHMOND, A. E., AND LANG, A. (1957) . Effect of kinetin on protein synthesis and survival of detached *Xanthium* leaves. *Science* **125,** 650–651.

SACHS, J. (1880) . Stoff und Form der Pflanzenorgane. *Arb. Botan. Inst. Würzburg* **3,** 452–488.

SACHS, J. (1882) . Stoff und Form der Pflanzenorgane. *Arb. Botan. Inst. Würzburg* **4,** 689–718.

SACHS, R. M. (1961) . Gibberellin, auxin and growth retardant effects upon cell division and shoot histogenesis. *Advan. Chem. Ser.* **28,** 49–58.

SACHS, R. M. (1965) . Stem elongation. *Ann. Rev. Plant Physiol.* **16,** 73–96.

SACHS, R. M., BRETZ, C. F., AND LANG, A. (1959) . Cell division and gibberellic acid. *Exptl. Cell Res.* **18,** 230–244.

SACHS, R. M., LANG, A., BRETZ, C. F., AND ROACH, J. (1960) . Shoot histogenesis: sub-apical meristematic activity in a caulescent plant and the action of gibberellic acid and AMO-1618. *Am. J. Botany* **47,** 260–266.

SINNOTT, E. W., AND BLOCH, R. (1945) . The cytoplasmic basis of intercellular pattern in vascular differentiation. *Am. J. Botany* **32,** 151–156.

SKOOG, F., AND MILLER, C. O. (1956) . Chemical regulation of growth and organ formation in plant tissues cultured *in vitro. Symp. Soc. Exptl. Biol.* **11,** 118–231.

STOWE, B. B., AND YAMAKI, T. (1957) . The history and physiological action of the gibberellins. *Ann. Rev. Plant Physiol.* **8,** 181–216.

THOMAS, T. H., WAREING, P. F., AND ROBINSON, P. M. (1965) . Chemistry and physiology of "dormins" in sycamore. Action of the sycamore "dormin" as a gibberellin antagonist. *Nature* **205,** 1270–1272.

TORREY, J. G. (1965) . Physiological bases of organization and development in the root. *In* "Encyclopedia of Plant Physiology" (W. Ruhland, ed.) , Vol. XV/1, 1256–1327. Springer, Berlin.

VARNER, J. E. (1966) . Hormonal control of enzyme production in barley endosperm. *Ann. N. Y. Acad. Sci.* (in press) .

VARNER, J. E., AND CHANDRA, G. R. (1964) . Hormonal control of enzyme synthesis in barley endosperm. *Proc. Natl. Acad. Sci. U.S.* **52,** 100–106.

WAREING, P. F., EAGLES, C. T., AND ROBINSON, P. M. (1964) . Natural inhibitors as dormancy agents. *In* "Régulateurs Naturels de la Croissance Végétale" (J. P. Nitsch, ed.) , pp. 377–386. C.N.R.S., Paris.

WENT, F. W. (1928) . Wuchsstoff und Wachstum. *Rec. Trav. Botan. Neerl.* **25,** 1–116.

WOLK, C. P. (1965) . Control of sporulation in a blue-green alga. *Develop. Biol.* **12,** 15–35.

WOLK, C. P. (1966) . Evidence of a role of heterocysts in the sporulation of a blue-green alga. *Am. J. Botany* **53,** 260–262.

WRIGHT, S. T. C. (1961) . A sequential growth response to gibberellic acid, kinetin and indolyl-3-acetic acid in the wheat coleoptile (*Triticum vulgare* L.) . *Nature* **190,** 699–700.

YOMO, H. (1958) . Studies on barley malt. 3. Sterilization of barley seeds and amylase formation of separated embryos and endosperms. *Hakko Kyokaishi* **16,** 444–448. (Japan.)

YOMO, H. (1960a) . Studies on the amylase activating substance. 4. On the amylase activating action of gibberellin. *Hakko Kyokaishi* **18,** 600–602. (Japan.)

YOMO, H. (1960b). Studies on the amylase activating substance. 5. Purification of the amylase activating substance. *Hakko Kyokaishi* **18,** 603–606. (Japan.)
YOMO, H., AND IINUMA, H. (1966). Production of gibberellin-like substances in the embryo of barley during germination. *Planta* **71,** 113–118.
ZACHAU, H. G., ÜTTING, D., AND FELDMANN, H. (1966). Nucleotide sequences of two serine specific transfer RNAs. I. *Angew. Chem. Intern. Ed. Engl.* **78,** 392.
ZEEVAART, J. A. D., AND LANG, A. (1963). Suppression of floral induction in *Bryophyllum daigremontianum* by a growth retardant. *Planta* **59,** 509–517.

Cell Death in Morphogenesis

JOHN W. SAUNDERS, JR.* AND JOHN F. FALLON

Department of Biology, Marquette University, Milwaukee, Wisconsin

Introduction

The founding of a new generation in most species is characterized by prodigal reproductive wastage. Seminal products are shed with abandon, only a minute fraction of their reproductive potential being realized; fertilized eggs fail to nidate, fall to predators or to parasites, or dry up when they are cast upon a shore or left behind by receding waters; of the fraction of potential young which does hatch or germinate, only a few individuals survive to breed and start the cycle anew. The probabilities are thus very high at any stage of the reproductive process that death will overtake an individual gamete, zygote, embryo, or young organism; and the successful organisms have evolved reproductive potentialities or devices which are commensurate with survival of the species in the face of the chances of reproductive death.

Even for the new individual which survives against greater or lesser odds, embryonic development is characterized by a further wastage. Death of cells is a normal component of most morphogenetic movements such as foldings, detachments, and the confluence of anlagen; it occurs prominently during histogenesis—for example, in the remodeling of cartilage and bone—and it is the means whereby many embryonic and larval organs are eliminated at metamorphosis. These deaths entail a loss of specific information held in nucleic acids and, in general, the abandonment to disorder of the high level of organization built into living cells.

An earlier generation of biologists emphasized a kind of chance causality for many deaths: death might ensue in cells crowded by pressure from their neighbors during morphogenetic movements; or dying cells might be considered the losers in competition for energy sources and oxygen. An older view also suggested for the phagocyte an assassin's

* Present Address: Laboratory of Anatomy, School of Veterinary Medicine, University of Pennsylvania, Philadelphia, Pennsylvania.

role in the elimination of cells as, for example, in the destruction of larval tissues in the metamorphosing insect. The modern insight, however, emphasizes the occurrence of cellular death during embryogenesis as not as much the consequence of chance or casual events, but rather as a phenomenon in the execution of a genetic program: a cell dies at a certain time because it is programmed to do so by intrinsic or extrinsic factors. With this insight, and with particular attention to the chick embryo, in the following discussion we shall analyze the occurrence of certain death programs and their control, and then direct attention to the events taking place when a cell becomes irreversibly committed to death as its morphogenetic endpoint. (For more general views of the topic of cell death in development, see Glücksmann, 1951; Saunders *et al.*, 1962; Zwilling, 1964; and Saunders, 1966.)

Integration of Patterns of Growth and Death in Shaping the Vertebrate Limb

In the higher vertebrates, limbs arise as paddlelike projections of the body wall, capped apically by a ridge of ectoderm. In the chick embryo, the wing and leg paddles arise at about 60 hours of incubation (stage 16, of the Hamburger–Hamilton series, 1951) and increase in apicobasal length, retaining the paddle-shaped outlines until the end of the fourth day (stage 24) when sculpturing of their definitive contours begins. As analyzed for the wing bud, this process involves continued cellular proliferation, the abundant production of intercellular materials, and rather dramatic cellular displacements (Saunders *et al.*, 1962; Amprino and Camosso, 1956). Spatiotemporally correlated with cell shiftings and the emergence of the wing and leg contours are localized zones of massive necrosis which sweep the length of the limb, appearing last in the soft tissues between the digits as their outlines are sculptured.

The occurrence of these zones of necrosis is quite predictable. Necrotic areas may be detected *in vivo* by the whitish opacity of the cells and by their ability to bind any of several basic vital dyes (Nile blue, neutral red, Bismarck brown, brilliant cresyl blue, azure B, methylene blue; cf. Saunders *et al.*, 1962), and they are easily found in sections stained according to standard histological practices. What one actually sees for the most part, are degenerating masses of cellular debris engulfed by neighboring cells. The latter, apparently stimulated to become phagocytic by the presence of morbid neighbors, engulf them in great numbers, swelling to enormous size with the volume of their load (Fig. 1).

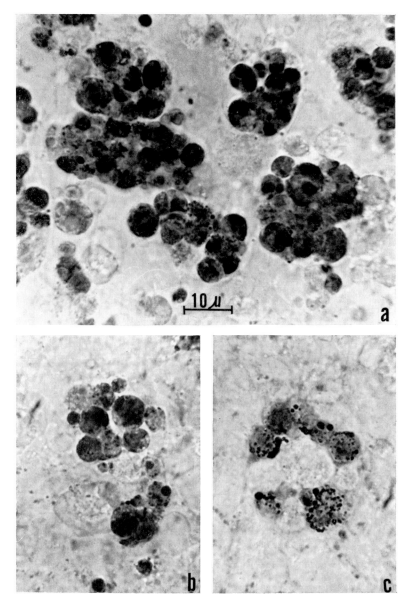

FIG. 1. Phagocytes from zones of massive necrosis in the limb buds of the 4-day chick embryo; vitally stained with neutral red (1:10,000 in isotonic salt solution) and gently flattened beneath a cover glass. All photographs at the same magnification. In a and b the cells are enormously distended with their content of red-stained

The pattern of early development of the appendages in amniotes is quite similar, and we were therefore somewhat unprepared to find that the correlation between the topographical distribution of cell deaths and the emergence of limb contours varies considerably from one kind of organism to another. Thus, in the chick embryo of stage 24 the leg bud shows a large zone of necrosis extending two-thirds of its length along the preaxial margin; the wing bud shows a similar zone of death along the posterior margin. Death and resorption of cells in these regions appear to contribute to the morphogenetic movements which model the contours of thigh and upper arm, respectively. Yet during the formation of the limbs in the duck, the homologous zones show no significant necrosis, but along the posterior margins of shank and tarso-metatarsus degenerations are found in patterns not unlike those of the chick (Figs. 2 and 3).

In the mouse embryo, which we have studied, zones of intensive necrosis do not occur in conjunction with the formation of proximal contours of the appendages, but the interdigital zones show abundant cell death prior to and during the emergence of the digits. Similar observations have been reported for the mouse and mole by Milaire (1963) and by Menkes et al. (1965) for mouse, rat, and human embryos. These are, of course, organisms in which the definitive digits are separate for the greater part of their length, and it appears that differential death may play a significant part in the carving of their contours. If so, it might be expected that failure of death to occur might result in a degree of soft tissue syndactyly, and that in forms with webbed feet, there might be reduction or absence of interdigital death.

The latter point has been examined for the duck embryo by Deleanu (1965) and by us. Here one finds that the distribution of necrosis is nicely correlated with the occurrence of webbing. Between digits I and II, which are not connected by webbing, the interdigital zone of the footplate shows a V-shaped wedge of necrosis extending from the distal margin, involving some ectodermal cells of the apical ridge remnant and a high percentage of the cells of the intervening mesenchyme. Between digits II and III, however, and between III and IV, only shallow zones of necrosis are found interdigitally at the margin of the footplate

---

cell debris. In c, the nucleus of the phagocyte appears as a clear zone surrounded by debris; the microscope was focused on the dark granules around the phagocytic vacuoles. In other preparations these are shown to be strongly positive for acid phosphatase and are presumably lysosomes.

and only the distal portions of the intervening tissue degenerate, the rest remaining as web (Fig. 3). One wonders what would be found in a similar study of other web-footed birds and of mammals with interdigital webbing.

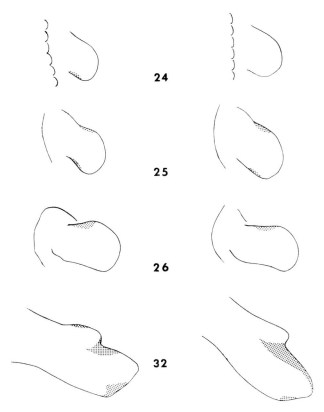

FIG. 2. The distribution of zones of cataclysmic necrosis at comparable stages in the superficial mesoderm of wing buds of the chick (left) and the duck (right) as revealed by vital staining with Nile Blue. The numbers are developmental stages for the chick embryo according to the seriation of Hamburger and Hamilton (1951).

Little attention has been given to the distribution of deaths in the footplates of syndactylous mutants. Milaire (1965) reported that, as one might expect, there is no significant interdigital necrosis in cases in which osseous syndactyly occurs in the hind limbs of mice of the *sm/sm* mutant genotype. The forelimbs often show soft-tissue syndactyly in these mutants, but we have found no reports of studies in which

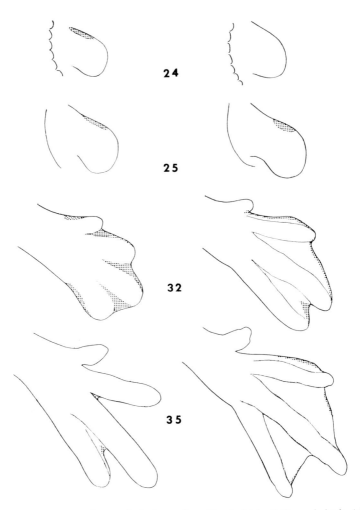

FIG. 3.   The pattern of necrosis in leg primordia of chick (left) and duck (right).
See legend for Fig. 2.

interdigital tissues of this or any similar mutant with soft-tissue syndactyly was analyzed for the presence of degenerations. Conceivably, the
occurrence of soft-tissue syndactyly could result from a failure of interdigital necrosis; but, the presence or absence of necrosis would hardly
be of consideration in the etiology of osseous syndactyly, for fusion of
the precartilaginous digital rudiments takes place prior to the time

necrosis of the intervening tissue is normally expected to occur, and thus there is essentially no interdigital tissue for death to eliminate.

Some light might be thrown on the significance of selective degeneration in digit formation if one were able to inhibit the necrosis of cells experimentally in specified locations. Menkes and Deleanu (1964) and Deleanu (1965) injected 5–20 μg of Janus green into the amniotic cavity of 6½-day chick embryos and found that survivors showed a high frequency of soft-tissue syndactyly in the hind limb. Embryos examined at appropriate stages by means of vital dyes showed absence of macrophages interdigitally. We have confirmed these findings: Fig. 4 shows controls and an unselected series of right leg buds from embryos sacrificed at intervals of 6 hours after administration of Janus green into the amniotic cavity of chick embryos at 6½ days. The failure of digital

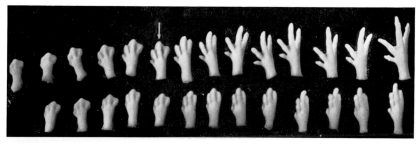

Fig. 4.   The normal development of the right foot of the chick embryo is shown in the upper row for control embryos sacrificed at 6½ days (far left) and at 6-hour intervals thereafter. In the lower row are shown right feet from embryos which received 7½ μg of Janus green in the amniotic fluid at 6½ days of incubation and were sacrificed simultaneously with their controls; all digits are joined by soft tissues. Arrow indicates stage illustrated in Fig. 5.

separation to occur is clearly shown in the figure. The diminution of interdigital necrosis during the critical stages of toe formation was revealed by treating each of the limbs with vital dyes and examining them for macrophages. Similar limbs fixed and sectioned for light microscopy likewise showed greatly reduced cellular degeneration (Fig. 5).

In other experiments we isolated the leg buds of duck and chick embryos of stages 18 to 21, stripped them of ectoderm by means of EDTA (ethylenediaminetetraacetate) and then covered them with trypsin-isolated ectodermal hulls from the wing buds of chick and of duck embryos, respectively (procedures of Zwilling, 1955). The chimeras were then grown as flank grafts on host chick embryos and, at appropriate

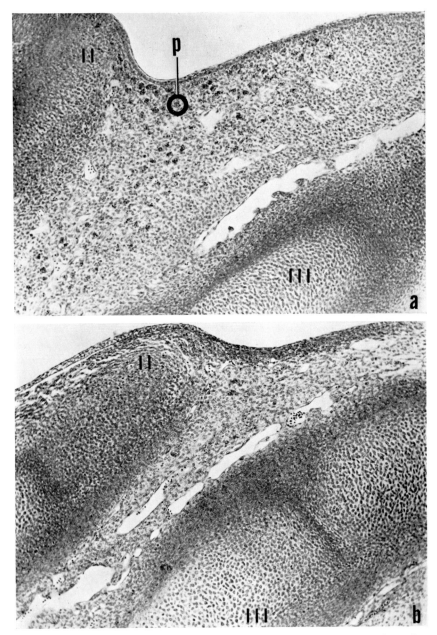

FIG. 5. The interzone between digits II and III is shown for the right foot of an
8-day control embryo (a) and for an embryo injected at 6½ days with Janus green

intervals, hosts were sacrificed and the grafts were vitally stained with Nile blue to reveal cellular debris. In limbs composed of duck mesoderm and chick ectoderm, webbing developed in the normal duck pattern: the interdigital area between I and II showed extensive necrosis and was completely eliminated; between digits II and III and III and IV, large-scale death occurred only marginally, and typical ducklike webbing remained (cf. Fig. 3). In the reciprocal combination, the

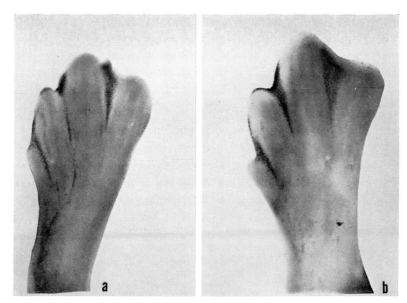

Fig. 6. Patterns of cell death revealed by staining with Nile blue; interdigital areas of necrosis are darkly stained; a: chimeric limb grown as a flank graft composed of the mesodermal core of a chick embryo leg bud and the ectodermal jacket from the wing bud of a duck embryo; b: foot of control chick embryo at a slightly earlier developmental stage. Note that the extent of interdigital necrosis in a is considerably less than in b.

initiation of necrosis was greatly retarded as compared to the normal condition for the chick foot: fewer cells degenerated (Fig. 6) and a thin interdigital webbing developed, quite similar to that seen after treatment of the chick embryo with Janus green (cf. Fig. 4).

(b). The embryos were sacrificed when necrosis was approximately at its peak, and the experimental and control sections were processed and stained simultaneously. Note the numerous phagocytes (p) containing heavily stained debris in a; none is found in b.

It is quite tempting to conclude that duck ectoderm inhibits the necrosis of the interdigital mesoderm and that treatment with Janus green does likewise, thus producing the webbed condition. This may be true, but failure of interdigital clefts to form may be just as reasonably interpreted as arising from effects of these treatments on patterns of growth in the limb, quite apart from effects on the death patterns, which may occur only concomitantly. Since this possibility has not yet been eliminated, it is premature to conclude that cell death is of primary causality in separation of the digits, and that failure of interdigital death to occur necessarily results in soft-tissue syndactyly.

Control of the Death Program

When this Society held the first "Growth Symposium" twenty-five years ago, there had emerged from the classic period of experimental embryology a number of principles—prospective fate, determination, differentiation, competence, induction, prospective potency—to name a few, which provided a conceptual framework giving coherence and meaning to large segments of embryological knowledge. In the excitement generated by new discoveries, particularly in molecular genetics, developmental principles are sometimes neglected today, but they should not be, for they enrich and give deeper meaning to the analytical data which issue from the application of our modern insights, and they are stimulating to the formulation of new questions in an appropriate developmental context.

It is not out of place for us, therefore, in a modern discussion of problems of morphogenetic death, to introduce some classic principles of development to assist us in putting these problems in context with those of growth and differentiation. It is appropriate to speak of the *prospective fate* of a cell or group of cells as being *death;* to say that the assignment to death is *determined* more or less reversibly, depending on circumstances, and to note that *competence* to respond by death to certain factors is characteristic of a certain *level of differentiation.*

Relatively early in development certain cells and tissues differentiate the competence to show a death pattern in response to environmental conditions which determine for others a pattern of growth and cytodifferentiation. At metamorphosis in holometabolous insects, larval tissues respond to existing hormonal conditions by degenerating, but imaginal cells react by growing and differentiating the adult organs. When the anuran tadpole enters metamorphosis under the influence of thyroid hormone, gills and tail, for example, degenerate but the limbs grow. Moreover, reaction competence for death, as for life, is often differentiated well in advance of the time it is actually exercised. Thus, the larval salivary glands of *Drosophila* normally begin to undergo histolysis in response to metamorphic hormones about 10 hours after puparium formation, but they actually have the competence to give this response immediately after the second moult; if grafted to late third instar larvae which are about to undergo metamorphosis, they degenerate simultaneously with the salivary glands of the host. This competence, however, is not present in salivary glands of larvae which have just completed the first moult (Bodenstein, 1943). What determines the origin of competence is not always clear. At this point one can only speculate about what "competence" for death in a cell or tissue, or for any other morphogenetic endpoint, may mean with respect to the state of the genome and the factors immediately determining its readout patterns.

Factors of the environment other than those provided or controlled by hormones likewise may determine that certain cells with the appropriate response competences shall die. Hamburger and Levi-Montalcini (1949), for example, showed that in the chick embryo sensory neurons of the spinal ganglia degenerate in a pattern which is related to the peripheral load encountered by outgrowing nerve processes. Normally, cataclysmic degeneration occurs among neuroblasts in the ventrolateral portions of spinal ganglia at the cervical and lumbar levels during days 5 to 9, but very little death is observed in ganglia at brachial and pelvic levels. However, unilateral extirpation of a limb primordium at very early stages, e.g., 2½ days, is followed by massive destruction of sensory neuroblasts during the 5- to 9-day period, probably those which normally would have innervated tactile receptors of the extirpated limb. Apparently death occurs among neurons which have sent their pioneering fibers into the periphery where the condition of insufficient load determines that they shall die, thus expressing a response pattern for which they may have differentiated a competence at the time they spun out their afferent fibers.

During the past several years we have carried out an intensive investigation of another embryonic site in which cataclysmic degeneration occurs with complete predictability (Saunders *et al.,* 1962; Fallon and Saunders, 1965). This site is in the superficial mesoderm of the posterior edge of the chick embryo wing bud near its junction with the body wall. For convenience we call this zone the "posterior necrotic zone" of the wing bud (hereafter, the "PNZ"). The PNZ is best seen at stage 24 (96 hours of incubation, Fig. 2) when, during a period of 8–10 hours, as many as 1500 to 2000 cells die and are ingested by phago-cytes, of which about 100 can be counted in each wing bud. The phago-cytes are readily seen in vitally stained limbs, the dye being strongly bound to the cellular debris within (Fig. 1). Usually this debris is resorbed about 10 hours after the onset of phagocytosis.

Apparently the prospectively necrotic cells of the PNZ become com-mitted very early to follow a death program. Prior to their demise, their location has been mapped for stages as early as stage 17, the stage at which the posterior outline of the wing bud can be recognized with certainty. If one excises the PNZ at this stage, or later, and grafts it to the dorsal side of the embryo to a site prepared by stripping ectoderm from over the somites, death is seen on schedule; that is, when the donor embryo achieves stage 24, massive necrosis is revealed in the graft upon application of vital dyes or through examination of histological sections. It is important to note that this occurs regardless of the stage of the host which may have already surpassed stage 24 at the time or may not have attained it as yet. Control tissues from the dorsal side of the wing bud similarly grafted do not degenerate. By stage 17, the PNZ cells, but not the nearby cells of the limb bud, have differentiated a program, an internal "death clock," which ticks off their necrosis at a preset time. The factors which "set" the death clock are completely unknown but, whatever they may be, probably no longer exist at stage 17, or the cells which occupy the same relative position after extirpation of the PNZ cannot respond to them; for death does not occur at the posterior junc-tion of wing bud and body wall after the PNZ is extirpated, regardless of the stage of operation, nor does it occur in other tissues grafted to the area.

It is tempting to suggest that the death clock which is set in the PNZ cells prior to stage 17 comprises a program of accelerated senescence: i.e., progressive and essentially irreversible deleterious changes leading to death. We have found no signs of such presumed changes; to the contrary, all indications are that the PNZ cells are quite "healthy" up to the time of their demise and, until then, can be diverted to a morpho-genetic fate involving their continued life and eventual histodifferentia-tion. Our first evidence for this was provided by results of experiments in which PNZ tissues from embryos of stages 17 to 23 were excised and grafted to a central position on the dorsal side of the wing bud. The grafts showed the characteristic pattern of degeneration only if the donor embryo were of stage 22 or 23; tissues from younger donors regularly showed no macrophages upon vital or supravital staining, and no significant amounts of pycnosis or other signs of cellular degeneration during histological examination. When host embryos were allowed to develop, they frequently showed an extra spur of cartilage covered with skin and feather germs in patterns similar to those found on the elbow.

From these results it emerges that, whereas the death clock is set in the PNZ and the cells proceed to death according to an intrinsic schedule, this schedule, nevertheless, does not involve irreversible changes until stage 22. Then the death program is fixed but, as we shall see, the cells subsequently recognized as dead at stage 24 were probably already moribund at stage 22. These findings also suggest that there are considerable differences between the kind of commitment to death shown by the PNZ cells and that which occurs, for example, in larval tissues of the insect or amphibian. In the latter forms the death clock is extrinsic to the cells which are to die and consists of a schedule of hormonal conditions, inocuous to other cells, to which the prospectively dying cells have differentiated the competence to give the death response. For the PNZ, however, the schedule is an intrinsic one, and death occurs without the imposition of conditions from without; certain external controls can be imposed experimentally, however, that turn off the death clock prior to stage 22.

Recently we have sought in organ culture experiments to gain some insight into the nature of external controls of the execution of the death pattern in the PNZ. Using Grobstein (1956) dishes containing Millipore filter culture wells with a variety of standard organ culture media and various modifications, we have determined that death occurs on schedule in explants of the PNZ. That is, when incubated at 37°C, PNZ tissues from the right wing bud show cataclysmic degeneration at the same time as do their left-wing counterparts on the donor embryo *in situ;* moreover, they show about the same number of macrophages. Control tissues, similarly cultured, do not show necrosis. Thus for PNZ cells the organ culture milieu provides conditions in which the normal prospective fate, death, is achieved.

If, however, one modifies these conditions by placing trans-filter to the PNZ a large slice of central wing or leg mesoderm from a 3- or 4-day embryo, then death fails to occur, depending on the age of the PNZ donor and the nature of the filter. With ultrathin filters (ca. 25 μ in thickness) having a porosity of 0.22 μ or greater, PNZ's do not show the death pattern if explanted prior to stage 20, but do show it sometimes, although usually on a reduced scale, when cultured at stage 20 or 21, and invariably show massive necrosis when put on the filter at stage 22 or 23. Somites explanted trans-filter, never prevent the occurrence of death in the PNZ nor do explants of heart, notochord, brain, and neural tube. Mesonephros, however, does prevent death from occurring.

The trans-filter factors which can turn off the death clock are apparently not mediated by cell contact, for electron micrographs of filters with 0.45 μ pores show that cell processes from each side of the membrane penetrate to a depth of 4 μ at the most. On the other hand, these factors do not pass, in effective amounts at least, when filters having a pore size of 0.05 μ are used, for under this circumstance PNZ cells trans-filter from central wing mesoderm invariably die on schedule. As yet, attempts to recover these factors from "conditioned" medium or to hold them in the filter in effective amounts have proved fruitless. It does appear, however, that they are cellular products which are synthesized in effective amounts or not, depending on the state of association of the producing cells. Thus wing bud mesoderm dissociated by trypsin and placed trans-filter to the PNZ will not prevent its necrosis, nor will it do so even when precultured in the dissociated state for 24 hours. If, at that time, the mesoderm is trypsinized and pelleted by centrifugation it can regain its lost property, but only after being cultured as a pellet for another 24 hours. In contrast, wing bud mesoderm dissociated by trypsinization and immediately pelleted and placed trans-filter to PNZ is quite effective in preventing its degeneration without being precultured.

One may now ask whether PNZ tissues prevented from degenerating *in vitro* at their scheduled time would die once the factors which prevented their necrosis were removed. An extensive series of replicate cultures was set up in which PNZ's from embryos of stage 19 were explanted, as before, trans-filter to central wing mesoderm. At stage 24 (determined by inspection of the control left wing of the PNZ donor) none of the PNZ explants showed necrosis. Thereafter, at intervals of 24 hours the trans-filter mesoderm was removed from 10 cultures, and the PNZ's were then placed in fresh medium and reincubated. Regularly, until 6 days had passed, these PNZ's showed massive necrosis within 12 hours of the removal. After 6 days, however, the PNZ remained non-necrotic indefinitely in the absence of trans-filter factors. It would seem therefore, that in the presence of certain externally supplied factors the death clock of the PNZ is, after a prolonged period, "turned off." The cells whose normal prospective fate is death finally become stabilized in a condition leading to indefinitely prolonged life

One wonders whether some other kinds of cells which die when experimentally deprived of certain associations likewise have an intrinsic death program and are only saved from degeneration by the fact that they normally do receive essential factors from other cells or tissues. What of the sensory neuroblasts of the lumbar level in the chick which, as noted above, degenerate when their pioneering fibers fail to contact an adequate periphery? Do they have an intrinsic death clock which could be turned off if appropriate contacts were made? Or, what of the cells of the superior colliculus in the mouse which degenerate promptly when the orbit is enucleated at birth (DeLong and Sidman, 1962) : do they have an intrinsic mechanism leading them to death on some schedule in the absence of sensory input? Perhaps there are many kinds of cells which have hitherto unrecognized death clocks which remain undetected because they are normally turned off by environmental factors before some critical period occurs, and thus they can survive and become stabilized in a final state. For cells of the PNZ, the influence requisite to achieving this stability is not available *in situ,* and they die on a rigid schedule.

Execution of the Death Sentence

For a number of systems which have a program for death, it seems that the cells prepare for their demise at least to the extent of producing or activating acid hydrolases for the future solubilization of their own remains. An interesting case, in this connection, is provided by the pupal intersegmental abdominal muscles of saturniid moths. Unlike various other tissues which break down when ecdysone is secreted at the break of pupal diapause, these muscles postpone their dissolution until adult development is complete. Apparently the endocrine signal provided by resumption of ecdysone secretion in the absence of juvenile hormone cues the production of hydrolytic enzymes in the prospectively degenerating muscles, for total and specific increases in catheptic activity occur quickly after the break of diapause, achieving an increase of 30% per day during the final phases of adult development prior to ecdysis. After ecdysis, the muscles break down rapidly, and this period is characterized by an increase in the nonsedimentable fraction of the enzyme, thus suggesting its release from lysosomes. Electron micrographs show lysosome-like bodies in the muscles of newly emerged adults. These are reported to decrease in number as histolysis of the muscle proceeds (Lockshin and Williams, 1964, 1965a,b,c,d) .

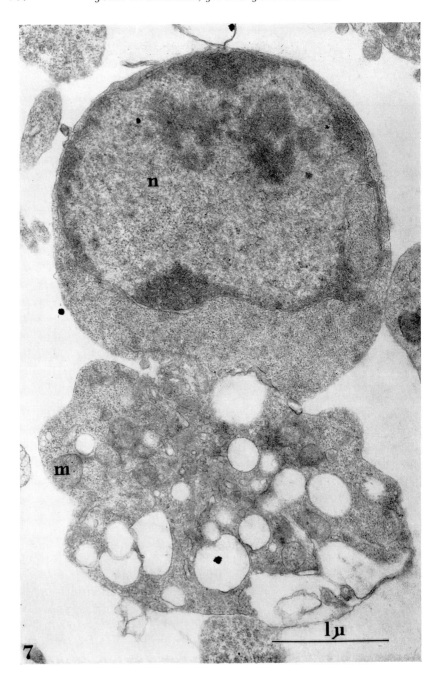

7

There is some evidence that withdrawal of nervous stimulation after adult ecdysis is critical for the onset of muscle breakdown, and Lockshin and Williams (1965c) have suggested that the flow of motor impulses somehow preserved the integrity of the lysosomal envelopes. Deprived of this input after adult ecdysis, the lysosomes release their enzymes and destroy the muscle.

The interpretation that action of lysosomal hydrolases on the cell content is the effective agent in rendering the cell morbid is difficult to substantiate. Certainly the release of lysosomal enzymes in many kinds of cells is not necessarily followed by death and, with but few exceptions, lysosomal rupture is equally well interpreted as following upon morbidity rather than causing it (see discussions by de Duve, 1963; Saunders, 1966). Nevertheless, it is tempting to suggest for the muscles studied by Lockshin and Williams that they early differentiate a death clock which is turned on by ecdysone and which operates a temporal pattern of enzyme synthesis. The time of occurrence of death, however, is dependent on the operation of programs extrinsic to the muscles themselves.

A somewhat similar metabolic preparation for death seems to occur in the Müllerian ducts of the chick embryo where there is a considerable synthesis of acid phosphatase, glucuronidase, cathepsin, and acid ribonuclease (Scheib, 1963; Hamilton and Teng, 1965) prior to their normal involution. Hamilton and Teng (1965) have pointed out that the total activity of acid ribonuclease increases greatly in both ducts of the male, but only in the right duct of the female; it is, of course, the left duct of the latter which persists and forms the definitive oviduct. There is some uncertainty about the precise mechanisms which trigger the degeneration normally (cf. Wolff, 1959; Scheib, 1963; Hamilton and Teng, 1965), but there is no question that sex hormones exercise a dramatic control *in vitro*. There is also need to investigate the role of macrophages in the production of hydrolytic enzymes which are assayed in excised Müllerian ducts. We have observed that large numbers of macrophages, heavily laden with refractile granules having high acid phosphatase activity, are present in the mesenteries and in the splanchnopleural and connective tissue investments of the ducts.

In cases such as the foregoing, although the cells seem to make preparations for their fate, they may, nevertheless, have their death post-

---

Fɪɢ. 7. Morbid cell, with nucleus (n) in an early phase of degeneration. The cell appears to have been fixed during the detachment of a highly vacuolate mass of cytoplasm containing degenerating mitochondria (m), various vesicles, and small fragments of rough endoplasmic reticulum. Photograph by Mrs. Marilyn Ricklin.

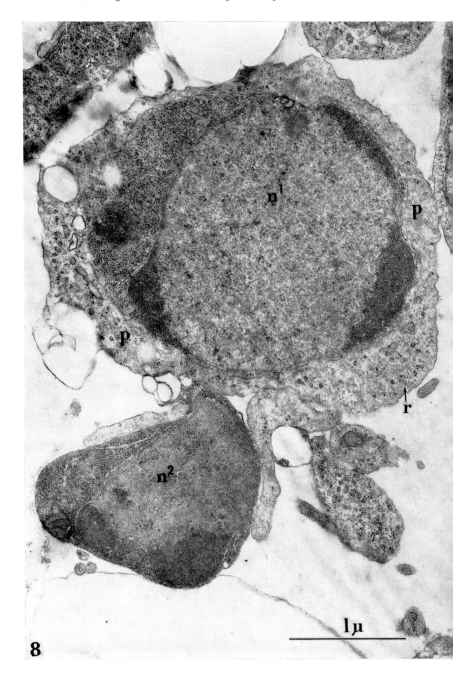

8

poned in the event that appropriate conditions for its occurrence are withdrawn experimentally. With the PNZ of the chick limb bud, on the contrary, death is inevitable unless extrinsic factors are supplied to prevent it prior to stage 22. Yet, in the PNZ no overt sign of the operation of the death clock has yet been detected before irreversible death changes set in: the light and electron microscopes reveal no distinctive cells; the activity of acid phosphatase, a lysosomal enzyme, shows no enhancement prior to frank necrosis; and a variety of histochemical stains for DNA, RNA, and histone and nonhistone protein provide no indication of differences among cells which could be correlated with the existence of a prospectively dying population amid prospectively living cells.

In the absence of other recognizable events programmed in the PNZ by the death clock, we next sought for clues to possible modifications in DNA-synthesizing activity in its prospectively necrotic cells (Held and Saunders, 1965). Chick embryos of stages 19 through 23 were injected intravascularly with a pulse dose of 2.5 μCi of tritiated thymidine of high specific activity, sacrificed at stage 24, sectioned, subjected to the Feulgen reaction, and radioautographed. The percentage of necrotic cells with radioactive label was then evaluated as a function of the stage at which the pulsed label was administered. Embryos injected at stages 19, 20, and 21 showed 43–47% necrotic nuclei in the PNZ labeled at stage 24, whereas those injected at stages 22 and 23 showed only 27% and 10% respectively; control areas showed no change in the percentage of labeled nuclei during these stages.

These results may be reasonably interpreted as showing that at stage 22, when the commitment of PNZ cells to death is irreversible, a significant percentage of them have ceased DNA synthesis, and that most of those which remain do so shortly thereafter. It is unlikely that this change is enforced by the assassination of healthy PNZ cells by phagocytes, for ingested cells cannot be found until later. What seems more likely is that the drastic alteration in the DNA-synthesizing pattern at stage 22 marks the onset of morbidity in a considerable segment of the cell population of the PNZ. Other cells, perhaps stimulated to cannibalistic

---

Fig. 8. Nucleus (n^1) of a degenerating cell surrounded by a thin film of its own cytoplasm and engulfed by a phagocyte (p). The cytoplasm of the phagocyte shows numerous polyribosomes (r). Another nucleus (n^2), at the right, is more advanced in degeneration. It was not ingested at the time of fixation, but appears to be embraced within arms of cytoplasm from a phagocyte, perhaps the same as the one which has engulfed n^1. Photograph by Mrs. Marilyn Ricklin.

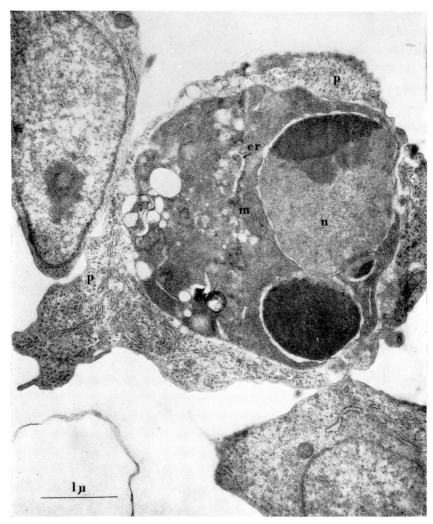

Fɪɢ. 9. Ingested cell with fragmenting nucleus (n) and vacuolate cytoplasm. Mitochondria (m), small vesicles, and fragments of endoplasmic reticulum (er) are distinguishable. Cytoplasm of the phagocyte (p) shows an unusually abundant endoplasmic reticulum and prominent ribosome clusters. Photograph by Mrs. Marilyn Ricklin.

activity by the presence of their morbid and moribund neighbors, then engulf them.

If this is so, however, the morphological changes in the first degenerating PNZ cells are not considerable prior to their ingestion. With the light microscope, cells with pycnotic nuclei are not readily found outside phagocytes in the PNZ until necrosis and phagocytosis are at their peak. Then they are seen with some frequency, suggesting that cells are now dying at such a rate that they undergo considerable cytological change before they can be ingested.

With the electron microscope we have not been able to identify morbid cells with certainty prior to the time some of them are ingested. There are, indeed, distinctive cells in the PNZ at stage 22 which show enhanced electron density marginally in the nucleus, a general "decay" of polysomes, and some inflation of Golgi vesicles and cisterns of the sparse endoplasmic reticulum; but, somewhat similar characteristics are found in embryonic chick cells at the end of telophase. Nevertheless, it is probable that some of these cells are morbid, for the same characteristics are found among ingested cells of later stages. Figure 7 illustrates a morbid cell with nucleus in early phases of degeneration which appears to be casting loose a vacuolated mass of cytoplasm containing degenerate mitochondria, Golgi vesicles, and endoplasmic reticulum. The nucleated remains, meanwhile apparently becoming increasingly electron dense (Fig. 8), may be engulfed sooner or later. Possibly cast-off cytoplasmic debris, too, is later phagocytized separately. More frequently, however, the entire cell appears to be engulfed (Fig. 9) and the "phagosomes" show debris in varying bizarre forms as digestion progresses (Fig. 10).

Among tissues of different species showing extensive morphogenetic necrosis there is considerable variation in the degree to which cytolysis proceeds prior to the onset of phagocytosis, and in the participation of endogenous lysosomal enzymes in autolysis of individual cells. Scharrer (1966), for example, has shown that during regression of the prothoracic gland of the cockroach rather considerable changes occur in nucleus and cytoplasm before the phagocytic hemocytes do their work. The nuclear substance of the glandular parenchymal cells begins to condense into patches of high electron density on the first day after the terminal moult and lysosome-like bodies of a kind not found in the nymphal glands appear. There are also membrane-bounded structures similar to autophagic vacuoles. Degeneration is quite advanced by the third day after the adult moult, and then hemocytes invade the gland in great numbers, ingesting the degenerating cells.

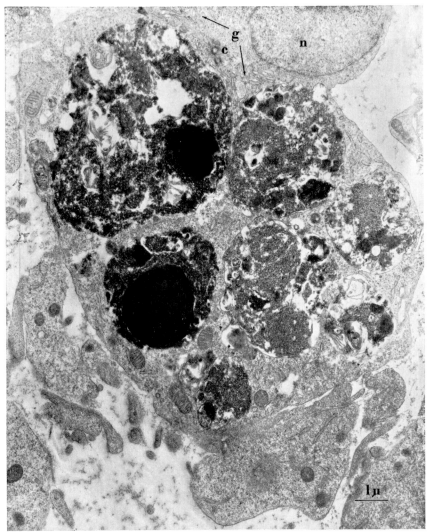

FIG. 10. Phagocyte engorged with cellular debris in various stages of degeneration. Typical of these cells is the abundant Golgi (g) lying near the nucleus (n) and the centriolar apparatus (c). Photograph by Mr. Donald Heinkel.

During metamorphosis in larvae of *Xenopus,* cytoplasmic bodies corresponding to lysosomes are not detected during early phases of muscle cell regression in the tail (Weber, 1964). The myofibrillar bundles first undergo a peculiar folding and lose their cross striations; the sarcoplasm becomes vesiculate; mitochondrial remnants and nuclei are cast into the intercellular spaces. Macrophages appear in considerable numbers only after degeneration is quite advanced, engulfing and digesting the cellular remains. With the appearance of the phagocytes, the activities of catheptic enzymes and of acid phosphatase increase dramatically. The population of macrophages rises rapidly, even in isolated tails regressing under the influence of thyroxine *in vitro,* and so does their content of lysosomal hydrolases (Weber, 1962, 1963). This indicates that macrophages may differentiate *in situ,* synthesizing *de novo* the enzymes used in solubilizing cellular remains. The neo-synthesis is inhibited by actinomycin D (Weber, 1965). Larval tail muscle cells in *Xenopus* thus behave in regression very much like those of the chick PNZ in that they die without a prior buildup of acid hydrolases, the latter apparently increasing in amount and becoming significant for the regression only as macrophages differentiate and produce the enzymes to hydrolyze the cellular debris they ingest (also see Tata, 1966).

Finally, it is perhaps worthy of note that regressive processes involving massive necrosis may occur without participation of macrophages at all. As one example, in the alate aphid, *Acyrthosiphon pisum,* which shows degeneration of the flight muscles soon after settling down on host plants, the muscle fibers undergo autolysis within the muscle sheath. Here there is no evidence of the penetration of phagocytic blood cells through the sheath or their accumulation outside it (Johnson, 1959; see also Jones, 1962, for a review of material on insect hemocytes).

General Conclusions

From the foregoing, conclusions can be drawn that the abundant death of cells and destruction of tissues and organs are integral parts of normal development, and that location and timing of these events are programmed by the genome and executed by mechanisms appropriately considered in the same conceptual categories as those which apply to control of growth and morphogenesis. The pattern of genetic readout may set up within a prospectively dying cell a death clock, or sequence of events which lead it normally to cease its own existence—i.e., to turn off its own readout—at a preset point in developmental time. This appears to be the case for certain degenerating limb bud cells of the chick embryo. For other kinds of cells the death program may call for the prospectively dying cells to prepare for their own demise—e.g., by synthesizing lysosomal enzymes—but the death clock for these cells actually consists of the creation at a point in developmental time of events extrinsic to them which then, directly or indirectly, act upon them to bring about their death.

Hopefully, the recognition and characterization of death clocks, and the analysis of their operation as aspects of genetic programming, is an approach which will offer further insights into the genetic and epigenetic control of development in higher organisms.

ACKNOWLEDGMENTS

Original research supported by grants under the direction of the senior author from the National Institutes of Health (C-1481, GM 07603, GM 09996), from the National Science Foundation (GS-794, G-14439, GB 4269), and from the Milwaukee Division of the American Cancer Society. The junior author was Pre-doctoral Trainee in Developmental Biology, supported by grant 8TI/HD-27 from the National Institutes of Health. Portions of the original work cited here issued from his doctoral research which will be published *in extenso* elsewhere.

We are particularly indebted to Miss Cecelia Reuss and to Miss Betty Murakami who contributed outstanding technical skills to many of the original studies reported here, to Mr. S. Ratajczak who prepared the illustrations, and to Mrs. Marilyn Ricklin and Mr. Donald Heinkel who supplied the electron micrographs.

REFERENCES

AMPRINO, R., AND CAMOSSO, M. (1956). Étude expérimentale de la morphogénèse de l'aile dans l'embryon de Poulet. I. Recherches par la méthode des marques coloreés. *Arch. Biol. (Liége)* **67**, 613-633.

BODENSTEIN, D. (1943). Factors influencing growth and metamorphosis of the salivary gland in *Drosophila. Biol. Bull.* **84**, 13-33.

DE DUVE, C. (1963). The lysosome concept. *In* "Lysosomes" (A. V. S. de Reuck and M. P. Cameron, eds.), pp. 1-31. Little, Brown, Boston, Massachusetts.

DELEANU, M. (1965). Toxic action upon physiological necrosis and macrophage reaction in the chick embryo leg. *Rev. Roumaine Embryol. Cytol.* **2**, 45-56.

DELONG, G. R., AND SIDMAN, R. L. (1962). Effects of eye removal at birth on histogenesis of the mouse superior colliculus: an autoradiographic analysis with tritiated thymidine. *J. Comp. Neurol.* **118**, 205-224.

FALLON, J. F., AND SAUNDERS, J. W., JR. (1965). *In vitro* analysis of the control of morphogenetic cell death in the wing bud of the chick embryo. *Am. Zoologist* **5**, 213-214.

GLÜCKSMANN, A. (1951). Cell deaths in normal vertebrate ontogeny. *Biol. Rev. Cambridge Phil. Soc.* **26**, 59-86.

GROBSTEIN, C. (1956). Trans-filter induction of tubules in mouse metanephrogenic mesenchyme. *Exptl. Cell Res.* **10**, 424-440.

HAMBURGER, V., AND HAMILTON, H. L. (1951). A series of normal stages in development of the chick embryo. *J. Morphol.* **88**, 49-92.

HAMBURGER, V., AND LEVI-MONTALCINI, R. (1949). Proliferation, differentiation and degeneration in the spinal ganglia of the chick embryo under normal and experimental conditions. *J. Exptl. Zool.* **111**, 457–502.

HAMILTON, T. H., AND TENG, C.-S. (1965). Sexual stabilization of Müllerian ducts in the chick embryo. In "Organogenesis" (R. DeHaan and H. Ursprung, eds.), pp. 681–700. Holt, New York.

HELD, W., AND SAUNDERS, J. W., JR. (1965). Incorporation of tritiated thymidine by nuclei in a zone of prospectively necrotic cells in the wing bud of the normal chick embryo. *Am. Zoologist* **5**, 214.

JOHNSON, B. (1959). Studies on the degeneration of flight muscles in alate aphids. II. Histology and control of muscle breakdown. *J. Insect Physiol.* **3**, 367–377.

JONES, J. C. (1962). Current concepts concerning insect haemocytes. *Am. Zoologist* **2**, 209–246.

LOCKSHIN, R. A., AND WILLIAMS, C. M. (1964). Programmed cell death. II. Endocrine potentiation of the breakdown of the intersegmental muscles of silkworms. *J. Insect Physiol.* **10**, 643–C49.

LOCKSHIN, R. A., AND WILLIAMS, C. M. (1965a). Programmed cell death. I. Cytology of degeneration in the intersegmental muscles of the pernyi silkmoth. *J. Insect Physiol.* **11**, 123–133.

LOCKSHIN, R. A., AND WILLIAMS, C. M. (1965b). Programmed cell death. III. Neural control of the breakdown of the intersegmental muscles of silkmoths. *J. Insect Physiol.* **11**, 601–610.

LOCKSHIN, R. A., AND WILLIAMS, C. M. (1965c). Programmed cell death. IV. The influence of drugs on the breakdown of the intersegmental muscles of silkmoths. *J. Insect Physiol.* **11**, 803–809.

LOCKSHIN, R. A., AND WILLIAMS, C. M. (1965d). Programmed cell death. V. Cytolytic enzymes in relation to the breakdown of the intersegmental muscles of silkmoths. *J. Insect Physiol.* **11**, 831–844.

MENKES, B., AND DELEANU, M. (1964). Leg differentiation and experimental syndactyly in chick embryo. *Rev. Roumaine Embryol. Cytol.* **1**, 69–77.

MENKES, B., DELEANU, M., AND ILIES, A. (1965). Comparative study of some areas of physiological necrosis at the embryo of man, some laboratory-mammalians and fowl. *Rev. Roumaine Embryol. Cytol.* **2**, 161–171.

MILAIRE, J. (1963). Étude morphologique et cytochimique du développement des membres chez la souris et chez la taupe. *Arch. Biol. (Liége)* **74**, 131–317.

MILAIRE, J. (1965). Étude morphogénétique de trois malformations congénitales de l'autopode chez la souris (syndactylisme—brachypodisme—hémimélie dominante) par des méthodes cytochimiques. *Mem. Acad. Roy. Belg. Classe Sci.* 16, Fasc. **3**, 119 pp.

SAUNDERS, J. W., JR. (1966). Death in embryonic systems. *Science* **154**, 604–612.

SAUNDERS, J. W., JR., GASSELING, M. T., AND SAUNDERS, L. C. (1962). Cellular death in morphogenesis of the avian wing. *Develop. Biol.* **5**, 147–178.

SCHARRER, B. (1966). Ultrastructural study of the regressing prothoracic glands of Blattarian insects. *Z. Zellfors. Mikroskop. Anat.* **69**, 1–21.

SCHEIB, D. (1963). Properties and role of acid hydrolases of the Müllerian ducts during sexual differentiation in the male chick embryo. In "Lysosomes" (A. V. S. de Reuck and M. P. Cameron, eds.), pp. 264–281. Little, Brown, Boston, Massachusetts.

TATA, J. R. (1966). Requirement for RNA and protein synthesis for induced regression of the tadpole tail in organ culture. *Develop. Biol.* **13**, 77–94.

WEBER, R. (1962). Induced metamorphosis in isolated tails of *Xenopus* larvae. *Experientia* **18**, 84–87.

WEBER, R. (1963). Behavior and properties of acid hydrolases in regressing tails of tadpoles during spontaneous and induced metamorphosis *in vitro*. *In* "Lysosomes" (A. V. S. de Reuck and M. P. Cameron, eds.), pp. 282–305. Little, Brown, Boston, Massachusetts.

WEBER, R. (1964). Ultrastructural changes in regressing tail muscles of *Xenopus* larvae at metamorphosis. *J. Cell Biol.* **22**, 481–487.

WEBER, R. (1965). Inhibitory effect of actinomycin D on tail atrophy in *Xenopus* larvae at metamorphosis. *Experientia* **21**, 665.

WOLFF, E. (1959). Endocrine function of the gonad in developing vertebrates. *In* "Comparative Endocrinology" (A. Gorbman, ed.), pp. 568–573. Wiley, New York.

ZWILLING, E. (1955). Ectoderm-mesoderm relationship in the development of the chick embryo limb bud. *J. Exptl. Zool.* **128**, 423–441.

ZWILLING, E. (1964). Controlled degeneration during development. *In* "Cellular Injury" (A. V. S. de Reuck and M. P. Cameron, eds.), pp. 352–362. Churchill, London.

Fact and Theory about the Cell Surface in Carcinogenesis

H. RUBIN

Department of Molecular Biology and Virus Laboratory, University of California, Berkeley, California

Any serious attempt to evaluate the current state of our knowledge about cancer leads us to some rather dismal conclusions. One of the most depressing things about cancer research is that we have foisted the delusion upon ourselves and upon the public that there has indeed been rapid progress in this field. This delusion has been nurtured by the assumption that knowledge which has accumulated so rapidly in certain fields of biology such as intermediary metabolism, replication of DNA, and the synthesis of proteins, is somehow immediately and directly applicable to the cancer problem. Thus we have expropriated various bits of information from selected fields of biology, depending on which is the fashion of the day, and applied them with little or no modification to an explanation of how cells become malignant. We have devised cancer theories involving the mitochondria, aerobic glycolysis, enzyme deletion, somatic mutation, chromosome aberration, and lysogeny, to mention only a few.

Some of the most energetic speculation about cancer has arisen from the tumor virus field, perhaps because there was some substantive framework on which to hang hypotheses. That is to say, viruses were actually discovered in cancers; they could cause cancers—whether directly or indirectly will not be considered here—and their implication as a cause of cancer offered the hope for controlling cancer by immunological means. When the information gained from the study of tumor viruses is scrutinized, however, it becomes clear that we have learned very little from these systems about the cellular changes which are the immediate causes of malignant behavior. If we say a virus is or is not present in a cell we say precious little about what it does to that cell to alter its behavior.

The contribution of the somatic mutation hypothesis to our understanding of the malignant process is even flimsier. The idea that a change in the genetic material of a cell could make it cancerous arose just as soon as we became aware of the theory of the gene, again an almost automatic extrapolation from the fashion of the day (see review by Strong, 1958). Since the cancerous behavior of a cell is perpetuated in its progeny, it would seem almost self-evident that there is a change in the genetic material of the cell.

Still, to the best of my knowledge, no one has presented concrete proof that a cancer has been caused by a somatic mutation. True enough, chromosome aberrations have been discovered in malignant cells, but the weight of evidence indicates that their role is, at best, secondary. It seems simply the path of least resistance to assume that transmission of the malignant property of cells to their progeny is a consequence of a change in the genetic material (i.e., DNA), since there is at present no other well-documented material basis for explaining cellular inheritance.

This brings us face to face with a nagging but crucial biological question. Are there ways of making hereditary changes in cells without altering the DNA of the cell? I am referring not only to agents of cytoplasmic inheritance such as certain viruses, plastids, episomes, etc., which have nucleic acid as their fundamental coding units. [We already have evidence for cytoplasmic inheritance of this sort in the case of the RNA-containing avian leukosis viruses (Rubin *et al.*, 1962). These viruses can be transmitted congenitally through the fertilized egg to the embryo only by the female parent. The male parent does not transmit the leukosis viruses congenitally through the spermatazoa even when high concentrations of virus can be demonstrated in the testes of viremic males at the time of fertilization. Evidently the virus genome is shed along with the cell's cytoplasm during spermiogenesis.] I am questioning whether or not there are other vehicles for perpetuating change. This will be discussed more extensively toward the end of this paper. At this point I should like only to suggest that the problem of carcinogenesis may not be very different from the problem of differentiation. In the case of differentiation we are presumably dealing with cells which have the same complement of genetic material but which maintain different forms and functions through successive cell generations, i.e., a hereditary but not necessarily a genic alteration. It seems to me that we often implicitly assume that differentiation merely involves the turning off or turning on of genes. In this we are expropriating the ideas of molecular genetics which were mainly conceived from work with bacteria. It might be useful to point out that even in bacteria these ideas are little more than vague concepts which have not yet given us any indication of how various regulatory processes interact with one another to produce the integrated functioning of the whole cell. To assume not only that these hypothetical processes *exist* in animal cells, but also that they are the ones central to the malignant transformation, is carrying absurdity to the second power.

What class of process then should we be looking for to implicate in the malignant transformation? As I have indicated there is no evidence of which I am aware to suggest that the malignant transformation results from a single, discrete, well-defined event such as a point mutation. There are all kinds and degrees of malignancy among cells, all characterized by the loss of differentiated function to a greater or lesser degree, and particularly by the loss of susceptibility to regulation of growth and movement.

Contact Inhibition

The little we know about regulation of growth and movement in animal cells suggests that cell surface macromolecules play a central role. For example, both direction and extent of cell movement appear to be controlled at the cell surface and are responsive to the nature of the surface contacted by the cell. If a cell is moving over a planar surface such as glass and encounters another cell, the phenomenon of contact inhibition occurs (Abercrombie *et al.*, 1957). Contact inhibition refers to the failure of cells in culture to move over one another. In a recent paper Carter has presented compelling evidence to indicate that contact inhibition is the result of the greater strength of adhesion of a cell to its substratum than to another cell (Carter, 1965). Carter has also shown that the direction of movement of cells on a gradient of differential adhesion is toward the region of strongest adhesion. Since the only variable in directing cell movement in Carter's experiment was the adhesiveness between cell and the differentially altered substratum, it is concluded that direction of movement is a surface-controlled phenomenon.

These observations have special relevance for understanding the malignant process. It is now a commonplace observation that cells escape from contact inhibition when they become malignant. That is to say, they can move over one another and over normal cells in tissue culture. Malignant cells by definition also have a tendency to invade other tissues. In so doing they must move away from their central mass into normal tissue in a form of directed movement, as if their adhesiveness to normal tissue were greater than their adhesiveness to cells of their own malignant type. The behavior of malignant cells therefore suggests that extensive changes have occurred in the cell surface.

I emphasize *extensive* changes because it seems unlikely that minor changes would produce the observed effect. Normal fibroblasts from as diverse sources as mice and chickens inhibit the movement of one another upon contact, as do cells as different as fibroblasts and epithelial cells. In both cases there must be substantial differences in the composition and arrangement of surface molecules of the opposing cells, but contact inhibition is maintained. We can conclude that contact inhibition is not a very precisely controlled phenomenon. This would be consistent with Carter's evidence that contact inhibition between cells occurs simply because the cells adhere more strongly to the culture dish than to one another.

The loss of sensitivity to contact inhibition by malignant cells would then appear to arise either from a decrease in the adhesiveness between the malignant cell and the surface of the dish or an increase in adhesiveness between the malignant and the normal cells. There are strong indications in the transformation of chicken cells into Rous sarcoma cells that a decrease in affinity between the cells and the dish occurs. The area of attachment between the transforming cell and the dish decreases. As a result, the cells round up and occasionally detach completely from the dish. There is no indication of increased adhesiveness between the malignant cells and normal cells. The loss of contact inhibition by a malignant cell would appear, therefore, to arise from a general decrease in its adhesiveness toward all surfaces rather than from a discrete change specifically altering its adhesiveness toward another cell.

Abercrombie *et al.* (1957) made a series of observations concerning contact inhibition between confronting explants of normal and malignant cells which are readily explained by Carter's postulated mechanism of differential adhesion, and not by other postulated mechanisms such as the formation of specific adhesions between cells. These observations are also consistent with the idea that the *loss* of contact inhibition by malignant cells is due to a decrease in differential adhesiveness arising chiefly from a decrease in adhesiveness to the dish. The relevant observations are enumerated below.

1. The movement of a malignant cell in a given direction is not obstructed when the cell is confronted by a normal cell.

2. By contrast, the movement of normal cells is obstructed when they are confronted by malignant cells.

In the first case, the differential adhesiveness of the malignant cell is decreased and it moves equally well over the substrate and over normal cells. In the second case, the differential adhesiveness of the normal cell toward the combination malignant cell and substrate is at least as great as it is toward the combination normal cell and substrate, and movement is obstructed.

3. The malignant cells are often found on top of but not underneath normal cells. This is to be expected under the assumption that the malignant cells are less adhesive to the substrate than are the opposing normal cells. If, however, contact inhibition were due to formation of specific adhesions between cells and not to a loss in general adhesiveness, the malignant cell would be as likely to be underneath as on top of the normal cells.

4. The more rounded malignant cells are more invasive than the spindle-shaped malignant cells, i.e., they penetrate further into an opposed population of normal cells. The degree of rounding of a cell is presumably an index of the cell's loss of adhesiveness to the substrate. The differential adhesiveness of the rounded cells toward the combination normal cell and substrate is less than that of the spindle-shaped cells which still are fairly adhesive to the substrate.

The results taken individually and collectively support the twin concepts that contact inhibition is a consequence of differential adhesiveness and that the loss of contact inhibition by malignant cells is a consequence of the decrease in general adhesiveness. This decrease is all that is needed to explain the most prominent behavioral characteristics of malignant cells, namely, their invasiveness and their tendency to detach from a mass of cells and metastasize to distant sites.

Studies of Cell Membranes

As already noted, the loss of adhesiveness in cells undergoing the malignant transformation in all likelihood arises from extensive changes in the cell's plasma membrane. Given the importance of the plasma membrane in the malignant transformation, how do we proceed to study this structure? Studies such as those of Abercrombie *et al.* (1957) on the interaction between intact living cells provided us with the key evidence implicating the cell membrane initially. Such studies, however, are basically descriptive and are unlikely to yield detailed information about membrane structure and its alteration in malignancy.

The most obvious alternative is to fractionate cells to obtain their membranes. Much effort has been expended in this direction with but little return in understanding membrane structure and function.

Why?

I believe the reasons are two-fold. First, the procedures commonly used in disrupting cells and isolating membranes are very likely to disrupt the weak bonds which hold lipids and proteins together in the intact, functioning membrane. Thus, it may be impossible with these disruptive procedures to detect those structural differences which might distinguish between membranes of normal and malignant cells.

Second, no biological test has been developed that can serve as a criterion for the functional integrity of the membranes. Since the most obvious function of membranes is to serve as a selectively permeable barrier between the inside and outside of the cell, it would appear *a priori* self-defeating to disrupt and isolate the membrane and then test it for this function. Unfortunately, no satisfactory substitute has been available for testing the biological integrity of isolated membrane components.

I should like to describe a technique, however, which I believe tests the functional integrity of components of the cell membrane. If my interpretation of the phenomena described below is correct, we are now in a position to study the functions of *isolated structural units of the membrane in solution*. This is accomplished by creating a drain on the membrane components of intact cells and requiring their replacement from the medium to achieve growth of the cells. If the demand is great enough, replacement can only be achieved by providing the structural components of the membrane itself as ready-made complex building blocks. Alterations of sufficient magnitude in the isolated building blocks are reflected in the failure of stressed cells to grow. The observations to be described suggest that this biological test can detect differences between the membrane structures of normal and malignant cells. The results also suggest that the cell membrane is made up of macro-molecules in constant flux, and in equilibrium with their environment. They indicate that the surface macromolecules are held loosely in position by weak bonds, and are constantly moving into and out of the membrane. Molecules released into the medium can be reinserted if they maintain their native configuration. The model is a dynamic one, which should be useful in interpreting a variety of membrane phenomena.

The Growth of Cells in Tissue Culture

To understand this system, I will have to backtrack and make a few comments about the pitfalls of extrapolating tissue culture observations for the explanation of *in vivo* phenomena. Wrenching cells from their normal surroundings and placing them into culture exposes them to a radical change in the surfaces which they contact. Instead of facing other cells or intercellular materials, they are flattened out on glass or plastic, come into contact with other cells only at their edges, and are washed over by a liquid medium. Cells may manifest certain features of behavior in culture which occur rarely, if at all, in the body. For example, the tendency of cells in culture is to be restricted to a monolayer as a result of contact inhibition, but they usually occur in three-dimensional masses in the body, where the differential adhesiveness required for the expression of contact inhibition apparently is not obtained. Therefore, we must be cautious about extrapolating the explanations for certain aspects of *in vitro* behavior to *in vivo* phenomena which may be only superficially similar. For example, I have already noted that contact inhibition has been explained at times as the result of a specific adhesion which forms upon contact between the plasma membranes of two cells. This explanation has then been invoked to explain the regulation of growth and movement *in vivo*. We now see that specific adhesion is not the basis for contact inhibition. Given what seems to be the correct explanation for contact inhibition, i.e., differential adhesiveness, we have no evidence that the appropriate conditions of differential adhesiveness necessarily exist *in vivo*. We are left with little reason to believe that contact inhibition is a tissue culture manifestation of growth regulatory phenomena which commonly occur *in vivo*.

The abnormal conditions of tissue culture can be useful, however, in bringing out properties of cells which would not be detectable by the behavior of the cells in their normal environment. Thus, contact inhibition does not distinguish between normal cells of different types or from different species, but it does distinguish normal from malignant cells. Knowing what we do about the role of differential adhesiveness in contact inhibition, we can infer that the general adhesiveness of malignant cells is low, and this in turn indicates that substantial changes in membrane structure accompany the malignant transformation.

One of the more perplexing aspects of animal cell behavior in culture is the difficulty encountered in growing the cells at low population densities (Rubin, 1966a). Not only do the cells grow poorly at low population densities, but they become highly vacuolated and stellate-shaped and many of them degenerate. It might be tempting to relate the failure of small numbers of cells to grow in culture to such superficially similar *in vivo* phenomena as the requirement for the inoculation of large numbers of cells to obtain successful transplantation of most tumors from one animal to another. The failure of cells in small numbers to grow in culture, however, might arise from an artifactual situation totally unrelated to the reason for the requirement of large numbers of cells to obtain successful tumor transplants *in vivo*. Nevertheless, the population requirement for cell growth in culture could tell us something about the limits of animal cell response to stressful conditions and perhaps point the way to an analysis of important properties of these cells.

I shall present evidence which leads me to believe that the failure of small numbers of cells to grow in culture is indeed an artifact of tissue culture and that the abnormal conditions of culture make it possible to achieve the previously elusive objective of assaying for the structural and functional integrity of the component parts of the cell membrane.

What are the abnormalities of tissue culture which are relevant to understanding why small numbers of cells fail to grow there? For reasons we do not comprehend, normal cells must attach to a surface and spread thereon before they can multiply. The spreading of a cell on a tissue culture dish can reach prodigious proportions; a suspended spherical cell 20 μ in diameter will have a maximum height of 1 μ in the region of the nucleus after attaching and flattening out on the dish. If proteins are excluded from the medium, a microexudate is formed which is detected by ellipsometry as a monomolecular film extending from the periphery of the cell to cover an area 100 times the cross-sectional area covered by that part of the cell visible in the optical microscope (Rosenberg, 1960). The crude evidence that is available indicates that the microexudate is made up of protein and lipid and is more than likely an extension of the membranous portion of the cell itself.

When proteins are present in the medium, they themselves adsorb to the surface of the dish and form a monomolecular film. No increase in the thickness of the film is detected by ellipsometry when cells are spread on a dish already covered by an adsorbed layer of protein. Since ellipsometry measures only film thickness, however, it cannot be determined whether the microexudate fails to form in the presence of preadsorbed proteins, or whether it does form and simply displaces the proteins. It is possible to settle this question, however, by labeling the cellular proteins with radioactive amino acids and detecting adsorbed proteins of cellular origin by autoradiography (M. Balls and A. Rein, unpublished). The results of such experiments indicate that the microexudate is indeed formed by cells despite the presence of adsorbed proteins on the dish. Apparently, the attractiveness of cell surface macromolecules for the dish is greater than that of serum macromolecules for the dish.

What is the expected fate of membrane macromolecules adsorbed at the solid-liquid interface on the surface of a culture dish? The molecules are subjected to interfacial forces which distort and rupture weak bonds of the type responsible for the secondary and tertiary structure of proteins leading to their denaturation (Cheesman and Davies, 1954). Lipids and proteins are also associated with each other through weak bonds which would be disturbed or disrupted by interfacial tension. The greater the open space surrounding a cell, the wider is the latitude for spreading and denaturation of the membrane microexudate, and the greater is the strain on the cell. Ultimately we would anticipate a breakdown in the permeability barrier of the cell which would lead to degeneration and death of the cell.

If another cell is close by, however, the spreading microexudate of one cell soon encounters a sister microexudate from its neighbor of equal adhesiveness to the substratum. Unlike the preadsorbed proteins of the medium, the microexudate proteins can be continuously replaced. The promixity of other cells therefore might be expected to spare a cell the debilitating effect of excessive microexudate formation with the attendant membrane damage, and permit survival and growth of the cell.

If this picture is correct, the capacity of cells to initiate growth should be dependent on the density of the cell population per unit area of the surface of the dish, and independent of either the concentration of cells per unit volume of the medium or the total number of cells in the dish. This expectation can be tested by studying the growth rate of cells as a function of population density, total dish area, and volume of fluid medium. When this is done (Fig. 1), it is found that cell population density per unit area of surface is the critical parameter determining growth rate. Large changes in the volume of medium or in total numbers of cells per culture have little or no effect on the growth rates of the cells. Under the conditions of culture used in these experiments, however, there must be at least 2500 chicken fibroblasts per square

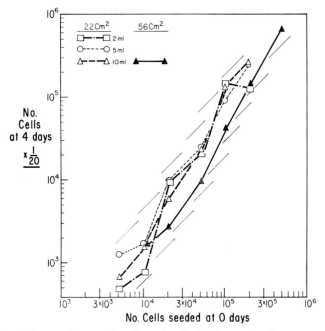

No. Cells seeded at 0 days

Fig. 1. Cell growth as a function of cell density and cell concentration. Chick embryo cells were seeded on plastic dishes 22 cm^2 or 56 cm^2 in floor surface area. The numbers of cells seeded are indicated on the abscissa. There were three groups of cultures in the 22-cm^2 dishes kept in either 2 ml, 5 ml, or 10 ml of medium. The cultures in the 56-cm^2 dishes were kept in 10 ml of medium. (The medium consisted of 4% calf serum, 1% chicken serum, 10% tryptose phosphate broth, and 85% mixture 199, with pH adjusted to about 7.5 with $NaHCO_3$.) The cultures were incubated at 37°C in a humidified incubator gassed with CO_2. At the end of 4 days of incubation they were suspended with trypsin and counted in a Coulter electronic counter.

The light, discontinuous lines, each with a slope of 1.0 are placed close to the experimental curves in such a way that the slope of each segment of the curves can be roughly estimated. If the growth rate were independent of the numbers of cells seeded, all the curves would have a slope of 1.0. The fact is that, except at the lowest and in some cases the highest cell numbers seeded, the curves have a slope greater than 1.0, indicating that the growth rate of cells increases with cell number seeded over a certain range.

Changing the amount of overlying fluid (i.e., varying the cell concentration per milliliter of medium) has little or no effect on the growth rate of the cells at most of the cell numbers tested. The area of the dish clearly has an effect, however. The rate of growth of a given number of cells on a 56-cm^2 dish is about the same as the rate of growth of less than half that number of cells on a 22-cm^2 dish. The results show that the critical parameter in determining the rate of cell growth is the population density of the cells per unit area of the floor surface of the dish.

centimeter of dish before the cells will grow at maximal rate. This cell density will be referred to as the critical density.

At the critical density, the cells after spreading on the dish cover only about $\frac{1}{50}$ of the surface area of the dish. This means that the average cell is on the order of 7 cell diameters distant from its neighbors. It might seem incredible that effects are produced over such distances on the surface of the dish if we were unaware of the existence of the microexudate which effectively extends the boundary of the cell far beyond its visible borders.

Demonstration of "Conditioning Factor"*

If the medium is harvested from cells growing at a density just above the critical level, it fails to enhance the growth of a separate population of cells seeded below the critical density. If the medium is obtained from cells growing at a density 10 times higher than the critical density, there is indeed enhancement of growth at a subcritical density of cells. The cells must be at 20 to 50 times the critical density, however, before they produce a medium of optimal enhancing effect, i.e., a medium which permit cells at a subcritical density to grow at a rare characteristic of cells growing at densities above the critical level.

These results suggest that the main growth-enhancing effect at cell densities just above the critical level is mediated by the equivalent of cell-to-cell contact along the surface of the dish, and not by free passage of material through the medium. When there is a very large excess of cells, however, a growth-enhancing substance can be detected in the medium. This substance will be referred to as "conditioning factor." I will refer to it as if it were a single substance, although I have no evidence that it is.

Conditioning factor not only allows cells at subcritical densities to grow at a maximal rate, but it prevents the morphological alterations usually seen at these densities in nonconditioned medium.

In effect, the conditioning factor allows cells at subcritical densities to take on the growth rate and healthy appearance of cells seeded at higher densities. I infer from these observations that the conditioning factor detectable in medium obtained from cultures of high cell densities is a solution of the same material which forms surface contacts between cells, and that this material permits growth of the cells at densities just above the critical level. In other words, I am suggesting that the condi-

* Rubin, 1966a.

tioning factor is made up of nothing less than the structural subunits of the cell membrane itself.

To hold with this point of view we have to revise the common picture of the cell membrane as the static sandwich-like structure seen in the electron microscope and designated the unit membrane (Robertson, 1964). It has already been suggested on other grounds that cellular membranes are made up of macromolecular lipoprotein complexes rather than of lipids and proteins in different phases (Gent et al., 1964; Tasaki and Singer, 1965; Green and Perdue, 1966). The novel func-tional aspect I should like to add to the macromolecular membrane theory, at least for the case of the plasma membrane, is that the macro

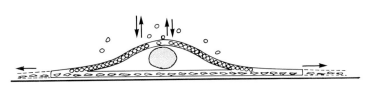

Fig. 2.   Anticipated fate of membrane macromolecules of spreading fibroblast under the dynamic macromolecular membrane model. The fibroblast attaches to the nega-tively charged dish and spreads there. The discontinuous lines represent the mono molecular microexudate film extending beyond the visible borders of the cell. The circles represent the intact macromolecular unit forming the cell membrane. They are distorted and denatured by interfacial tension at the surface of the dish beneath the cell and beyond its borders in the microexudate. They are also released into the medium unaltered in the form of conditioning factor, and can be replaced into the surface at any location on the cell.

molecular units are in a state of flux, constantly being released from and replaced into the membrane. This follows almost from first principles since the membrane units must be held in association with each other by weak bonds which will occasionally be broken by thermal energy. To a greater or lesser extent depending on the energy of association, some of these units will appear in the medium (Fig. 2).

Following this line of reasoning, we can anticipate that the condition ing factor has the properties of lipoprotein molecules, which are of course very large and notoriously unstable (Lindgren and Nichols, 1960). It is possible to study the size and stability of the conditioning factor by subjecting it to a variety of physical treatments and assaying its remaining biological activity.

It can be shown that the conditioning factor is very large since it can be concentrated by prolonged centrifugation at 50,000 $\times$ g. The pellet following such centrifugation has no activity but the fluid overlying the pellet does, indicating that the factor loses activity upon forced packing. On the whole, only about one-fourth of the total original activity is recovered after centrifugation, and all of it is in the fluid immediately overlying the pellet.

The conditioning factor is nondialyzable although there is some loss of activity in prolonged dialysis unless the salt concentration is kept low. It passes without retention over a Sephadex G-25 column. (Filtration on columns of higher porosity is complicated by dilution effects which interfere with detection of biological activity.) The findings indicate that the conditioning factor is either a large molecule or a large aggregate of smaller molecules.

It is also highly unstable. Its activity is destroyed by exposing it to a temperature of 56°C for 10 minutes, to sonic vibration for 10 minutes, or to slow stirring by a magnetic bar in the cold for 4 to 8 hours. It is extremely sensitive to increases in pH or salt concentration, losing activity quickly at room temperature when the pH is raised from the usual 7.6 to 8.5, or when the salt concentration is raised from the usual 0.14 M to a higher level of 0.8 M. The instability to physical treatments is in accord with the expectation that the conditioning factor is a macromolecule having a native configuration maintained by weak bonds. The conditioning factor is also inactivated by very low concentrations of surface active agents such as dextran sulfate (1 μg/ml) and lysolecithin (30 μg/ml) which are known to disrupt cell membranes.

The findings are consistent with the idea that the conditioning factor is a lipoprotein derived from the cell membrane. The crucial step in identifying the conditioning factor, however, is to isolate it and characterize it chemically. The main problem in establishing the chemical composition of the conditioning factor is that the common procedures for purifying macromolecules inactivate its biological activity. The efforts to purify it are being pursued, but in the meantime we have been examining the nature of macromolecules released from cells without regard to the biological activity of these molecules.

It is quite evident from our work that both proteins and lipids are indeed released from cells growing in culture. Similar findings had been made with red cells (Lovelock, 1954; Vandenheuvel, 1962). Chick fibroblasts maintained in the absence of serum release about 0.2 mg of protein per 10^7 cells in 24 hours. We have also identified a variety of phospholipids in the medium following incorporation of P^{32} into cellular phospholipids (J. Peterson, unpublished). The identification in the medium of lipids and proteins derived from cells provides at least the minimal material basis for the idea that the conditioning factor is a lipoprotein probably derived from the cell surface.

If we accept this tentative identification of the conditioning factor we may look upon its growth-enhancing effect as due to the replacement of structural subunits of the cell surface which have been lost through adsorption to the surface of the dish, or through release into the medium. The conditioning factor could then be considered a sealing substance which prevents the cell from becoming a leaky sieve after spreading on the dish. In accord with this idea, we have obtained evidence that small numbers of cells become leaky shortly after they attach to a tissue culture dish and that the leakage does not occur in the presence of conditioned medium (Rein and Rubin, unpublished). We have also found that small numbers of cells lose their capacity to grow within a few hours after spreading on a dish if kept in fresh medium during that time, even though conditioned medium is later substituted for the fresh medium. If the cells are kept in suspension during their sojourn in fresh medium, however, they maintain their capacity for growth in conditioned medium. This finding supports the view that the failure of small numbers of cells to grow is the result of damage to the membrane of the isolated, spreading cell produced by interfacial forces on the surface of the dish (Rein and Rubin, unpublished).

Conditioning of Medium by Rous Sarcoma Cells*

If the conditioning factor is indeed a derivative of the cell membrane, it should be markedly altered during the malignant transformation which alters so markedly the adhesiveness of the cell. The transformation of chicken cells in culture by infection with Rous sarcoma virus offers an excellent opportunity for testing a change in the conditioning factor, since a high proportion of normal chicken cells can be transformed to sarcoma cells with reasonable synchrony within a few days after infection. With this system it is possible to test the production of conditioning factor by normal and malignant cells derived from the same tissue of a single embryo.

* Rubin, 1966b.

When chicken cells are infected with RSV they remain normal in appearance for about 3 days, and during this time they condition the medium at least as well as do uninfected cells. Concurrently with their transformation, however, the cells desist from the production of a biologically active conditioning factor, and begin the release of material which *inhibits* the growth of small numbers of normal cells under the usual tissue culture conditions.

Investigation of the inhibitory factor has just begun. Like the conditioning factor it appears to be macromolecular, passing over a Sephadex G-25 column. Its production by transformed cells is variable, and sometimes with repeated transfer the cells start producing an effective conditioning factor again, although it may have different properties from that produced by normal cells.

The production of an inhibitory factor by freshly transformed Rous sarcoma cells is reflected in the difficulty one encounters in growing pure cultures of such cells even in large numbers. When the Rous sarcoma cells form a small minority of the population, however, and normal cells a majority, the Rous sarcoma cells grow at least as well as do the normal cells. If a small number of Rous sarcoma cells is cultivated in an active conditioned medium obtained from normal cells, the sarcoma cells grow at a respectable rate.

We infer from these observations that Rous sarcoma cells produce a substance which disrupts their own surface structure. This disruption interferes with growth of the cells spread on the dish where their membranes are subject to stress. When suspended in soft agar where there is less membrane distention, the Rous sarcoma cells grow more extensively than do the normal cells, and presumably the same is true in the whole animal. So, again, it is only through the artifact of tissue culture that we are able to measure cellular alterations quantitatively.

The question of the chemical nature of the inhibitory factor is entirely speculative. If we accept the assumption that it acts on the cell membrane, a surface-active agent would be the most likely candidate. Surface-active agents have been implicated previously in two types of cellular pathology following virus infection. In one case it has been found that lysophosphatides are produced in excess during infection with Sendai virus, and that these lysophosphatides cause hemolysis of red blood cells (Rebel *et al.*, 1962). If they can cause lysis of red blood cells, the lysophosphatides are probably also capable of disrupting the surface of the infected tissue cell and they might very well be responsible for death of the infected cell.

In the second case, evidence has been presented that phospholipids
produced during infection with Newcastle disease virus can induce the
formation of giant cells (Kohn, 1965). Since giant cells are multinucleated syncytia formed through the fusion of the plasma membranes
of two or more cells, we again have a case of membrane alteration produced by surface-active agents. It is possible that the production of
smaller amounts of surface-active agents by infected cells would disrupt
the cell membrane sufficiently to account for malignant behavior but
not enough to cause cell fusion or lysis.

General Discussion

The study of conditioned medium and its effect on the growth of
small numbers of cells has suggested a dynamic macromolecular model
of the cell membrane in constant flux with its internal and external
environment, and has provided us with what we believe to be a biological test for membrane function. We conclude that the arrest of conditioning factor production at the time of the malignant transformation,
and at the onset of release into the medium of an inhibitory factor,
reflects the production of material which disrupts the structure and
function of the membrane and accounts for the invasive character of
the malignant cell. These concepts must be considered only working
hypotheses at this time, but they offer us a self-consistent explanation of
certain aspects of cell behavior and growth. They also offer us the
promise of a fresh new method for investigating the problems of membranes and malignancy.

Can the ideas derived from studies in viral carcinogenesis be applied
to an understanding of chemical carcinogenesis? The latter is an area
of active work and speculation, but we again encounter a tendency to
hang theories of carcinogenesis on the molecule of the day. Thus, there
is much discussion of complexes formed between carcinogens and nucleic
acids, or carcinogens and proteins, depending on one's point of view
(Brookes and Lawley, 1964; Heidelberger, 1964). One particular approach which has not received much attention involves the possible
effect of chemical carcinogens on cellular membrane systems. The most
potent carcinogens, such as methylcholanthrene, the benzypyrenes, and
the dibenzanthracenes behave like lipids with regard to solubility, and
bear some structural similarity to cholesterol which is an important
component of animal cell membranes, and to steroids in general. On
theoretical grounds, Willmer (1961) has suggested that these polycyclic

aromatic hydrocarbons are likely to localize preferentially in membranes, and to exert their primary carcinogenic effect there. The difficulty preventing acceptance of this idea is its failure to explain how the alteration is perpetuated in progeny cells in the absence of the original carcinogenic agent itself.

We must ask again, is there any basis for assuming that an alteration in a cell's membrane can be reproduced in the absence of genic change? The best documented indication that this can occur has been described in the case of *Paramecium aurelia* (Beisson and Sonneborn, 1965). By grafting pieces of cortex of one paramecium onto a whole cell, a modified cortical pattern was produced and maintained through as many as 700 cell fissions, i.e., permanently. It was concluded that the "presence, location, orientation and shape of newly formed structures is determined by the cortical environment existing at the time of their development." Breeding experiments showed that there were no genic changes. It was also shown by the existence of normal as well as abnormal regions on the same cell that the cortical mutations were not due to failure of the genes to produce the requisite molecules. Nor were the mutations due to persisting differences in local concentrations of molecules since the regions of altered cortical organization persisted as they moved around the cell in successive cell generations. The conclusion we are forced to make from these observations is that the higher levels of organization of cortical units in the surface of *Paramecium* are determined by the arrangement of pre-existing units.

There is evidence among multicellular organisms that membrane structure can influence the prospective fate of cells although there is as yet no evidence that the membrane structure of metazoan cells predetermines a similar structure in progeny cells. Curtis (1962) has shown that transplantation of the cortex from the grey-crescent region of an uncleaved fertile amphibian egg to the ventral margin of a second egg induces a whole second embryonic axis. Transplantation of the underlying yolk cytoplasm has no effect. [Earlier work, however, indicated that a yolk gradient may be important in determining where the active organizing site of the cortex will be located (Dalcq and Pasteels, 1937).]

The suggestion arising from these studies is that the pre-existing pattern of the structures in which cell surface macromolecules occur determines the pattern of these structures in subsequent cell generations. In both cases the effects are produced in and by the outermost regions of the cell. The results recall the ideas of Paul Weiss (1962) who suggested that certain macromolecules with a hydrophilic group at one end and a hydrophobic group at the other would be arranged at an oil-water interface with each group buried in the medium appropriate to it. In the cell this would result in a certain arrangement of surface macromolecules depending on the types and quantities of these macromolecules present in the cell, and the conditions of the internal and external environments. This surface arrangement would then determine the selective permeability properties of the cell and the distribution of other cellular molecules, progressing concentrically into the interior of the cell (Fig. 3).

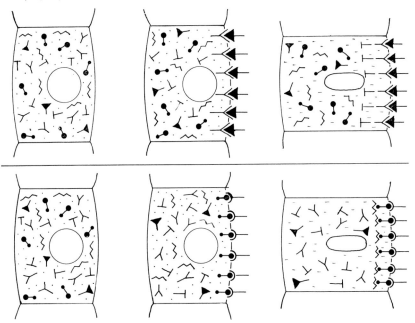

FIG. 3. "Molecular model of the induction of dichotomous differentiation among cells of the same kind" (Weiss, 1962). The presence of certain molecules in the environment of a cell can affect the distribution of cell surface macromolecules and through them the distribution of intracellular molecules, thereby determining the differentiative fate of the cell.

As a model for determining the distribution of molecules in complex mixtures, Weiss describes the crystallization of hydroxylapatite on collagen fibrils (Fig. 4). The deposition always begins at the 640 Å repeat period of collagen (Glimcher, 1959). If the collagen fibril is reconstituted in such a way as to have a repeat period other than 640 Å no crystal nucleation occurs. A specific steric arrangement of collagen must therefore be obtained before a particular higher order of complexity can be developed.

Perhaps more germane to the subject of this paper is the finding that the physical thickness and bulk properties of a substratum influence its

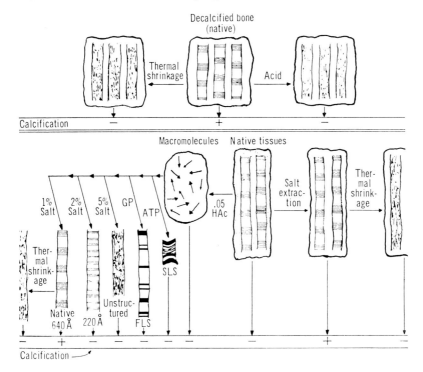

FIG. 4. "Diagram summarizing the success (+) or failure (—) of calcification of different varieties of collagen in metastable solutions of calcium phosphate." (Adapted by Weiss, 1962, from Glimcher, 1959.) Crystal nucleation of metastable calcium phosphate on collagen occurs only when the collagen has polymerized into fibrils with the native 640-Å repeat period. The native collagen when present in ordinary connective tissue ("native tissue") does not, of course, become calcified *in vivo* but does so *in vitro*, indicating that the microenvironment plays a crucial role in this process in addition to the role played by the arrangement of collagen molecules as expressed in their periodicity.

interaction with cells (Rosenberg, 1962). Rosenberg deposited varying numbers of fatty acid monolayers at constant surface pressure on solid bases of different compositions. He found that the time courses for attachment and for spreading varied with the number of fatty acid monolayers and with the type of material used in the base. I interpret these results to signify that the material used as base influences the configuration and distribution of fatty acids in the first monolayer, which in turn influences the succeeding monolayers. In this way structural effects can be propagated through many layers.

It remains to be seen, of course, whether similar effects influence either the distribution of molecules as new surface materials are laid down in cells, or can account for the close-in interactions of cells in the induction of differentiation. The results, however, tempt one strongly to suggest an explanation for the phenomenon of plastic film carcinogenesis (Oppenheimer *et al.,* 1955). This is the remarkable case in which cancer can be induced by simply inserting a film of inert material into tissue. As long as the material is in a continuous sheet and not in the form of a perforated film or a powder, a relatively high incidence of cancer is induced (Alexander and Horning, 1958). It is likely that cancer is in this case the consequence of the nature of the physical surface encountered by the cell. I am tempted to conclude that the distribution of molecules in the surface of the cell is affected by the strange substratum in contact with the cells in a manner analogous to the Rosenberg effects of base layer materials on overlying fatty acid monolayers.

The finding of perpetuated membrane alterations in cells and propagated monolayer effects in model systems lends credibility and substance to the idea that the malignant transformation arises from a heritable disruption in the distribution and configuration of cell surface macromolecules. Once the cell surface pattern is altered radically enough, it can no longer be restored to normal, and the cell becomes progressively more malignant as the pattern increasingly approaches a random distribution of molecules.

This view of the malignant transformation leads to two distinct predictions about the nature of the malignant cell—that there is no genic change, and that there is an inheritable alteration in the arrangement or the lack of arrangement of macromolecules in the surface of the cell. Techniques of cell hybridization and nuclear transplantation may be useful in determining whether or not genic changes have occurred. The use of conditioning factors and related materials from normal and malignant cells should give us some insight into the question of inheritable cell surface alterations. If my interpretation of its nature is correct, the conditioning factor is especially attractive material for analysis of certain higher order phenomena because it provides a biological test for complex structural subunits of the cell, and fills the yawning gap for analytical tools between the cell and the molecule.

Summary

I have presented evidence to support the proposition that contact inhibition among normal cells results from the greater adhesiveness of the cells to the tissue culture substrate than to each other. The loss of contact inhibition in malignant cells therefore can be attributed mainly to a loss of adhesiveness to the culture dish. This explanation suggests the occurrence of marked changes in the plasma membrane of malignant cells. It is at variance with the popular notion that the loss of contact inhibition is due to a change in some specific recognition mechanism which occurs among normal cells.

The failure of small numbers of cells in culture to grow is attributed to the denaturation of the components of their plasma membranes at the surface of the culture dish. Conditioned medium obtained from cultures of large numbers of cells enhances the growth of small numbers of cells. The active factor in conditioned medium is large and unstable. Reasons have been given for believing it to be a structural unit of the cell membrane itself which acts by maintaining the integrity of the membranes of cells cultured in small numbers.

From these and other observations, I have developed a rough functional model of the plasma membrane as a structure consisting of lipoprotein subunits held loosely in place and in equilibrium with the internal and external environment. This model provides great flexibility to the membrane and great sensitivity for response to external conditions.

When cells undergo the malignant transformation following infection with Rous sarcoma virus, they stop producing active conditioning factor and start producing a substance which inhibits the growth of cells spread on a solid substrate. I have speculated that the inhibitory substance produced by the cells undergoing transformation is a surface-active agent which disrupts the arrangement of macromolecules in the plasma membrane.

I have discussed Willmer's argument (1961) that the carcinogenic polycyclic aromatic hydrocarbons are most likely, because of their steriodal configuration and solubility properties, to localize in membranes. This seems a perfectly logical assumption and it would be eminently reasonable to conclude that the primary carcinogenic effect is exerted here by disruption of membrane structure. The main obstacle to acceptance of this mechanism for chemical carcinogenesis is its failure to explain how the disrupted structure is maintained in progeny cells once the carcinogen is diluted out. I have argued that changes in the arrangement of membrane molecules can be perpetuated without genic change because the arrangement of molecules in a growing membrane depends on the pre-existing arrangement of the molecules already present in the membrane. The strongest support for this idea comes from the study of the distribution of cortical granules in *Paramecium*, but supporting evidence that membrane structure influences the fate of lines of cells is adduced from higher organisms.

I suggest that one of the most important problems for metazoan biologists is to find appropriate means for determining whether or not membrane changes can be perpetuated hereditarily without genic change. If they can, it would be of prime importance to know how the patterns can be modified hereditarily, and what role such modifications play in differentiation and in malignancy.

ACKNOWLEDGMENT

These investigations were supported by research grants CA 04774 and CA 05619 from the National Cancer Institute, Public Health Service.

REFERENCES

ABERCROMBIE, M., HEAYSMAN, J., AND KARTHAUSER, H. (1957). Social behavior of cells in tissue culture. III. Mutual influence of sarcoma cells and fibroblasts. *Exptl. Cell Res.* **13,** 276–291.

ALEXANDER, P., AND HORNING, E. S. (1958). Observations on the Oppenheimer method of inducing tumours by subcutaneous implantation of plastic films. *In* "Carcinogenesis, Mechanisms of Action," pp. 12–22. Little, Brown, Boston, Massachusetts.

BEISSON, J., AND SONNEBORN, T. M. (1965). Cytoplasmic inheritance of the organization of the cell cortex in *Paramecium aurelia. Proc. Natl. Acad. Sci. U.S.* **35,** 275–282.

BROOKES, P., AND LAWLEY, P. D. (1964). Reactions of some mutagenic and carcinogenic compounds with nucleic acids. *J. Cellular Comp. Physiol.* **64,** Suppl. 1, 111–128.

CARTER, S. B. (1965). Principles of cell motility: The direction of cell movement and cancer invasion. *Nature* **208,** 1183–1187.

CHEESMAN, D. G., AND DAVIES, J. T. (1954). Physicochemical and biological aspects of proteins at interfaces. *Advan. Protein Chem.* **9,** 440–498.

CURTIS, A. S. G. (1962). Morphogenetic interactions before gastrulation in the amphibian, *Xenopus laevis*—the cortical field. *J. Embryol. Exptl. Morphol.* **10,** 410–422.

DALCQ, A., AND PASTEELS, J. (1937). Une conception nouvelle des bases physiologique de la morphogénèse. *Arch. Biol. (Liége)* **48,** 669–710.

GENT, W. L. G., GRIGSON, N. A., GAMMACK, D. B., AND RAPER, J. H. (1964). The lipid-protein unit in myelin. *Nature* **204,** 553–555.

GLIMCHER, M. J. (1959). Molecular biology of mineralized tissues with particular reference to bone. *In* "Biophysical Science—A Study Program" (J. L. Oncley, F. O. Schmitt, R. C. Williams, M. D. Rosenberg, and R. H. Bolt, eds.), pp. 359–393. Wiley, New York.

GREEN, D. E., AND PERDUE, J. F. (1966). Membranes as expressions of repeating units. *Proc. Natl. Acad. Sci. U.S.* **55,** 1295–1302.

HEIDELBERGER, C. (1964). Studies on the molecular mechanism of hydrocarbon carcinogenesis. *J. Cellular Comp. Physiol.* **64,** Suppl. 1, 129–148.

KOHN, A. (1965). Polykaryocytosis induced by Newcastle disease virus in monolayers of animal cells. *Virology* **26,** 228–245.

LINDGREN, F., AND NICHOLS, A. V. (1960). Structure and function of human serum lipoproteins. *In* "The Plasma Proteins" (F. Putnam, ed.), pp. 1–58. Academic Press, New York.

LOVELOCK, J. E. (1954). Physical instability and thermal shock in red cells. *Nature* **173,** 659–661.

OPPENHEIMER, B. S., OPPENHEIMER, E. T., DANISHEFSKY, I., Stout, A. P., and Eirich, F. R. (1955). Further studies on polymers as carcinogenic agents in animals. *Cancer Res.* **15,** 333–340.

REBEL, G., FONTANGES, R., AND COLOBERT, L. (1962). Nature lipoidique des substances responsables de l'activite hemolytique de myxovirus para influenza I (virus Sendai). *Ann. Inst. Pasteur* **102,** 137–152.

ROBERTSON, J. D. (1964). Unit membranes: A review with recent new studies of experimental alterations and a new subunit structure in synaptic membranes. *In* "Cellular Membranes in Development" (M. Locke, ed.), pp. 1–81. Academic Press, New York.

ROSENBERG, M. D. (1960). Microexudates from cells grown in tissue culture. *Biophys. J.* **1,** 137–159.

ROSENBERG, M. D. (1962). Long range interactions between cell and substratum. *Proc. Natl. Acad. Sci. U.S.* **48,** 1342–1349.

RUBIN, H. (1966a). A substance in conditioned medium which enhances the growth of small numbers of chick embryo cells. *Exptl. Cell Res.* **41,** 138–148.

RUBIN, H. (1966b). The inhibition of chick embryo cell growth by medium obtained from cultures of Rous sarcoma cells. *Exptl. Cell Res.* **41,** 149–161.

RUBIN, H., FANSHIER, L., CORNELIUS, A., AND HUGHES, W. (1962). Tolerance and immunity after congenital and contact infection with an avian leukosis virus. *Virology* **17,** 143–156.

STRONG, L. C. (1958). Genetic concept for the origin of cancer: Historical review. *Ann. N. Y. Acad. Sci.* **71,** 810–838.

TASAKI, I., AND SINGER, I. (1965). A macromolecular approach to the excitable membrane. *J. Cellular Comp. Physiol.* **66,** 137–146.

VANDENHEUVEL, F. A. (1962). The origin, metabolism and structure of normal human serum lipoproteins. *Can. J. Biochem. Physiol.* **40,** 1299–1326.

WEISS, P. (1962). From cell to molecule. *In* "The Molecular Control of Cellular Activity" (J. M. Allen, ed.), pp. 1–72. McGraw-Hill, New York.

WILLMER, E. N. (1961). Steroids and cell surfaces. *Biol. Rev. Cambridge Phil. Soc.* **36,** 368–398.

Starting Points for Research in the Ontogeny of Behavior

MARCUS JACOBSON

Department of Biological Sciences, Purdue University, Lafayette, Indiana

Many of the experimental methods used in the past have proved to be of inadequate power to resolve the primary mechanisms of behavior. At the very lowest power of resolution are the methods of eliciting reflexes in response to tactile or other stimulation of the embryo or fetus. Little can be inferred about the primary causes of behavior from observing such remote effects as reflex movements. The strategy of experiments of this kind has been to compile a timetable of the behavioral repertoire of embryos, and if possible, to correlate this with the histological appearance of the nervous system during its development and maturation. This was a reasonable starting point at the time when neurons were regarded only as units with all-or-none activity, and when the reflex arc was thought to be the module from which all neuronal circuits were constructed and from which all behavior emerged. This conception of the nervous system has gradually had to be enlarged to take into account the evidence of graded electrical activity in dendrites (Grundfest, 1957, 1958; Bullock, 1959a), of the delicate gradations of neuronal activity which result from synaptic excitatory and inhibitory interaction (Eccles, 1964), and of the patterned spontaneous activity which occurs in some neurons regardless of input (Adrian, 1931; Hagiwara and Watanabe, 1956; Bullock, 1959b, 1961; Strumwasser, 1965).

The period of greatest vogue for cataloging the reflex abilities of embryos (Coghill, 1929, 1940; Tracy, 1926; Orr and Windle, 1934; Kuo, 1932, 1938, 1939; Tuge, 1937; Windle, 1940, 1944, 1950) was clouded by the controversy about the order in which reflexes developed (summarized by Windle, 1940; Hooker, 1942, 1952, 1958; Hamburger, 1963). Coghill's theory that local reflexes were individuated out of a total pattern was derived mainly from his observations of the ontogeny of reflex

behavior of salamanders (Coghill, 1929, 1940). Evidence that quite localized reflexes were the first to appear in the mammalian fetus (Windle,
1940, 1944) cast doubt on the universality of Coghill's theory. Holtzer
and Kamrin (1956) have questioned the validity of Coghill's theory, even
in the salamander. They found that brachial segments of the spinal
cord of the larval salamander developed normally and mediated normal
limb reflexes even when totally isolated from the rest of the nervous
system.

In spite of skillful histological studies of the developing nervous system, very little anatomical evidence has been found to support the
concept of individuation of reflexes from a total pattern. Seeking
correlations between the structure and functions of neurons remains
one of the major tasks of neurobiology, a task made more rewarding but
certainly not easier by the use of electron microscopy. The correlations
that have been made between the anatomical maturity and the reflex
activity of the developing nervous system are fairly simple. For example,
the onset of reflexes has been correlated with the completion of the reflex
arc from cutaneous sensory receptors through the central nervous system
to the skeletal muscles (Coghill, 1929; Windle and Orr, 1934; Youngstrom, 1938; Windle, 1940, 1944; Hogg, 1941; Harris and Whiting, 1954;
Whiting, 1955; Hamburger, 1964; Humphrey, 1964). Once the orderly
connection of neurons into a reflex arc has been demonstrated histo-
logically and functionally, the precise chronology of its development,
which mainly interested Coghill, is of secondary importance to the
question of the nature of the forces that ordered the neurons to form
a reflex arc.

As starting points for a program of research into the ontogeny of
behavior it seems important to identify early stages in the causal chain
leading to mature behavior. The difficulty here is knowing what to look
for, and having found something, to decide where it fits into the causal
chain. Too often in the past, explanations of the ontogeny of behavior
have been given in terms of phenomena which are secondary effects far
removed from their primary causes. The point of departure which I
have chosen is the conclusion that the development of the nervous system
and of embryonic behavior is the result of developmental processes
which may be modified only to a very limited extent by experience and
learning. The evidence for this contention has been provided in several
papers of Weiss (1936, 1941, 1952, 1965) and Sperry (1945b, 1951a,b,
1963, 1965). Even if their conclusion is only partly true, it will have
served the important purpose of turning attention to the genetic mechanisms responsible for ordering neurons into functional assemblies.

Without becoming dogmatic it is difficult to draw up a list of investigations which are close to the core of the problem of the ontogeny of behavior, but the following seem to be worth including. (1) Investigating the mechanisms which play a part in the formation of neuronal connections. Determining the nature and development of neuronal specificity and the part it may play in the selection of orderly connections by developing and regenerating neurons. (2) Discovering the factors which determine and regulate the intrinsic excitatory state of the neuron. This includes the regulation of synthesizing processes and growth of neurons and the development of their synaptic and electrical mechanisms. (3) Detecting the molecular events that are involved in the storage, transfer, and retrieval of information concerning innate and learned activity in the neurons. Determining whether, or to what extent, the information is coded as a unique macromolecule for each kind of behavior, or whether the information consists of nonspecific changes of excitability and connectivity distributed in a specific pattern of neurons for each form of behavior.

Electrical Activity of Neurons during Maturation

Electrical recordings from the developing nervous system can give important information about the time of onset of neuronal activity during development, about ontogenetic changes in the electrical activity of neurons, and can be used to test when and how functional connections are formed during the development of the nervous system. Electrical methods can sometimes provide a simple and direct indication of when a developing structure becomes functional. An illustration of this is the success of electrical recording in demonstrating that developing nerve fibers can conduct impulses before they become myelinated (Ulett et al., 1944; Del Castillo and Vizoso, 1953), thus solving a problem that could not be settled on anatomical evidence alone (Tilney and Casamajor, 1924; Langworthy, 1929; Angulo y Gonzalez, 1929; Windle et al., 1934).

Methods of recording the integrated activity of a large population of neurons in a volume of brain by means of large electrodes has yielded very meager information about the functions and development of the nervous system (Jasper et al., 1937; Peters et al., 1950, 1958; Crain, 1952; Ellingson and Wilcott, 1960; Crescitelli and Nilsson, 1966). This is largely because it has not proved possible to identify the origin of the components of the complex changes of potential which have been recorded. Single unit recording with microelectrodes has proved to be the most reliable method of investigating the functional characteristics of neurons because it has the great advantage of precise localization of the origin of the recorded activity (Frank, 1959). We do not know, however, what kind of information has been lost by selecting the activity of one neuron from the total pattern which is distributed among thousands or millions of neurons even in the simplest kind of behavior. Single unit analysis tends to select the invariant or universal properties of classes of neurons and to discard information about the great variations that must occur in the activity of large numbers of neurons to produce the variabil- ity so often observed in behavior. Single unit recording from the develop- ing nervous system is a very recent development. No one has yet been able to identify the first electrical or secretory activity of the young neuron. We are still largely ignorant of the processes leading to the mature elec- trical activity of neurons. I suspect that extracellular microelectrode recording from immature neurons will prove very rewarding in mapping the pattern of connections as they develop. Intracellular recording from immature neurons has shown maturational changes in the excitatory (EPSP) and inhibitory postsynaptic potentials (IPSP) (Naka, 1964a,b; Purpura *et al.,* 1960, 1964, 1965). In general, the maturational changes recorded intracellularly from immature spinal motoneurons (Naka, 1964a,b) and from immature neocortical neurons of the cat (Purpura *et al.,* 1965) are similar, although the electrical properties of spinal motoneurons mature in the last few weeks before birth while the maturation of neocortical neurons is delayed and occurs during the first month after birth. Maturation of the spike-generating mechanism in spinal motoneurons of the cat is completed by the late prenatal stage, but maturation of the EPSP is delayed until the last days of prenatal life (Naka, 1964a). Intracellular records from immature spinal moto- neurons of the cat fetus show well-developed inhibition via recurrent collaterals and via Renshaw cells 2 to 3 weeks before birth (Naka, 1964b). The well-known fatigability of responses evoked by repetitive stimulation of immature neurons is probably the result of the rapid development of inhibition which is very marked in immature spinal and cortical neurons (Naka, 1964a,b; Purpura, 1961; Purpura *et al.,* 1965). Progressive shortening of the initially long latencies and long durations of evoked EPSP's and IPSP's which have been recorded in immature spinal cord and brain has been attributed to an increase in conduction velocity, increasing synchronization, and increase in the rate of release of transmitters as maturation proceeds (Skoglund, 1960; Marty and

Scherrer, 1964; Naka, 1964a,b; Purpura *et al.*, 1964, 1965). Slowness of EPSP's of immature cortical neurons may be related to the predominance of axodendritic synapses prior to the third postnatal week, after which axosomatic synapses increase and the EPSP's become faster (Voeller *et al.*, 1963; Purpura *et al.*, 1965). Spontaneous potentials which have been recorded intracellularly from immature neocortical neurons of the cat show considerable variation in prepotential, time course, and voltage (Purpura *et al.*, 1965). This instability of the spike-generating mechanism in immature neurons has not been explained, but could be due to changes occurring during the maturation of intraneuronal mechanisms maintaining an excitatory state. Cell injury is an unlikely cause of the instability, as a steady resting potential was maintained during recording.

The importance of continuous activity in the nervous system in the absence of external stimulation is now fully appreciated, although this was not true in the recent past when many neurophysiological experiments were performed in animals in which spontaneous neuronal firing was reduced or abolished by deep anesthesia. Spontaneous activity has been recorded mainly in sensory systems (for review see Granit, 1955), and from spinal internuncial, corticoreticular, and hippocampal neurons (Amassian and Devito, 1954; Frank and Fuortes, 1956; Hunt and Kuno, 1959; Kandel and Spencer, 1961). Possible mechanisms which may result in spontaneous repetitive firing of neurons are the prolonged action of transmitter or the intraneuronal maintenance of an excitatory state (Kandel and Spencer, 1961; Eccles, 1964). In contrast with the activity normally recorded continuously from sensory and internuncial neurons, motoneurons normally do not fire action potentials when they are at rest, but become active only when stimulated trans-synaptically or antidromically. For this reason it is difficult to accept the suggestion that early repetitive somatic movements in the chick embryo may be due to spontaneous bursts of action potentials from spinal motoneurons (Hamburger *et al.*, 1965). I suspect that these movements may arise from spontaneous activity in interneurons rather than in spinal motoneurons, but this needs to be confirmed by microelectrode recording from the spinal cord of the chick embryo.

The function of an assembly of neurons in which the connections have been microprecisely determined during development need not be invariant. Variations in neuronal excitability could result from a variety of causes such as changes in the endogenous level of excitability or as the result of the action of inhibitory or excitatory synaptic transmitters

(Eccles, 1964), or from electrical interaction between overlapping dendrites (Grinnell, 1966; Nelson, 1966). These might result in changes of the threshold at which single or repetitive firing occurs, or in changes of the rate of spontaneous firing. An example of how changes in the rate of spontaneous firing within a prewired neuronal circuit can affect behavior is provided by studies of the motoneurons in the thoracic ganglia of the cockroach (Horridge, 1962, 1964). Spontaneous activity in these motoneurons sets the posture of the legs and alterations of the relative frequency of firing of the neurons to various leg muscles result in new postural settings. Horridge (1962) discovered that a leg connected to an isolated thoracic ganglion can be trained to adopt a particular posture by giving the limb an electric shock when it was held in any other posture, and it has been found that during training a sustained increase occurred in the frequency of the spontaneous firing in the neurons which produce the trained posture (Horridge, 1964; Hoyle, 1965).

The ways in which the frequency of firing of spontaneously active neurons is regulated either by endogenous or exogenous factors are not understood. It is worth speculating, however, whether or not the patterning of spontaneous discharge could be regulated during development to produce some kind of innate behavior. So much attention has been paid to the ontogeny of reflex behavior that behavior arising from spontaneous firing of neurons has largely been overlooked. Hamburger and his associates have drawn attention to the periodic movements of the head and trunk which start in the $3\frac{1}{2}$–4-day chick embryo soon after the motor nerves have made contact with muscles, and have suggested that these movements are produced by bursts of spontaneous activity in the motoneurons (Hamburger and Balaban, 1963; Hamburger et al., 1965). They suggest that repetitive movements in the chick embryo may become modified and directed at new goals, for example, pecking through the shell at hatching or movements involved in social or sexual displays in adult chickens. Gobbling and strutting in the turkey may originate from periodic discharge of neurons starting in the embryo (Schleidt, 1964). The original suggestion that the periodicity of spontaneous movements might persist and determine the general level of motor activity in the adult was made by Tracy (1926) from his observations of spontaneous movements in fish embryos.

One can conceive of spontaneous neuronal activity being regulated in a variety of ways concerned with adjusting the ionic equilibrium across the neuronal membrane and by regulating the production or destruction of inhibitory and excitatory synaptic transmitters. Perhaps activation or repression of gene loci controlling membrane permeability and active transport may be a means of regulating the level of excitability of neurons, but without any experimental evidence this is simply a guess.

Effects of Growth Factors and Hormones on Neuronal Maturation

There is considerable evidence of growth-promoting substances which select particular kinds of neurons at critical phases of their development. A protein nerve growth factor (NGF) specifically controls the differentiation and growth of embryonic sympathetic ganglion cells and dorsal root ganglion cells (Levi-Montalcini, 1964a,b; Levi-Montalcini *et al.*, 1964). Antiserum to NGF destroys these ganglion cells if given to rats in the prenatal or neonatal period, but has no effect on mature ganglion cells. The origin of NGF is not known: although it is secreted by the salivary glands it is not formed by them, and it has been found in the blood plasma. NGF increases RNA and protein synthesis and appears to have effects similar to those of pituitary growth hormone, testosterone, thyroid, and other anabolic hormones. Inhibitors of protein and RNA synthesis such as puromycin and actinomycin inhibit the action of NGF as well as the actions of anabolic hormones. Perhaps the action of NGF is like that of testosterone, to stimulate DNA-dependent RNA polymerase (Frieden, 1964). These substances, however, select specific target cells and the mechanism of their specificity at the cellular level remains to be explained.

A single injection of testosterone given to female or castrated male rats within the first few hours after birth results in male sexual behavior at maturity (Segal and Johnson, 1959; Harris and Levine, 1962, 1965; Grady *et al.*, 1965). Harris and Levine (1965) have postulated that prior to a critical period in the development of mammals the central nervous structures controlling sexual behavior in both males and females are undifferentiated, but are of the female type. During this critical phase testosterone from the testes acts on the brain to determine that subsequent sexual behavior is of the male type, while female sexual behavior ensues in the absence of testosterone. The target cells for this action of testosterone are probably in the hypothalamus (Harris and Levine, 1965), but in addition, granule cells of the hippocampus and pyramidal cells in Ammon's horn bind selectively with tritiated testosterone (Altman and Das, 1965b).

The effect of thyroid hormones on the maturation of the nervous system is well known and has recently been reviewed by Eayrs (1960). As a rule, thyroid hormones stimulate neuronal maturation: for example, thyroid implanted in the fourth ventricle stimulates early maturation of the neurons in the abducens nucleus, resulting in premature maturation of the lid-closure reflex (Kollros, 1942). Thyroxine has a specific action on Mauthner's neurons in amphibians, causing them to regress during metamorphosis. Local application of thyroxine to the medulla of frog tadpoles results in premature regression of Mauthner's neurons and an increase in size of the surrounding neurons (Weiss and Rosetti, 1951). The nature of this kind of neuronal specificity is unknown.

Growth hormone administered to pregnant rats results in a remarkable neuronal hyperplasia in the fetuses. The brain of the fetus shows from 10 to 20% increase in weight, DNA content, cortical cell density, number and length of cortical dendrites, and in the ratio of neurons to glia (Zamenhoff, 1942; Clendinnen and Eayrs, 1961; Zamenhoff *et al.*, 1966). The growth hormone is effective only during the period of proliferation of matrix cells, which in the rat brain continues into the early neonatal period (Altman and Das, 1965a,b). The functional results of the increase in the number of neurons and probably also in the number of neuronal connections is not entirely clear. The offspring of rats treated with growth hormone during pregnancy showed a 40% increase in the retention of a conditioned response compared with a control group of normal rats (Block and Essman, 1965).

Effects of Function on Neuronal Maturation

No definite answer is yet possible to the question of whether or not maturation of neurons is dependent on, or influenced by, function. The complex inhibitory and excitatory interactions which develop in the spinal cord of the cat before birth (Naka, 1964a,b) are only potentially functional in the fetus and may be regarded as developing with forward reference to postnatal function. Neonatal experience would seem most likely to intervene in the maturation of neocortical neurons which occurs during the first weeks following birth. Purpura and Housepian (1961), however, have shown that a slab of immature neocortex of the cat isolated from the rest of the brain continues normal anatomical and electrical maturation. The maturation of the visual pathways and visual cortex also do not seem to require prenatal stimulation. In the newborn kitten which has no patterned visual experience, connections between the retina and geniculate nucleus (Wiesel and Hubel, 1963a), and between the retina and striate cortex, are fully ordered both retinotopically and functionally in the manner found in the adult cat (Hubel and Wiesel, 1963a).

If newborn kittens are deprived of patterned vision in one eye for 2 to 3 months, no defect in the concentric organization of receptive fields can be recorded from the lateral geniculate nucleus even though geniculate cells show moderate or severe signs of atrophy (Wiesel and Hubel, 1963a). The number of striate cortical cells which can be driven binocularly from the deprived eye is very greatly reduced, however, and receptive field abnormalities are found in the small percentage of cells still driven from the deprived eye (Wiesel and Hubel, 1963b). Since retinostriate connections are normally formed in the cat before birth, the effect of monocular visual deprivation after birth seems to be to break down existing connections rather than to prevent their normal formation. The matter is greatly complicated, however, by the finding that if both eyes are closed by lid suture at birth, the damage caused to retinocortical connections is less than the damage caused by monocular visual deprivation (Wiesel and Hubel, 1965a). This suggests that the effect may be due to some kind of interaction in the cortex between the optic fibers from the two eyes. The effect is permanent since very minimal recovery is shown even months after the eyes have been opened following a period of neonatal visual deprivation (Wiesel and Hubel, 1965b).

The question of how much of the circuitry of the visual system is prewired during development and the extent to which it may be modified by experience is crucial to any understanding of the ontogeny of behavior. There is a wealth of evidence summarized by Sperry (1951a,b, 1963, 1965) that the formation of specific neuronal connections in the visual system of fishes and amphibians cannot be altered by training, and that the maladaptive behavior resulting from rotation of the eye persists indefinitely in spite of experience. One should also consider the evidence regarding the atrophic effects of disuse and the effects of use in maintaining the integrity of neurons and perhaps also of the connections between them (Hydén, 1943, 1960; Riesen, 1961; Mendelson and Ervin, 1962; Sharpless, 1964; Gyllensten et al., 1965). These changes, however, have not been shown to affect the way in which neurons become connected together and at present we cannot ascribe the development of a single neuronal circuit to the action of use and experience.

Use and disuse may produce alterations within prewired arrays of neurons, but the evidence is overwhelmingly in favor of the view that neuronal connections concerned with quite specific and complete behavior patterns are genetically determined and cannot be influenced by stimulation, experience, or learning. Localized destruction of a part of the forebrain in the male stickleback results in conversion of normal aggressive, sexual and parental behavior into bizarre forms of behavior (Segaar, 1962, 1965). The abnormal behavior which occurs during regeneration of the missing part of the brain has no permanent effect, however, and normal behavior is fully restored following regeneration. Self-stimulation of the fetus by its own movements, a kind of sensory feedback, has been suggested as a factor causing maturation of fetal behavior (Lehrman, 1953; Schneirla, 1956; Gottlieb and Kuo, 1965). There is no experimental support of this thesis, however, and some evidence against it (Oppenheim, 1956). It has frequently been pointed out that the intensity and variety of stimulation to which the embryo or fetus is subject would appear to be too limited to play any role in the ontogeny of behavior. The limited learning capacity of embryos (Yerkes, 1903; Burnett, 1912; Moore and Welch, 1940; Munn, 1940; Hunt, 1949; Carmichael, 1951) is in very sharp contrast with their rich repertoire of innate behavior.

The danger of losing sight of the total pattern of neuronal activity giving rise to behavior is greatest when techniques of very high resolving power and selectivity are used to study the molecular mechanisms in neurons. Even the simplest kinds of behavior result from activity distributed in a population, usually heterogeneous, of thousands or millions of neurons and perhaps also of glia. Therefore, one should appreciate the limitations of methods of detecting molecular changes either in a single neuron or in a bulked sample of brain. In searching for a molecular unit of behavior or of memory, we may be in danger of substituting the banality of molecules for the banality of reflexes. Even the very sophisticated experiments of Hydén and his collaborators (Hydén, 1943; Hydén and Egyhazi, 1962, 1964; Hydén and Lange, 1965) are not above the criticism that their results have frequently been overinterpreted to show specific changes in neurons which are more likely to be a nonspecific result of neuronal activity and which need not be related to any specific kind of behavior or learning. The effect of neuronal activity lasting several days resulting in increased RNA (Hydén, 1943; Edström and Eichner, 1958; Hydén, 1960; Hydén and Pigón, 1960; Hydén and Egyhazi, 1964; W. E. Watson, 1965) and increase in protein synthesis

(Hydén, 1943; Altman, 1963) is now well established. However, the rapid increase in RNA in neurons after stimulation described by Hydén (1943) has not been confirmed (Liu *et al.*, 1950; Bertram and Barr, 1949; Grampp and Edström, 1963; W. E. Watson, 1965). Hydén and Egyhazi (1962, 1964) found changes in adenine-uracil ratios in RNA in Deiter's neurons following their activity in a specific task such as learning to balance on a wire, but found no change in the same neurons stimulated by passively tumbling the rats. There is no evidence that the Deiter's neurons received the same amount of stimulation in the learning and in the control experiments. A relationship between the learning curve and the RNA of cortical neurons active during learning of transfer of handedness in rats was found by Hydén and Lange (1965). Adenine–uracil-rich RNA, of the messenger RNA type, was formed during the third to fifth day of learning while the learning curve was rising. From the ninth to tenth day the learning curve reached a plateau. At the same time the adenine–uracil-rich RNA disappeared and guanine–cytosine-rich RNA of the ribosomal type appeared. They concluded that the ribosomal type of RNA "takes over the long-term synthesis of proteins necessary to sustain neural function of the new behavior." The specificity of these changes in RNA and protein synthesis is still not clear, and additional evidence will be required to decide whether coding of information specific to the learned behavior occurs or whether the synthesizing activity merely reflects an enhancement of the functional activity of the neuron. Bonner (1964) has suggested that neuronal stimulation results in derepression of DNA. This could conceivably result in neuronal growth or synthesis of transmitters, but it is difficult to conceive how it could be made specific for every kind of learning or memory unless a large part of the genome was devoted to this function.

Memory and learning as well as instinctive behavior (which may be regarded as a kind of memory gained by the species during its evolutionary experience) must involve an organized spatial and temporal pattern of activity within many neurons. Perhaps it is the total pattern which is specific and it would then be unreasonable to look for the engram completely coded within each neuron. The information is much more likely to be distributed among many neurons. The molecular mechanisms underlying behavior may be of a nonspecific kind directed at changing the total pattern of activity in a population of neurons. Nonspecific mechanisms may result in changes in the rate and amount of neuronal growth, or in the formation and function of synapses, or in the intrinsic excitatory state of neurons. By acting only on selected neurons within a large population and so changing the total pattern of activity, a few nonspecific changes may result in very great variability of behavior. One problem then is to find a way in which specific neurons are selected for these changes, or the way in which the appropriate neuronal circuits, prewired and ready for action, are chosen from a large pool of prewired circuits available for selection. I suspect that both kinds of mechanisms may operate; the activity of an individual neuron or of the circuitry-linking groups of neurons may be uniquely determined during development, and in addition all or some neurons within a predetermined circuit may be selected for activity during any kind of behavior, perhaps by intraneuronal synthesis of a specific macromolecule. The most reasonable hypothesis is that information for innate behavior and for long-term memory is stored in the neurons and perhaps also in the glia in some stable form (Agranoff *et al.*, 1965, 1966; Flexner *et al.*, 1965). The most implausible hypothesis is that the information concerning every contingency of neuronal activity related to specific patterns of activity during innate or learned behavior is coded in the form of specific macromolecules. Such a specific mechanism would require at least three characteristics, none of which have yet been demonstrated. First, the specific mechanism demands that there be a different protein representing every memory or every kind of innate behavior. Second, the main parameters of neuronal coding, impulse frequency and spatial distribution of excitatory and inhibitory activity, would have to be preserved by transducing them into a macromolecular code. Finally, there would have to be a mechanism for recovering the information from the macromolecular store and rapidly transducing it back into electrical activity, either in the form of graded potentials in the dendrites or directly into spike activity at the axon hillock region. Other alternatives are that the information-containing macromolecules might be transferred down the axon to the presynaptic region and control the release of synaptic transmitter, or that the excitability of the postsynaptic regions in the dendrites, soma, or axon, might be altered in some way not yet understood. At least one of these requirements needs to be demonstrated before strong claims can be made for the storage of specific memory and innate behavior in macromolecular form in the neuron.

Are Neuronal Connections Predetermined during Development?

A feature of development which is unique to the nervous system is the formation of connections between neurons at relatively great distances from each other by means of their dendrites and axons. Whether these connections are entirely predetermined or whether some indeterminacy exists is the point at issue. It has been argued that in the formation of neuronal connections a considerable degree of indeterminacy "seems inevitable when we compare the final complexity of brain organization with the relatively small genetic information-capacity likely to be available for its specification" (McKay, 1960). There are only about one thousand genes containing about 10^5 bits of information in the bacterial cell, and about one million genes containing about 10^{10} bits of information in the fertilized mammalian egg (Perutz, 1958; Raven, 1961; J. D. Watson, 1965). Even if the difference in the genetic information content of bacterial and mammalian cells is largely devoted to organizing the nervous system it is clearly not possible for a separate gene to determine the exact connections of 10^{10} neurons in the human brain or even of 10^8 neurons in the brain of the octopus (Young, 1963). A selective mechanism, in which all the information for uniquely specifying the connections of each neuron is coded in the DNA is clearly implausible. This might be taken as an indication of the indeterminacy of neuronal connections if it could be confirmed by anatomical and physiological evidence that could discriminate between neuronal connections which are genetically predetermined and those which are indeterminant and may be subject to revision or remodeling. There is no such evidence. Sholl's (1956) evidence that the dendritic domains of cortical neurons are indeterminate has been disputed by Colonnier (1964), who found a correlation between the shapes of neurons in the visual cortex and the functional classes recorded in the cortex by Hubel and Wiesel (1962, 1963b). On the other hand, there is overwhelming evidence that the organization of neurons into topographically ordered systems plays an important part in determining the functions of the nervous system.

Striking examples of the importance of spatial interrelationships determining function may be found in the point-to-point projection of sensory receptors to the sensory centers of the brain, which has been found in visual, auditory, and somatosensory systems of all vertebrates. In some cases the topographical order between adjacent axons is maintained from beginning to end, for example, in the ascending somatosensory tracts through the cord, brainstem, and thalamus to the cerebral cortex. In other cases, the fibers lose their topographical order within the afferent pathway, but regain an orderly arrangement before they reach their termination. An example of this is the projection of the retina to the optic tectum of amphibians (Maturana *et al.*, 1960; Gaze

and Jacobson, 1962a; Jacobson, 1962). Other examples of the importance of topographical order in the function of the nervous system
may be found in the specificity with which afferent fibers from muscle
spindles connect with the appropriate alpha motoneurons of the spinal
cord (Granit, 1955; Eccles, 1964). An idea of how finely specified the
Purkinje cells of the cerebellum must be can be gained from the fact
that there are an average of 510 Purkinje cells per square millimeter in
the Purkinje layer (Fox and Barnard, 1957), and as a rule each
Purkinje cell synapses with only one climbing fiber (Ramon Y Cajal,
1911; Scheibel and Scheibel, 1958). Other examples are to be found in
the visual system, in which the position of an object in an animal's visual
space is actually represented by the activity of neurons at one point
within the map of the retinal projection onto the visual centers of the
brain (Polyak, 1941, 1957; Talbot and Marshall, 1941; Gaze, 1958;
Daniel and Whitteridge, 1961; Gaze and Jacobson, 1962a; Jacobson,
1962; Jacobson and Gaze, 1964; Schwassmann and Kruger, 1965). In
the sense that some neurons respond to a specific parameter of the visual
stimulus such as an object of a certain size, shape, or orientation, there
are units which may be said to be functional analogs of specific attributes
of the stimulus (Hubel and Wiesel, 1962, 1963b, 1965; Maturana *et al.,*
1960; Gaze and Jacobson, 1963b; Jacobson and Gaze, 1964). The specific operational characteristics of these units in the visual system seem
to be mainly or entirely due to their geometrical and topographical
organization. In the case of units which respond selectively to a specific
size, shape, or orientation of the stimulus, it has been found that the
specificity depends on conformity of the stimulus with the size, shape,
and orientation of the receptive field (Hubel and Wiesel, 1962, 1963b,
1965; Gaze and Jacobson, 1963b). The receptive field of retinal ganglion cells is a reflection of the spatial arrangement of the dendrites of
the retinal ganglion cells and of the special pattern of inhibitory and
excitatory synapses on the ganglion cell dendrites (Maturana *et al.,*
1960; Brown, 1965). The axons of the retinal ganglion cells do not
only connect selectively with their determined positions in the map of
the retina on the optic tectum of the frog and the goldfish, but axons
conveying information about specific attributes of the stimulus are
clearly segregated so that they terminate in different strata of the tectum
(Maturana *et al.,* 1960; Jacobson and Gaze, 1964). In the cortex a more
generalized analog with a higher order of abstraction from the sensory
stimulus is synthesized by convergence of several "simple" units onto a
"complex" cortical cell, and of "complex" onto "hyper-complex" units

(Hubel and Wiesel, 1962, 1965). To achieve the observed kind of anamorphic synthesis the connections of the cortical cells must be spatially organized in a very specific manner which presumably depends on the distribution of afferent axons on their dendritic trees (Hubel and Wiesel, 1962, 1965; Colonnier, 1964). We thus have no doubt that in the visual system the operational characteristics of neurons which are concerned with the perception of space and form are mainly determined by the position, shape, and specific pattern of interconnections of the neurons.

Specificity of connections to very restricted regions of the neuron is now well established by anatomical and physiological methods. In the pyramidal cells of the cerebral cortex excitatory synapses are mainly restricted to specialized postsynaptic structures, the dendritic spines, while inhibitory synapses occur at the dendritic bases and on the neuron soma (Anderson *et al.*, 1963; Blackstad and Flood, 1963). While behavior undoubtedly depends on the activity of a certain number of neurons connected in specific order, anatomical relationships alone are not sufficient. There must also be some way of determining which neurons are excitatory and which are inhibitory, and this in turn depends not only on the development of specific synthetic mechanisms for inhibitory and excitatory synaptic transmitters, but also on the spatial distribution of inhibitory and excitatory terminations on the postsynaptic membrane. Eccles (1964) suggests that the specific location of inhibitory synapses on or close to the soma, and of the excitatory synapses on the dendrites, results from specific biochemical differences between soma and dendrites and some form of selective chemical sensing by the presynaptic terminals.

Formation of Connections between the Retina and Brain

A special case of the problem of how functional connections are formed between neurons in the developing nervous system is the manner in which optic nerve fibers of different functional types and from different places in the retina bcome connected with the appropriate places in the visual centers of the brain. Most work on the formation of neuronal connections has been done on fish and amphibians because of the capacity of their nervous system for regeneration even in the adult. As far as one can see, the same factors regulate the formation of neuronal connections during development of the visual system as during regeneration of the optic nerve. The subject of optic nerve regeneration has

been dealt with in reviews by Sperry (1951a,b) and Gaze (1960). Therefore, I shall only touch briefly on what is known of the factors regulating the formation of neuronal connections in the visual system to show
how little we understand the underlying mechanisms.

The observation that the visuomotor behavior of fishes and frogs is
fully restored after regeneration of the optic nerve led Sperry (1951a)
to conclude that the regenerating optic nerve fibers regain their correct
central connections. This was later confirmed by the most direct means
available: that of mapping the retinotectal projection by recording electrical responses from the optic nerve fibers at their terminations in the
tectum (Gaze, 1959; Gaze and Jacobson, 1959, 1963a; Maturana *et al.*,
1959; Jacobson and Gaze, 1965). The histological appearance of the
optic nerve after regeneration leaves one in no doubt that the relative
positions of the optic fibers have been grossly altered at the site of
transection of the nerve. Therefore, there must be an unscrambling
mechanism which insures that each optic nerve fiber reaches its appropriate place in the tectum. There is also good evidence that the selection
of the correct pathway into the tectum is made by the regenerating optic
fibers at several points during their growth (Attardi and Sperry, 1960;
Jacobson, 1961a,b; Arora and Sperry, 1962). We are quite ignorant of
the mechanisms which enable the optic nerve fibers to select the appropriate pathway and the correct neurons on which to terminate in the
tectum. That it is not due to a relocation of synapses during learning,
however, was made clear by the elegant experiments in which Sperry
combined rotation of the eye with transection of the optic nerve in
frogs, and then tested their visual pursuit reflexes after regeneration of
the optic nerve (Sperry, 1944, 1951a). After recovering vision, the frogs
misdirected their pursuit of a fly by the same angle as the eye had been
rotated. For example, when vision returned following 180° rotation of
the eye plus section of the optic nerve (the other eye having been
removed), the amphibian would follow a series of vertical stripes moving
in the nasotemporal direction across the visual field, whereas optokinetic
responses are normally evoked only to movement in the temporonasal
direction. When a lure was waved in the nasosuperior quadrant of the
visual field, the amphibian attempted to capture the lure with snapping
movements directed at the temporoinferior visual field quadrant. These
maladaptive responses have never been known to be corrected by experience (Sperry, 1944, 1951a,b; Stone, 1944, 1953). In one newt, maladaptive motor responses were observed for 4½ years following rotation
of the eye, but recovery of normal optokinetic responses and accurate

localization of the lure occurred immediately after the eye was rotated back to its normal position (Stone, 1953). The conclusions drawn from these and other experiments are that the normal topographical representation of the retina on the optic tectum is restored irrespective of whether the retina is upright or upside down or whether the optic tract is connected to the ipsilateral or contralateral optic lobe (Sperry, 1945a). In addition, the regenerating optic nerve fibers become chaotically scrambled at the site of section of the optic nerve (Sperry, 1944; Gaze and Jacobson, 1963a). Therefore, it is necessary to postulate a mechanism which insures that each optic nerve fiber connects with its correct tectal locus. Since these misdirected responses are never corrected as a result of experience, it is clear that the formation of central connections by regenerating optic nerve fibers in the frog is governed by genetic mechanisms and not by the adequacy of the functional effect. None of the experiments so far devised, however, gives any further insight into the nature of these processes. At present it is only possible to say that each axon in the optic nerve probably has a unique characteristic which is related to its function and to the position of its ganglion cell in the retina, and which specifies the connections which it makes in the optic tectum. The retinal specificities must be mirrored in the tectum so that functional connections can be formed only between optic axons and tectal cells with matching specificities.

It is not known to what extent the axons are guided along the correct pathway to their terminations and to what extent they find their correct terminations by random branching within the tectum. There is evidence that both mechanisms may operate. Optic fibers have to select the appropriate pathway during development as well as during regeneration at several points along the optic tract. One of the selections has to be made at the point at which the optic tract splits into two brachia: the medial brachium supplying the medial half of the tectum and the lateral brachium supplying its lateral half (Jacobson, 1961a,b; Gaze and Jacobson, 1963a). An experiment proving that the optic fibers to each half of the tectum select the appropriate brachium even at the earliest stages of optic nerve regeneration in the frog is shown in Fig. 1. At this stage of regeneration, first demonstrated by Jacobson (1961a), the optic nerve fibers have entered the tectum but have not established point-to-point connection. If one brachium is cut, however, the responses on that side of the tectum are completely abolished. The responses that have been recorded with extracellular microelectrodes from the frog's tectum during this early stage of regeneration of the

optic nerve are totally unlike normal responses: they have very large
receptive fields, very low voltage (less than 20 μV), and do not have the
functional differentiation of the several classes of units normally recorded in the optic tectum (Maturana *et al.*, 1960; Gaze and Jacobson,
1963b). The simplest and most probable explanation of these results
is that there has been extensive overlap of the fine terminal arboriza-

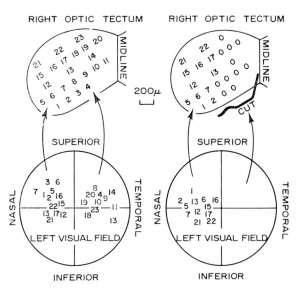

Fig. 1.   The projection of the left visual field on to the right optic tectum 52 days
after transection of the left optic nerve is shown in the diagram at the left. Each
number on the tectum represents an electrode position at which action potentials
were evoked in response to a light in the visual field at the position with the corresponding numbers. The nasal part of the field projects appropriately to the lateral
part of the tectum and the temporal field to the medial part of the tectum, but the
projection within each half of the tectum is disorderly.
    The diagram at the right shows the same projection mapped immediately after
cutting the optic fibers in the medial brachium of the tectum. Responses were
absent at the electrode positions marked 0 indicating that visual projection to these
positions entered the tectum only through the fibers which had been cut.

tions of the optic nerve fibers in the tectum. The responses are thus not
from single units as in normal frogs, but from the overlapping fine
branches of many fibers. This is probably the reason for the large receptive fields and for the lack of the normal functional distinctions between
different fibers.

    To determine whether the change in organization in receptive fields in cases of early regeneration of the optic nerve could have been due to changes within the retina rather than to changes within the tectum, an experiment was done in one frog in which responses were recorded both from the optic nerve and from the tectum early in regeneration. Although the responses from the tectum were of the nonselective type shown in Fig. 1, normal unit responses were recorded from the optic nerve. The conclusions from this experiment are that early in regeneration the optic nerve fibers from the retina have their normal functional characteristics, select the appropriate brachium to enter the tectum, but branch extensively within the tectum prior to making their final connections with the appropriate tectal neurons. The retinotectal maps obtained from frogs several months after the onset of optic nerve regeneration are normal in most cases, which means that the terminal branches of each optic nerve fiber finally connect only with the appropriate tectal neurons. There are, however, a small number of cases of anomalous regeneration in which optic axons formed connections with incorrect places in the tectum (Gaze and Jacobson, 1962b, 1963a). One type of anomalous regeneration which has given a clue to the mechanism of formation of connections during regeneration involves connections organized correctly in one axis of the retina and tectum, but randomly in the other axes (Gaze and Jacobson, 1963a). In this pattern, shown in Fig. 2, points in nasotemporal sequence in the retina connect in the correct mediolateral sequence on the rostral part of the tectum. The organization which is correct in the mediolateral axis is apparent on the rostral part of the tectum; the retinal projection to the caudal part of the tectum is diffuse or random. From this it appears as if the organization of retinotectal connections unfolds from the rostral to the caudal poles of the tectum. These observations have parallels in the development and differentiation of the tectum; thus stratification is first seen in the rostral pole of the tectum and extends caudally as more optic fibers grow into the tectum (Herrick, 1942; Kollros, 1953). Cholinesterase develops first at the rostral pole of the tectum, and during development there is a rostrocaudal gradient of cholinesterase in the tectum (Boell et al., 1955). We do not as yet know anything about maturation of electrical activity in the tectum which would reflect the order with which the ingrowing optic fibers form their synapses in the tectum. Sperry (1965) has suggested that direct anatomical demonstration of the course and termination of developing and regenerating nerve fibers is the most suitable way of observing where the specific connections are made. Without electrophysiological recording, however, there is no

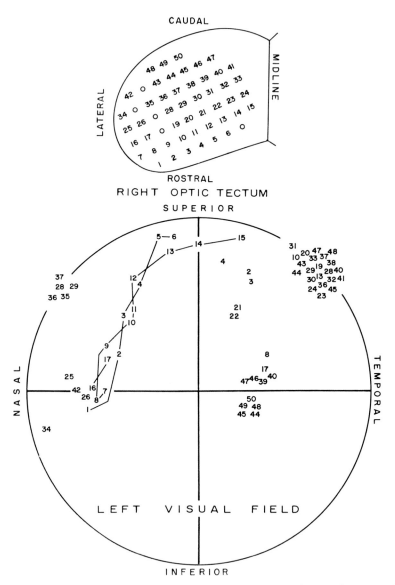

FIG. 2. The projection of the left visual field on to the right optic tectum 246 days after transection of the left optic nerve. The conventions are the same as in Fig. 1. The projection is correctly organized *within* rows 1 to 6, 7 to 15, and 16 to 17 in the nasotemporal axis of retina and mediolateral axis of tectum, but there is no order *between* these rows or for positions 19 to 50. (Redrawn from Gaze and Jacobson, 1963a.)

certain way of knowing whether or not functional connections have been established. Anatomical and electrical methods complement each other and are limited when used alone. Electrical recording is limited mainly by the extent to which it may be difficult to identify the origin of the electrical activity. The only way in which it is possible to obtain a point-to-point retinotectal map is to record either presynaptically from the terminals of optic nerve fibers or postsynaptically from tectal neurons. It is therefore certain that the responses do not come from optic fibers on their way to their terminations. It is extremely difficult to trace the course of single optic nerve fibers for any appreciable distance in serial sections of the tectum (Jacobson and Gaze, 1965). Since the fine branches of the axon tip are beyond the resolution of light microscopy, the only reliable method of determining where these terminals go is by the use of the electron microscope (Gray and Hamlyn, 1962). Noback and Purpura (1961) have given examples of attempts to determine cortical neuronal connections with the light microscope which have been found to be incorrect when examined more critically with the electron microscope. They have advocated caution in accepting "studies purporting to analyze the extent by which one neuron is capable of being affected by other neurons when such analyses are based on the assumption that two closely applied structures that cannot be adequately resolved with light microscopy may be synaptically related." More critical experiments are needed to determine whether the optic axons select their appropriate terminations by branching extensively, whether they follow a more direct course, or whether the selection is made neither by random contact nor by guidance but by some other yet unknown mechanism.

The recovery of a projection retinotopically organized only in the nasotemporal but not in the dorsoventral axis of the retina suggests that the organization of the projection is determined separately in these two axes of the retina. Other experiments have yielded evidence that the organization of the connections between retina and tectum is determined by two gradients acting at right angles in the nasotemporal and dorsoventral retinal axes determining the order of connections in the lateromedial and rostrocaudal axes of the tectum. The evidence for this has come from experiments in which compound eyes were formed surgically in *Xenopus* embryos (Gaze *et al.*, 1963, 1965). The operation consisted of grafting the nasal half of the eyecup from one *Xenopus* embryo in place of the temporal half of the eyecup from another embryo and vice versa, so as to form double-nasal and double-temporal eyecups. This operation was performed at stage 30 to 32 before any nervous connections had been formed between the retina and the brain. These animals were then kept until they were small adults, and then the projection from the compound retina was mapped electrophysiologically. The results show that optic fibers from corresponding positions in each half-retina project to the same position in the optic tectum (Fig. 3). Fibers from each half-retina project to the whole tectum and not as in normal animals to half the tectum. In each case the pattern of projection is retinotopically organized in a way that is appropriate to the original half-retina, but is a mirror image of this pattern for the grafted half-retina. The projection from each half of the compound eye appears to have spread out to occupy the whole tectum and does not seem to have connected only with half the tectum as it might have if the specification of each cell were absolute and not relative to its neighbor. This rules out a discontinuous mosaic of specificities in the retina and tectum and indicates a continuous gradient of specificities. These results are consistent with the idea that independent parallel specification of the retina and tectum occur so that each cell in the retina and tectum acquires a specific identification in a biaxial gradient system. The specification of a cell in the gradient only depends on whether the cell is above or below its neighbors in the gradient system (Fig. 5). If the number of cells is halved by bisecting the retina or presumably also by halving the tectum, the gradient will still be complete but its slope will be steepened. Thus, if the retina is halved we would expect the remaining half-retina to connect to the whole tectum and this is what appears to have occurred. Another possible interpretation to these results favored by Sperry (1965) is that only the half of the tectum which receives optic nerve fibers develops to twice its normal size while the deafferented half of the tectum atrophies. There is good evidence, however, that removal of an eye in a frog or a salamander embryo does not result in total atrophy of the tectum, but only in a reduction of the number of cells in certain layers (Dürken, 1913; Larsell, 1931; McMurray, 1954). The reason appears to be that the tectum has afferent connections other than those from the eye, and that tectal neurons survive if they have several sources of afferent supply, only one of which has been destroyed. In view of these findings one would not expect to find either total failure of development or atrophy of half the optic tectum after removal of half the retina. For the same reason, total atrophy of half the tectum would not follow the formation of double-nasal or double-temporal eyes in *Xenopus*. Although the evidence which has been cited would not lead one to expect complete atrophy of half the tectum, it may be necessary to perform some additional experiments to distinguish between the

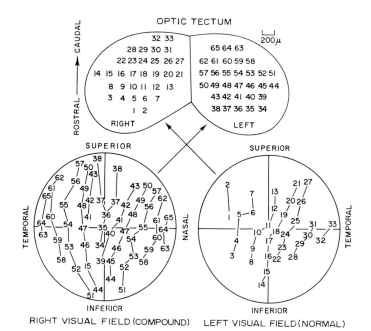

Fig. 3. Map of the contralateral retinotectal projection from the normal left eye and from the compound double-nasal right eye in *Xenopus*. The conventions are the same as in Fig. 1. The projection from the left eye to right tectum is normal, while that from the right double-nasal eye shows reduplication of stimulus positions about the vertical meridian.

Retinotectal magnification factors are calculated by finding the stimulus positions most distant from each other on the appropriate meridian of visual field and measuring the angular distance between them; then finding the distance in microns between the corresponding points on the tectum. For the compound eye each half of the visual field has to be treated separately along the horizontal meridian. In this experiment the magnification factor values are:

	Normal eye	Compound eye
MFH	8.9	12.7
MFV	9.0	6.2

The ratio MFH:MFV for the normal eye is thus 0.99 while for the compound eye it is 2.05. (Redrawn from Gaze *et al.*, 1965.)

spreading out and atrophy theories. To test this, one would have to label the two halves of the tectum by some distinctive means and see whether or not only half the tectum develops and hypertrophies to the size of the whole tectum. As this is not at present possible, we tried another approach. This involved measurement of the number of microns of tectum devoted to the representation of each degree of the retina, the retinotectal magnification factor, in normal *Xenopus* and in *Xenopus* with compound eyes. The magnification factor is therefore a measure of the amount of tectal representation for different parts of the retina (Jacobson, 1962). In normal *Xenopus* there is little variation of magnification factor with body length and weight. The MF measured along

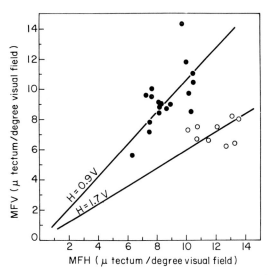

Fig. 4. Graph of vertical magnification factor (MFV) against horizontal magnification factor (MFH) from normal eyes (closed circles) and from compound eyes (open circles). The line H = 0.9 V represents the mean ratio MFH:MFV for normal eyes while the line H = 1.7 V represents the mean ratio MFH:MFV for compound eyes. (Redrawn from Gaze et al., 1965.)

any meridian of the retina, for example, the horizontal magnification factor (MFH) or the vertical magnification factor (MFV), are the same: about 10 μ of tectum per degree of retina. The ratio MFH:MFV is 1 for normal *Xenopus*. In double-nasal or double-temporal compound eyes the MFH is double the MFV, however, so that the ratio MFH:MFV is 2 (Gaze et al., 1963). This is shown in Figs. 3 and 4.

This result is compatible with the hypothesis that in the embryo the pattern of retinotectal connections appears to be determined by a system of gradients across the retina and the tectum in which each retinal ganglion cell acquires a unique value in the gradient system which is matched by a comparable value in the tectal cells with which it connects (Fig. 5). If the retina is reduced in size in the embryo at a stage before the gradient system is set up, a complete gradient is nevertheless established across the reduced retina, and since the tectal gradi-

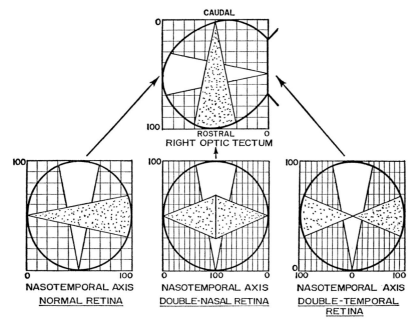

FIG. 5.   Diagram of the gradient system which is postulated as specifying the retina and tectum. The normal retina and tectum are superimposed on a grid giving the values of the gradient in the two axes of the retina and the corresponding values in the tectal axes. The values arbitrarily extend from 0 to 100. The effect of vertically bisecting the eye and transplanting half the eye to produce double-nasal and double-temporal compound eyes in *Xenopus* embryos at stage 30 is shown.

The compound eyes have two gradients each extending from 0 to 100 as mirror images across the horizontal axis of the eye. The tectal gradients remain unaltered. As a result, the magnification factors (number of microns of tectum representing one degree of retina) is doubled in the NT axis of the retina. (Redrawn from Gaze *et al.*, 1963.)

ents are normal, the fibers from the reduced retina will spread out to connect with the whole tectum. Once the gradients have become established, however, halving the retina or halving the tectum would not produce this result since each cell in the retina or the tectum had already acquired its unique value.

This prediction was confirmed in a series of experiments designed to determine whether reduction in the number of regenerating optic nerve fibers or in the size of the tectum receiving the regenerated fibers can alter the normal retinotectal projection in adult goldfish (Jacobson and Gaze, 1965). In these experiments the retinotectal projection was first mapped in adult goldfish and it was then shown that cutting half through the optic nerve close to the retina produced a very sharply defined area of tectal deafferentation. In another group of adult goldfish the optic nerve was cut half through as in the previous experiment, but it was also crushed proximal to the cut so that regeneration might occur first from the optic nerve fibers which had simply been crushed while

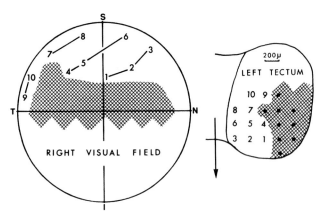

Fig. 6. The projection of the right visual field on the left optic tectum of an adult goldfish, mapped 55 days after crushing and temporal hemisection of the right optic nerve. The closed circles on the tectum represent electrode positions from which no responses could be obtained. The cross-hatched area in the field would normally have projected to the cross-hatched region of the tectum. (From Jacobson and Gaze, 1965.)

regeneration might be delayed from fibers which had been cut and crushed. The object was to see whether or not the optic fibers from half the retina would spread out to occupy the whole tectum. The results of mapping the retinotectal projection of half the optic nerve fibers into the whole tectum make it clear that the regenerating fibers have connected only with those parts of the tectum with which they normally connect and have left the remaining half of the tectum unconnected (Fig. 6). As a corollary to this experiment, the optic nerve was crushed and half the tectum was excised in several adult goldfish and the retinotectal projection was mapped after regeneration. The results also show clearly that the regenerating fibers connect only with their appropriate positions in the tectum (Fig. 7). Therefore, in adult goldfish the connections which regenerating optic nerve fibers make in the tectum are fully determined, and the fibers connect with the appropriate cells in the tectum irrespective of the relative numbers of optic fibers and tectal cells. The elastic properties of the system demonstrated in larval *Xenopus* have presumably been lost in adult goldfish (Jacobson and Gaze, 1965).

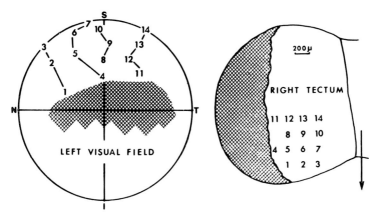

FIG. 7. The projection of the left visual field on the residual medial part of the right optic tectum, mapped 127 days after removing the lateral part of the tectum and crushing the left optic nerve. No responses were evoked from the cross-hatched part of the field which normally would have projected to the lateral part of the tectum, while the projection was correctly organized to the residual medial half of the tectum. (From Jacobson and Gaze, 1965.)

Specification of Retinal Ganglion Cells

The eye is the only part of the nervous system in which it is not difficult to determine with fair precision when the change occurs from an equipotential system to a system with more limited developmental potential. This can be done in several ways by studying the effects of surgically altering the eyecup at different stages of development by rotating it, by reducing its size, or by increasing its size by grafting two eyecups together. By testing the animal's visual capacities, or by electrophysiological mapping of the retinotectal projection to the retina after these operations, it is possible to determine exactly when the retinal ganglion cells acquire their unique location in the retina. DeLong and

Coulombre (1965) excised quadrants of the retina of chick embryos and
studied the defects in retinotectal projection by anatomical methods
after the chicks hatched. They found no defects in the retinotectal projection following removal of a quadrant of the presumptive retina
before 70 to 74 hours of incubation, but ablation of retina after
74 hours resulted in a localized defect in the retinal projection to
the tectum. From these results one may conclude that the retina
of the chick is equipotential until about 70 hours of incubation (stage
19 of the Hamburger and Hamilton series, 1951). At present it is
difficult to relate the time of specification of the retina with the stages
in the histogenesis of the retina in the chick. Studies of the histogenesis
of the chick retina by means of thymidine-H[3] autoradiography (Fujita
and Horii, 1963) indicate that matrix cells cease DNA replication at
the center of the retina on the fifth day and this extends out to the
periphery of the retina on the sixth to eighth day of incubation. Parallel
changes were observed in the optic tectum of the chick embryo by Fujita
(1964) who found that neuroblast differentiation started first at the
ventrolateral pole of the tectum on the fifth and sixth day and proceeded dorsomedially about a day later. The times given for retinal
histogenesis are definitely too late, however, as I have seen differentiated
retinal ganglion cells in the chick at 3 to 4 days, and this is supported
by the finding that optic nerve fibers can be seen growing in the retina
of the $3\frac{1}{2}$-day chick embryo (Rogers, 1957).

The timing of retinal specification has been determined with much
greater precision in amphibians, and it is therefore easier to relate the
specification to other events; for example to the synthesizing activities
of the differentiating retinal ganglion cells. The functional specification
of the retina of amphibians has been studied by rotating the eye at
different stages of development before the outgrowth of the optic nerve,
and then determining the visuomotor behavior of the mature animal
(Fig. 8). Stone (1944, 1948, 1960) showed that before larval stage 34
the optic cup of *Amblystoma* can be rotated without affecting normal
vision. Rotation of the optic cup during stages 34–36 resulted in progressive confusion of visuomotor responses, however, and rotation after
stage 36 invariably resulted in reversal of visuomotor behavior. Since
the optic axons only start invading the tectum during stage 38, it is
clear that the retinal specification is fully expressed in both dorsoventral
(DV) and anteroposterior (AP) axes before the eye is connected with
the brain. By rotating the eye in *Triturus* at different stages of develop-

ment, Székely (1954, 1957) has been able to show that the AP axis of
the eye is specified before the DV axis (Fig. 8).

I have repeated these experiments by rotating the eyecup of *Xenopus*
embryos through 180° at stages 29 to 35 (Nieuwkoop and Faber, 1956).

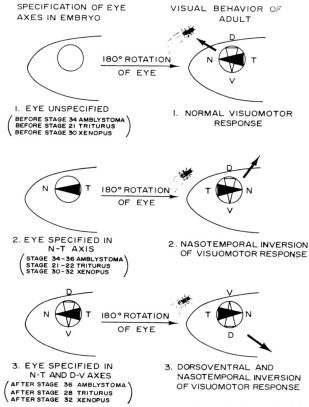

Fig. 8.   Diagram showing the method of determining the time of axial specification
of the eye by observing visuomotor reflexes in adult amphibians in which the eye
had been rotated 180° at various embryonic stages. Data for *Triturus* from Székely
(1954, 1957); for *Amblystoma* from Stone (1960); for *Xenopus* from the author's
observations.

These animals were reared through metamorphosis, their visuomotor
reflexes were tested, and then the projection from retina to tectum was
mapped electrophysiologically. The details of the method of mapping
are given in other papers (Jacobson, 1962; Gaze and Jacobson, 1963a;
Gaze *et al.*, 1963, 1965). Normal vision and normal retinotectal maps

were found in two animals in which the eye had been rotated before
stage 29. Two others in this group failed to give responses. Inverted
optokinetic responses were found in two animals in which the eye had
been rotated at stages 32 and 35. In these animals the retinotectal projection was also rotated. A similar result was obtained by Gaze (1959,
1960) after rotation of the eye and regeneration of the optic nerve in
adult *Xenopus*. The most interesting result was obtained in one
Xenopus in which the eye had been rotated at stage 30 (Fig. 9). The
retinotectal projection from the rotated left eye was inverted in the
NT axis of the eye and in the rostrocaudal axis of the tectum, but was
normal in the DV axis of the eye and mediolateral axis of the tectum.
The right eye was normal and served as a control. The latter experiment
proves that the specification of retinal ganglion cells in *Xenopus* occurs
in two stages. The cells are first specified in the NT axis of the retina
at about stage 30, after which they have the information which enables
them to form the correct sequence of connections in the rostrocaudal
axis of the tectum. During the next few hours the ganglion cells are
given the information which specifies them in the DV axis of the
retina and enables them to form the correct connections in the mediolateral axis of the tectum. After this, the retinal ganglion cells have the
information about their relations to other ganglion cells in both axes
of the retina, and inversion of the retina at subsequent stages of development results in inversion of vision and in an inverted order of
connections with the optic tectum.

The histological appearance of the retina during the period of specification is one of total undifferentiation. Autoradiographic studies have
recently been started to attempt a correlation between the specification
of the ganglion cells and their histogenesis. A single injection of 0.5 μCi
of thymidine-H³ (specific activity 14.5 Ci/mM) was made into the yolk
sac of a series of *Xenopus* embryos from stage 28 to stage 36. The
embryos were killed from 1 to 24 hours after the injection, and autoradiographs were made of serial sections through the eye and brain and
examined with the light microscope. The results showed that cessation
of DNA replication occurs first in the ganglion cells at the center of the
retina at stage 28 to 29 and extends from the center radially to the
periphery of the retina (Fig. 10). By stage 33, DNA synthesis has stopped
in all the retinal ganglion cells except those at the periphery. Thus, all
retinal ganglion cells are formed during the period of axial polarization
of the retina. During this period from stage 30 to 33 many cells distributed throughout the bipolar and receptor layers still incorporate

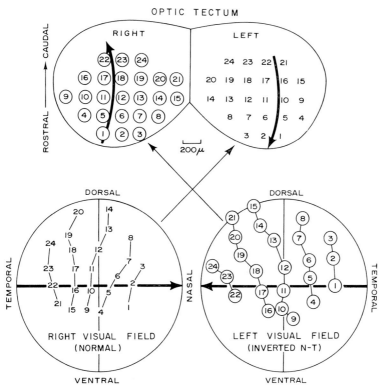

Fig. 9. Map of the contralateral retinotectal projection in adult *Xenopus* from the normal right eye and from the left eye which had been rotated 180° at embryonic state 30. Each number on the tectum represents an electrode position at which an optimal response was evoked when the stimulus (a small light) was at the position indicated by the same number in the visual field.

The projection from the right eye is normal: The correct projection of the naso-temporal retinal axis is shown as an arrow from back to front of the left tectum. The projection from the left eye shows nasotemporal inversion but is normal dorso-ventrally. The arrow pointing from front to back of the right tectum indicates the inverted order of projection. This shows that nasotemporal specification of retinal ganglion cells had occurred before rotation of the eye at stage 30, but that dorso-ventral specification occurred in accordance with the position of the retina after rotation.

thymidine-H[3] in preparation for cell division as may be seen in Fig. 10. The object of these studies was to correlate the sequence of formation of retinal cells with the axial specification of the retina, that is, with the time at which each retinal ganglion cell is given the information

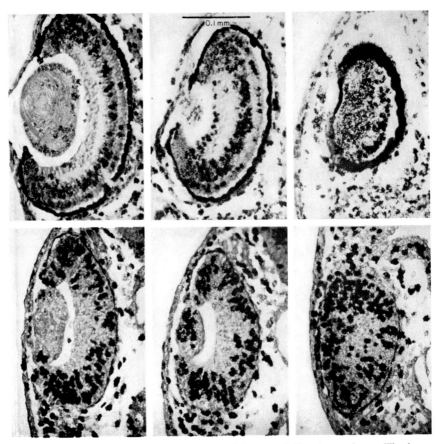

FIG. 10.   Thymidine-H³ autoradiographs of the eye of *Xenopus* embryos. The lower three photographs show serial sections through the eye of a stage 32 embryo which had been injected with thymidine-H³ at stage 30 and killed 3 hours later. The retinal cells nearest the lens have not incorporated thymidine-H³ while most of the remaining cells are labeled.

The upper three photographs show serial sections through the eye of a stage 38 embryo injected with thymidine-H³ at stage 30 and killed 24 hours later. The ganglion cells in the central region of the retina are unlabeled, indicating that their final DNA synthesis was before stage 30. The peripheral ganglion cells and cells in the bipolar and receptor layers have been labeled, indicating that they continued to synthesize DNA in preparation for division after stage 30. Specification of the ganglion cells occurs at about stage 30.

about its precise position in the retina. No correlation could be detected between the order of generation of ganglion cells which occurred in radial fashion starting from the center of the retina and the biaxial specification of the ganglion cells. However, the radial sequence of ganglion cell formation may have other correlations. For example, it may be correlated with differences in growth rate of the optic nerve fibers or it may be correlated with differential adhesiveness of optic fibers, the adhesiveness diminishing from center to periphery. Dissociated cells always reaggregate in hierarchial order in which the more adhesive cells take up a position internal to the less adhesive cells (Steinberg, 1963, 1964; Steinberg and Roth, 1964). During development or regeneration of the optic nerve, partial sorting out of optic nerve fibers could occur if the fibers from the center of the retina were more adhesive than those arising more peripherally. The evidence that some complex morphogenetic events may be due mainly to random motility of cells and their differential adhesiveness has recently been summarized by DeHaan (1958) and by Trinkaus (1965). The long path which the optic fibers have to travel to reach their terminations would increase their tendency to unscramble as a result of selective adhesiveness.

Another possibility is that a nerve growth-promoting factor may act on the ganglion cells to produce differences in their time of differentiation and in the rate of growth of their axons, in a manner similar to the action of the NGF on sympathetic ganglion cells and dorsal root cells (Levi-Montalcini, 1964a,b; Levi-Montalcini *et al.*, 1964). This growth-promoting factor may either act with uniform intensity over the whole retina but exert its effect for different times depending on the order of generation of the ganglion cells, or the action may be gradient-wise in the two axes of the retina. In either case the growth rate for optic nerve fibers would be specific for different parts of the retina and the arrival of fibers in the tectum would occur in a succession which would have validity in terms of retinal area. It is known that in amphibians the optic fibers are tangled in the optic nerve, but become segregated into thick and thin fibers at the chiasma, and there is evidence of retinotopic organization of the fibers in the optic tract. The gradual increase of dimensional organization of the visual tract along its axis is consistent with an organizing force exerting a summative effect along the axis of the tract.

The axial specification of retinal ganglion cells occurs only after cessation of their DNA replication, but before overt cytological differentiation. This is now being studied with higher resolution autoradiography and electron microscopy. The finding that the ganglion cells stop dividing before they become specified, but the bipolar and receptor cells do not, is understandable if one considers that the bipolar and receptor cells make short connections within the retina while the ganglion cells form their connections in the visual centers of the brain some distance away. It seems as if, to insure maximum resolution of the specification, each ganglion cell acquires its specific identification only after it stops dividing. If that were not so, the specificity would become distributed among the daughter cells. Moreover, since the specification of the ganglion cell determines the selection of pathways along which the axon grows and its point of termination in the tectum, ganglion cell specification might be expected to occur before axonal growth commences.

Spatial specification precedes morphological development of retinal ganglion cells by many hours and this suggests that the macromolecules conferring neuronal specificity may be synthesized very shortly after DNA replication ceases, followed only later by synthesis of macromolecules involved in cellular differentiation. The spatial specification of each retinal ganglion cell may depend upon the synthesis of a unique macromolecule according to the cell's position within the retina. Sperry's hypothesis that neuronal specificity may be based on a single large molecule with a very wide range of graded forms seems very reasonable (Sperry, 1965). The mechanism of neuronal specification may either be selective or instructive in the sense that these terms are used in connection with antibody formation. A selective mechanism has already been considered improbable because of the limited information capacity of the genome. In an instructive mechanism substances acting gradientwise in the two axes of the retina might interfere with any of the stages of protein synthesis; replication of DNA, transcription of its code into the nucleotide sequence of RNA, translation of the latter into amino acid sequence, and folding of the peptide chain, resulting in a specific protein for each cell. For example, the mechanism of antibody formation suggested by Pauling (1940) and recently revised by Haurowitz (1965), in which the anitgen interferes with folding of peptide chains, might be a means of specifying neurons. Several proteins could be subjected to a wide range of configurational changes under the influence of one or more antigen molecules acting gradientwise across the retina. This is merely one possibility; any other instructive mechanism for labeling each neuron in a distinct way related to its position would do.

Seen in this way, the organization of the nervous system is brought about by the development of regional macromolecular specificities in parallel between neurons which become connected together. However, this oversimplified model does not take into account the anamorphic changes that occur as the map is projected through several orders of neurons. For example, a series of parallel specificities may account for the topographical order of visual projections, but does not account for the changes in receptive field organization which occur as the fibers project from retina to lateral geniculate nucleus, then to striate cortex, extrastriate cortex, and to other parts of the brain. As Hubel and Wiesel have shown, new kinds of organization of increasing complexity are created at higher levels of the projection by convergence and synthesis of inputs from lower levels. To produce this kind of synthesis the specificities cannot be laid down simply in parallel as matching macromolecular maps. Moreover, the model fails to account for the congruence between sensory and motor mechanisms which result in sensorimotor coordination. The way in which optic afferents to the tectum connect with efferents from the tectum to bulbar and spinal motoneurons is not known even in the frog. This congruence between tectal input and output is apparently maintained even when optic fibers from each half of a compound eye spread out to occupy the whole tectum. The complexity of connections in the tectum has thwarted all attempts to determine the kinds of operations it performs. The beautiful cytoarchitectonic diagrams of the tectum appear to have about the same relationship to the structures they depict as a city map has to the activities of its inhabitants. The functions of the optic tectum are even more enigmatic when one considers how much processing of visual information is already performed in the retina of the fish and frog before it is relayed to the tectum (Maturana et al., 1960; Jacobson and Gaze, 1964). Some optic nerve fibers in the goldfish (Jacobson and Gaze, 1964) have retinal receptive fields as highly organized as some recorded in the cat's striate cortex (Hubel and Wiesel, 1962). In that case, the connections within the retina of the goldfish need to be as finely determined as the connections between the retina and cortex of the cat. Undoubtedly, the specificity with which neuronal connections are formed within the retina needs more study. Perhaps the secrets of the ontogeny of behavior may be learned from the retina, which is a brain in miniature containing an epitome of most of the processes of neuronal development, organization, and function.

ACKNOWLEDGMENT

Part of the work reported in this paper was supported by Grant GB-4622 from the National Science Foundation.

REFERENCES

ADRIAN, E. D. (1931). Potential changes in the isolated nervous system of *Dytiscus marginalis. J. Physiol. (London)* **72,** 132–151.

AGRANOFF, B. W., DAVIS, R. E., AND BRINK, J. J. (1965). Memory fixation in gold-fish. *Proc. Natl. Acad. Sci. U.S.* **54,** 788–793.

AGRANOFF, B. W., DAVIS, R. E., AND BRINK, J. J. (1966). Chemical studies on memory fixation. *Brain Res.* **1,** 303–309.

ALTMAN, J. (1963). Differences in the utilization of tritiated leucine by single neu-rones in normal and exercised rats: An autoradiographic investigation with microdensitometry. *Nature* **199,** 777–779.

ALTMAN, J., AND DAS, G. D. (1965a). Post-natal origin of microneurones in the rat brain. *Nature* **207,** 953–956.

ALTMAN, J., AND DAS, G. D. (1965b). Autoradiographic and histological evidence of postnatal hippocampal neurogenesis in rats. *J. Comp. Neurol.* **124,** 319–336.

AMASSIAN, V. E., AND DEVITO, R. V. (1954). Unit activity in reticular formation and nearby structures. *J. Neurophysiol.* **17,** 575–603.

ANDERSON, P., ECCLES, J. C., AND LØYNING, Y. (1963). Recurrent inhibition in the hippocampus with identification of the inhibitory cell and its synapses. *Nature* **198,** 541–542.

ANGULO Y GONZALEZ, A. W. (1929). Is myelogeny an absolute index of fetal behavioral capacity? *J. Comp. Neurol.* **48,** 459–464.

ARORA, H. L., AND SPERRY, R. W. (1962). Optic nerve regeneration after surgical cross-union of medial and lateral optic tracts. *Am. Zoologist* **2,** 610.

ATTARDI, D. G., AND SPERRY, R. W. (1960). Central route taken by regenerating optic fibers. *Physiologist* **3,** 12.

BERTRAM, E. G., AND BARR, N. L. (1949). Cytological changes in motor nerve cells following prolonged electrical stimulation. *Anat. Record* **103,** 567.

BLACKSTAD, T. W., AND FLOOD, P. R. (1963). Ultrastructure of hippocampal axoso-matic synapses. *Nature* **198,** 542–543.

BLOCK, J. B., AND ESSMAN, W. B. (1965). Growth hormone administration during pregnancy: A behavioral difference in offspring rats. *Nature* **205,** 1136–1137.

BOELL, E. J., GREENFIELD, P., AND SHEN, S. C. (1955). Development of cholinesterase in the optic lobes of the frog *(Rana pipiens). J. Exptl. Zool.* **129,** 415–452.

BONNER, J. (1964). The next new biology. *Plant Sci. Bull.* **11,** 1–7.

BROWN, J. E. (1965). Dendritic fields of retinal ganglion cells of the rat. *J. Neuro-physiol.* **28,** 1091–1100.

BULLOCK, T. H. (1959a). Neuron doctrine and electrophysiology. *Science* **129,** 997–1002.

BULLOCK, T. H. (1959b). Initiation of nerve impulses in receptor and central neurons. *Rev. Mod. Physiol.* **31,** 504–514.

BULLOCK, T. H. (1961). The origins of patterned nervous discharge. *Behaviour* **17,** 48–59.

BURNETT, T. C. (1912). Some observations on decerebrate frogs with special refer-ence to the formation of associations. *Am. J. Physiol.* **30,** 80–87.

CARMICHAEL, L. (1951). Ontogenetic development. *In* "Handbook of Experimental Psychology" (S. S. Stevens, ed.), pp. 281–303. Wiley, New York.

CLENDINNEN, B. G., AND EAYRS, J. T. (1961). The anatomical and physiological effects of prenatally administered somatotrophin on cerebral development in rats. *J. Endocrinol.* **22,** 183–193.

COGHILL, G. E. (1929). "Anatomy and the Problem of Behavior." Cambridge Univ. Press, London and New York.

COGHILL, G. E. (1940). Early embryonic somatic movements in birds and mammals other than man. *Soc. Res. Child Develop. Monograph* **5** (2), 1–48.

COLONNIER, M. (1964). The tangential organization of the visual cortex. *J. Anat.* **98,** 327–344.

CRAIN, S. M. (1952). Development of electrical activity in the cerebral cortex of the albino rat. *Proc. Soc. Exptl. Biol. Med.* **81,** 49–51.

CRESCITELLI, F., AND NILSSON, S. V. C. (1966). Electroretinogram of the frog during embryonic development. *Science* **151,** 1545–1547.

DANIEL, P. M., AND WHITTERIDGE, D. (1961). The representation of the visual field on the cerebral cortex in monkeys. *J. Physiol. (London)* **159,** 203–221.

DEHAAN, R. L. (1958). Cell migration and morphogenetic movements. In "A Symposium on the Chemical Basis of Development" (W. D. McElroy and B. Glass, eds.), pp. 339–374. Johns Hopkins Press, Baltimore, Maryland.

DEL CASTILLO, J., AND VIZOSO, A. D. (1953). The electrical activity of embryonic nerves. *J. Physiol. (London)* **122,** 33–34P.

DELONG, R. G., AND COULOMBRE, A. J. (1965). Development of the retinotectal topographic projection in the chick embryo. *Exptl. Neurol.* **13,** 351–363.

DÜRKEN, B. (1913). Über einseitige Augen extirpation bei jungen Froschlarven. *Z. Wiss. Zool.* **105,** 192–242.

EAYRS, J. T. (1960). Influence of the thyroid on the central nervous system. *Brit. Med. Bull.* **16,** 122–126.

ECCLES, J. C. (1964). "The Physiology of Synapses." Springer, Berlin.

EDSTRÖM, J. E., AND EICHNER, D. (1958). Relation between nucleolar volume and cell body content of ribonucleic acid in supraoptic neurons. *Nature* **181,** 619.

ELLINGSON, R. J., AND WILCOTT, R. C. (1960). Development of evoked responses in visual and auditory cortices of kittens. *J. Neurophysiol.* **23,** 363–375.

FLEXNER, L. B., FLEXNER, J. B., DE LA HABA, G., AND ROBERTS, R. B. (1965). Loss of memory as related to inhibition of cerebral protein synthesis. *J. Neurochem.* **12,** 535–541.

FOX, C. A., AND BARNARD, J. W. (1957). A quantitative study of the Purkinje cell dendritic branchlets and their relationship to afferent fibers. *J. Anat.* **91,** 299–313.

FRANK, K. (1959). Identification and analysis of single unit activity in the central nervous system. In "Handbook of Physiology" (J. Field, ed.), Sect. 1, Vol. I, pp. 261–277. Am. Physiol. Soc., Washington, D. C.

FRANK, K., AND FUORTES, M. G. F. (1956). Unitary activity of spinal interneurones of cats. *J. Physiol. (London)* **131,** 425–435.

FRIEDEN, E. H. (1964). Sex hormones and the metabolism of amino acids and proteins. In "Actions of Hormones on Molecular Processes" (G. Litwack and D. Kritchevsky, eds.), pp. 509–559. Wiley, New York.

FUJITA, S. (1964). Analysis of neuron differentiation in the central nervous system by tritiated thymidine autoradiography. *J. Comp. Neurol.* **122,** 311–328.

FUJITA, S., AND HORII, M. (1963). Analysis of cytogenesis in chick retina by tritiated thymidine autoradiography. *Arch. Histol. Japan.* **23,** 359–366.

GAZE, R. M. (1958). The representation of the retina on the optic lobe of the frog. *Quart. J. Exptl. Physiol.* **43**, 209–214.

GAZE, R. M. (1959). Regeneration of the optic nerve in *Xenopus laevis. Quart. J. Exptl. Physiol.* **44**, 290–308.

GAZE, R. M. (1960). Regeneration of the optic nerve in Amphibia. *Intern. Rev. Neurobiol.* **2**, 1–40.

GAZE, R. M., AND JACOBSON, M. (1959). The response of the frog's optic lobe to stimulation of the eye by light after section and regeneration of the optic nerve. *J. Physiol. (London)* **148**, 45P.

GAZE, R. M., AND JACOBSON, M. (1962a). The projection of the binocular visual field on the optic tecta of the frog. *Quart. J. Exptl. Physiol.* **47**, 273–280.

GAZE, R. M., AND JACOBSON, M. (1962b). Anomalous retino-tectal projection in frogs with regenerated optic nerves. *J. Physiol. (London)* **163**, 39P.

GAZE, R. M., AND JACOBSON, M. (1963a). A study of the retino-tectal projection during regeneration of the optic nerve in the frog. *Proc. Roy. Soc. (London)* **B157**, 420–448.

GAZE, R. M., AND JACOBSON, M. (1963b). "Convexity detectors" in the frog's visual system. *J. Physiol. (London)* **169**, 1–3P.

GAZE, R. M., JACOBSON, M., AND SZÉKELY, G. (1963). The retinotectal projection in *Xenopus* with compound eyes. *J. Physiol. (London)* **165**, 484–499.

GAZE, R. M., JACOBSON, M., AND SZÉKELY, G. (1965). On the formation of connections by compound eyes in *Xenopus. J. Physiol. (London)* **176**, 409–417.

GOTTLIEB, G., AND KUO, Z. Y. (1965). Development of behavior in the duck embryo. *J. Comp. Physiol. Psychol.* **59**, 183–188.

GRADY, K. L., PHOENIX, C. H., AND YOUNG, W. C. (1965). Role of the developing rat testis in differentiation of the neural tissues mediating mating behavior. *J. Comp. Physiol. Psychol.* **59**, 176–182.

GRAMPP, W., AND EDSTRÖM, J. E. (1963). The effect of nervous activity on ribonucleic acid of crustacean receptor neuron. *J. Neurochem.* **10**, 725–731.

GRANIT, R. (1955). "Receptors and Sensory Perception." Yale Univ. Press, New Haven, Connecticut.

GRAY, E. G., AND HAMLYN, L. H. (1962). Electron microscopy of experimental degeneration in the optic tectum of the chicken. *J. Physiol. (London)* **162**, 39–41P.

GRINNELL, A. D. (1966). A study of the interaction between motoneurones in the frog spinal cord. *J. Physiol. (London)* **182**, 612–648.

GRUNDFEST, H. (1957). Electrical inexcitability of synapses and some of its consequences in the central nervous system. *Physiol. Rev.* **37**, 337–361.

GRUNDFEST, H. (1958). Electrophysiology and pharmacology of dendrites. *Electroencephalog. Clin. Neurophysiol.* **10**, Suppl., 22–41.

GYLLENSTEN, L., MALMFORS, T., AND NORRLIN, M. (1965). Effect of visual deprivation on the optic centre of growing and adult mice. *J. Comp. Neurol.* **124**, 149–160.

HAGIWARA, S., AND WATANABE, A. (1956). Discharges in motoneurons of cicada. *J. Cellular Comp. Physiol.* **47**, 415–428.

HAMBURGER, V. (1963). Some aspects of the embryology of behavior. *Quart. Rev. Biol.* **38**, 342–365.

HAMBURGER, V. (1964). Ontogeny of behavior and its structural basis. In "Comparative Neurochemistry" (D. Richter, ed.), pp. 21–34. Macmillan (Pergamon), New York.

HAMBURGER, V., AND BALABAN, M. (1963). Observations and experiments on spontaneous rhythmical behavior in the chick embryo. *Develop. Biol.* **7,** 533–545.

HAMBURGER, V., AND HAMILTON, H. L. (1951). A series of normal stages in the development of the chick embryo. *J. Morphol.* **88,** 49–92.

HAMBURGER, V., BALABAN, M., OPPENHEIM, R., AND WENGER, E. (1965). Periodic motility of normal and spinal chick embryos between 8 and 17 days of incubation. *J. Exptl. Zool.* **159,** 1–14.

HARRIS, G. W., AND LEVINE, S. (1962). Sexual differentiation of the brain and its experimental control. *J. Physiol. (London)* **163,** 42–43P.

HARRIS, G. W., AND LEVINE, S. (1965). Sexual differentiation of the brain and its experimental control. *J. Physiol. (London)* **181,** 379–400.

HARRIS, J. E., and WHITING, H. P. (1954). Structure and function in the locomotor system of the dogfish embryo. The myogenic state of movement. *J. Exptl. Biol.* **31,** 501–524.

HAUROWITZ, F. (1965). Antibody formation and the coding problem. *Nature* **205,** 847–851.

HERRICK, C. J. (1942). Optic and postoptic systems in the brain of *Amblystoma tigrinum. J. Comp. Neurol.* **77,** 191–353.

HOGG, L. D. (1941). Sensory nerves and associated structures in the skin of human fetuses 8 to 14 weeks of menstrual age, correlated with functional capability. *J. Comp. Neurol.* **75,** 371–410.

HOLTZER, H., AND KAMRIN, R. P. (1956). Development of local coordination centers. I. Brachial centers in the salamander spinal cord. *J. Exptl. Zool.* **132,** 391–408.

HOOKER, D. (1942). Fetal reflexes and instinctual processes. *Psychosomat. Med.* **4,** 199–205.

HOOKER, D. (1952). "The Prenatal Origin of Behavior." Univ. of Kansas Press, Lawrence, Kansas.

HOOKER, D. (1958). Evidence of prenatal function of the central nervous system in man. "James Arthur Lecture on the Evolution of the Human Brain." Am. Museum Nat. Hist., New York.

HORRIDGE, G. A. (1962). Learning of leg position by the ventral nerve cord in headless insects. *Proc. Roy. Soc. (London)* **B157,** 33–52.

HORRIDGE, G. A. (1964). The electrophysiological approach to learning in isolatable ganglia. *Animal Behavior* **1,** Suppl., 163–182.

HOYLE, G. (1965). Neurophysiological studies on "learning" in headless insects. *In* "The Physiology of the Insect Central Nervous System" (J. E. Treherne and J. W. L. Beament, eds.), pp. 203–232. Academic Press, New York.

HUBEL, D. H., and WIESEL, T. N. (1962). Receptive fields, binocular interaction, and functional architecture in the cat's visual cortex. *J. Physiol. (London)* **160,** 106–154.

HUBEL, D. H., AND WIESEL, T. (1963a). Receptive fields of cells in striate cortex of very young visually inexperienced kittens. *J. Neurophysiol.* **26,** 994–1002.

HUBEL, D. H., AND WIESEL, T. N. (1963b). Shape and arrangement of columns in the cat's striate cortex. *J. Physiol. (London)* **165,** 559–568.

HUBEL, D. H., AND WIESEL, T. N. (1965). Receptive fields and functional architecture in two nonstriate areas (18 and 19) of the cat. *J. Neurophysiol.* **28,** 229–289.

HUMPHREY, T. (1964). Some correlations between the appearance of human fetal reflexes and the development of the nervous system. *Prog. Brain Res.* **4,** 93–133.

HUNT, C. C., AND KUNO, M. (1959). Properties of spinal interneurones. *J. Physiol.* *(London)* **147**, 346-363.

HUNT, E. L. (1949). Establishment of conditioned responses in chick embryos. *J. Comp. Physiol. Psychol.* **42**, 107-117.

HYDÉN, H. (1943). Protein metabolism in the nerve cell during growth and function. *Acta Physiol. Scand.* **17**, 1-150.

HYDÉN, H. (1960). The neuron. *In* "The Cell" (J. Brachet and A. E. Mirsky, eds.), Vol. 4, pp. 215-323. Academic Press, New York.

HYDÉN, H., AND EGYHAZI, E. (1962). Nuclear RNA changes of nerve cells during learning experiments in rats. *Proc. Natl. Acad. Sci. U.S.* **48**, 1366-1373.

HYDÉN, H., AND EGYHAZI, E. (1964). Changes in RNA content and base composition in cortical neurons of rats in a learning experiment involving transfer of handedness. *Proc. Natl. Acad. Sci. U.S.* **52**, 1030-1035.

HYDÉN, H., AND LANGE, P. W. (1965). A differentiation in RNA response in neurons early and late during learning. *Proc. Natl. Acad. Sci. U.S.* **53**, 946-952.

HYDEN, H., AND PIGÓN, A. (1960). A cytophysiological study of the functional relationships between oligodendroglial cells and nerve cells of Dieter's nucleus. *J. Neurochem.* **6**, 52-72.

JACOBSON, M. (1961a). The recovery of electrical activity in the optic tectum of the frog during early regeneration of the optic nerve. *J. Physiol. (London)* **157**, 27-29P.

JACOBSON, M. (1961b). Recovery of electrical activity in the optic tectum of the frog during early regeneration of the optic nerve. *Proc. Roy. Phys. Soc. Edinburgh* **28**, 131-137.

JACOBSON, M. (1962). The representation of the retina on the optic tectum of the frog. Correlation between retinotectal magnification factor and retinal ganglion cell count. *Quart. J. Exptl. Physiol.* **47**, 170-178.

JACOBSON, M., AND GAZE, R. M. (1964). Types of visual response from single units in the optic tectum and optic nerve of the goldfish. *Quart. J. Exptl. Physiol.* **49**, 199-209.

JACOBSON, M., AND GAZE, R. M. (1965). Selection of appropriate tectal connections by regenerating optic nerve fibers in adult goldfish. *Exptl. Neurol.* **13**, 418-430.

JASPER, H. H., BRIDGMAN, C. S., AND CARMICHAEL, L. (1937). An ontogenetic study of cerebral electrical potentials in the guinea pig. *J. Exptl. Psychol.* **20**, 63-71.

KANDEL, E. R., AND SPENCER, W. A. (1961). Electrophysiology of hippocampal neurons. II. After-potentials and repetitive firing. *J. Neurophysiol.* **24**, 243-259.

KOLLROS, J. J. (1942). Localized maturation of lid-closure reflex mechanism by thyroid implants into the tadpole hind brain. *Proc. Soc. Exptl. Biol. Med.* **49**, 204-206.

KOLLROS, J. J. (1953). The development of the optic lobes in the frog. *J. Exptl. Zool.* **123**, 153-187.

KUO, Z. Y. (1932). Ontogeny of embryonic behavior in Aves. *J. Exptl. Zool.* **61**, 395-430.

KUO, Z. Y. (1938) Ontogeny of embryonic behavior in Aves. XII. The stages of embryonic movements in the chick. *Am. J. Psychol.* **51**, 361-379.

KUO, Z. Y. (1939). Studies in the physiology of the embryonic nervous system. *J. Exptl. Zool.* **82**, 371-396.

LANGWORTHY, O. R. (1929). A correlated study of the development of reflex activity in fetal and young kittens and the myelinization of tracts in the nervous system. Contrib. Embryol. Carnegie Inst. 20, 127–172.

LARSELL, O. (1931). The effect of experimental excision of one eye on the development of the optic lobe and opticus layer in larvae of the tree frog (Hyla segilla). J. Exptl. Zool. 58, 1–20.

LEHRMAN, D. S. (1953). A critique of Konrad Lorenz's theory of instinctual behavior. Quart. Rev. Biol. 28, 337–363.

LEVI-MONTALCINI, R. (1964a). Growth and differentiation in the nervous system. In "The Nature of Biological Diversity" (J. M. Allen, ed.), pp. 261–295. McGraw-Hill, New York.

LEVI-MONTALCINI, R. (1964b). Growth control of nerve cells by a protein factor and its antiserum. Science 143, 105–110.

LEVI-MONTALCINI, R., SHENKEIN, I., BUEKER, E. D., CRAIN, S. M., RENITEZ, H., and VATTER, A. E. (1964). Symposium on the nerve growth factor. Ann. N. Y. Acad. Sci. 118 (3), 1–86.

LIU, C., BAILEY, H. L., AND WINDLE, W. F. (1950). An attempt to produce structural changes in nerve cells by intense functional excitation induced electrically. J. Comp. Neurol. 92, 169–191.

MACKAY, D. M. (1960). Modelling of large-scale nervous activity. Symp. Soc. Exptl. Biol. 14, 192–198.

McMURRAY, V. M. (1954). Development of the optic lobes in Xenopus laevis. The effect of repeated crushing of the optic nerve. J. Exptl. Zool. 125, 247–263.

MARTY, R., AND SCHERRER, J. (1964). Critères de maturation des systèmes afférents corticaux. Prog. Brain Res. 4, 222–234.

MATURANA, H. R., LETTVIN, J. Y., McCULLOCH, W. S., AND PITTS, W. H. (1959). Evidence that cut optic nerve fibers in a frog regenerate to their proper places in the tectum. Science 130, 1709–1710.

MATURANA, H. R., LETTVIN, J. Y., McCULLOCH, W. S., AND PITTS, W. H. (1960). Anatomy and physiology of vision in the frog (Rana pipiens). J. Gen. Physiol. 43, Suppl., 129–175.

MENDELSON, J. H., AND ERVIN, F. H. (1962). Influences of afferent neurons on efferent neurons. In "Neural Physiopathology and Behavior. I. Effects of Deafferentiation on Brain Function" (R. G. Grenell, ed.), pp. 178–210. Harper, New York.

MOORE, A. R., AND WELCH, J. C. (1940). Associative hysteresis in larval Amblystoma. J. Comp. Psychol. 29, 283–292.

MUNN, N. L. (1940). Learning experiments with larval frogs. J. Comp. Psychol. 29, 97–108.

NAKA, K.-I. (1964a). Electrophysiology of the fetal spinal cord. I. Action potentials of the motoneuron. J. Gen. Physiol. 47, 1003–1022.

NAKA, K.-I. (1964b). Electrophysiology of the fetal spinal cord. II. Interaction among peripheral inputs and recurrent inhibition. J. Gen. Physiol. 47, 1023–1038.

NELSON, P. G. (1966). Interaction between spinal motoneurons of the cat. J. Neurophysiol. 29, 275–287.

NIEUWKOOP, P. D., AND FABER, J. (1956). "Normal Table of Xenopus laevis (Daudin)." North-Holland Publ., Amsterdam.

NOBACK, C. R., AND PURPURA, D. P. (1961). Postnatal ontogenesis of cat neocortex. J. Comp. Neurol. 117, 291–308.

OPPENHEIM, R. W. (1966). Amniotic contraction and embryonic motility in the chick embryo. *Science* **152,** 528–529.

ORR, D. W., AND WINDLE, W. F. (1934). The development of behavior in chick embryos: The appearance of somatic movements. *J. Comp. Neurol.* **60,** 271–285.

PAULING, L. (1940). A theory of the structure and process of formation of antibodies. *J. Am. Chem. Soc.* **62,** 2643–2657.

PERUTZ, M. F. (1958). Some recent advances in molecular biology. *Endeavour* **17,** 190–203.

PETERS, J. J., VONDERAHE, A. R., AND POWERS, T. R. (1950). The functional chronology in developing chick nervous system. *J. Exptl. Zool.* **133,** 505–518.

PETERS, J. J., VONDERAHE, A. R., AND POWERS, T. H. (1958). Electrical studies of functional development of the eye and optic lobes in the chick embryo. *J. Exptl. Zool.* **139,** 459–468.

POLYAK, S. L. (1941). "The Retina." Univ. of Chicago Press, Chicago, Illinois.

POLYAK, S. L. (1957). "The Vertebrate Visual System." Univ. of Chicago Press, Chicago, Illinois.

PURPURA, D. (1961). Analysis of axodendritic synaptic organizations in immature cerebral cortex. *Ann. N. Y. Acad. Sci.* **94,** 604–654.

PURPURA, D. P., AND HOUSEPIAN, E. M. (1961). Morphological and physiological properties of chronically isolated immature neocortex. *Exptl. Neurol.* **4,** 377–401.

PURPURA, D. P., CARMICHAEL, M. W., AND HOUSEPIAN, E. M. (1960). Physiological and anatomical studies of development of superficial synaptic pathways in neocortex. *Exptl. Neurol.* **2,** 324–347.

PURPURA, D. P., SHOFER, R. J., HOUSEPIAN, E. M., AND NOBACK, C. R. (1964). Comparative ontogenesis of structure-function relations in cerebral and cerebellar cortex. *Prog. Brain Res.* **4,** 187–221.

PURPURA, D. P., SHOFER, R. J., AND SCARFF, T. (1965). Properties of synaptic activities and spike potentials of neurons in immature neocortex. *J. Neurophysiol.* **28,** 925–942.

RAMON Y CAJAL, S. (1911). "Histologie du Système Nerveux de l'Homme et des Vertébrés," Vol. 2. Maloine, Paris.

RAVEN, C. (1961). "Oogenesis: The Storage of Developmental Information." Macmillan (Pergamon), New York.

RIESEN, A. H. (1961). Stimulation as a requirement for growth and function in behavioral development. *In* "Functions of Varied Experience" (D. W. Fiske and S. R. Maddi, eds.), pp. 57–80. Dorsey Press, Homewood, Illinois.

ROGERS, K. T. (1957). Early development of the optic nerve in the chick. *Anat. Record* **127,** 97–107.

SCHEIBEL, M. E., AND SCHEIBEL, A. B. (1958). A symposium on dendrites. Formal discussion. *Electroencephalog. Clin. Neurophysiol.* **10,** Suppl., 43–50.

SCHLEIDT, W. M. (1964). Über die Spontaneität von Erbkoordinationen. *Z. Tierpsychol.* **21,** 235–256.

SCHNEIRLA, T. C. (1956). Interrelationships of the "innate" and the "acquired" in instinctive behavior. *In* "L'instinct dans le Comportement des Animaux et de l'Homme" (P.-P. Grassé, ed.), pp. 387–432. Masson, Paris.

SCHWASSMANN, H. O., AND KRUGER, L. (1965). Organization of the visual projection upon the optic tectum of some freshwater fish. *J. Comp. Neurol.* **124,** 113–126.

SEGAAR, J. (1962). Die Funktion des Vorderhirns in bezug auf das angeborene Verhalten des dreidornigen Stichlingsmännchen (*Gasterosteus aculeatus* L.) zugleich ein Beitrag über Neuronenregeneration im Fischgehirn. *Acta Morphol. Neerl. Scand.* **5,** 49–64.

SEGAAR, J. (1965). Behavioural aspects of degeneration and regeneration in fish brain: A comparison with higher vertebrates. *Prog. Brain Res.* **14,** 143–231.

SEGAL, S. J., AND JOHNSON, D. C. (1959). Inductive influence of steriod hormones on neural growth. *Arch. Anat. Microscop. Morphol. Exptl.* **48,** 261–265.

SHARPLESS, S. (1964). Reorganization of function in the nervous system; use and disuse. *Ann. Rev. Physiol.* **26,** 380–388.

SHOLL, D. A. (1956). "The Organization of the Cerebral Cortex." Methuen, London.

SKOGLUND, S. (1960). The spinal transmission of proprioceptive reflexes and the postnatal development of conduction velocity of different hindlimb nerves in the kitten. *Acta Physiol. Scand.* **49,** 318–329.

SPERRY, R. W. (1944). Optic nerve regeneration with return of vision in anurans. *J. Neurophysiol.* **7,** 57–69.

SPERRY, R. W. (1945a). Restoration of vision after crossing of optic nerves and after contralateral transplantation of the eye. *J. Neurophysiol.* **8,** 15–28.

SPERRY, R. W. (1945b). The problem of central nervous reorganization after nerve regeneration and muscle transposition. *Quart. Rev. Biol.* **20,** 311–369.

SPERRY, R. W. (1951a). Mechanisms of neural maturation. *In* "Handbook of Experimental Psychology" (S. S. Stevens, ed.), pp. 236–280. Wiley, New York.

SPERRY, R. W. (1951b). Regulative factors in the orderly growth of neural circuits. *Growth Symp.* **10,** 63–87.

SPERRY, R. W. (1963). Chemoaffinity in the orderly growth of nerve fiber patterns and connections. *Proc. Natl. Acad. Sci. U.S.* **50,** 703–710.

SPERRY, R. W. (1965). Embryogenesis of behavioral nerve nets. *In* "Organogenesis" (R. L. DeHaan and H. Ursprung, eds.), pp. 161–186. Holt, New York.

STEINBERG, M. S. (1963). Reconstruction of tissues by dissociated cells. *Science* **141,** 401–408.

STEINBERG, M. S. (1964). The problem of adhesive selectivity in cellular interactions. *In* "Cellular Membranes in Development" (M. Locke, ed.), pp. 321–366. Academic Press, New York.

STEINBERG, M. S., AND ROTH, S. A. (1964). Phases in cell aggregation and tissue reconstruction. An approach to the kinetics of cell aggregation. *J. Exptl. Zool.* **157,** 327–338.

STONE, L. S. (1944). Functional polarization in retinal development and its reestablishment in regenerated retinae of rotated eyes. *Proc. Soc. Exptl. Biol. Med.* **57,** 13–14.

STONE, L. S. (1948). Functional polarization in developing and regenerating retinae of transplanted eyes. *Ann. N. Y. Acad. Sci.* **49,** 856–865.

STONE, L. S. (1953). Normal and reversed vision in transplanted eyes. *A.M.A. Arch. Ophthalmol.* **49,** 28–35.

STONE, L. S. (1960). Polarization of the retina and development of vision. *J. Exptl. Zool.* **145,** 85–93.

STRUMWASSER, F. (1965). The demonstration and manipulation of a circadian rhythm in a single neuron. *In* "Circadian Clocks" (J. Aschoff, ed.), pp. 442–462. North Holland Publ., Amsterdam.

SZÉKELY, G. (1954). Zur Ausbildung der lokalen funktionellen Spezifität der Retina. *Acta Biol. Acad. Sci. Hung.* **5**, 157–167.

SZÉKELY, G. (1957). Regulationstendenzen in der Ausbildung der "Funktionellen Spezifität" der Reinaanlage bei *Triturus vulgaris. Arch. Entwicklungsmech. Organ.* **150**, 48–60.

TALBOT, S. A., AND MARSHALL, W. H. (1941). Physiological studies on neural mechanism of visual localization and discrimination. *Am. J. Ophthalmol.* **24**, 1255–1264.

TILNEY, F., AND CASAMAJOR, L. (1924). Myelogeny as applied to the study of behavior. *Arch. Neurol. Psychiat.* **12**, 1–66.

TRACY, H. C. (1926). The development of motility and behavior in the toadfish (*Opsanus tau*). *J. Comp. Neurol.* **40**, 253–369.

TRINKAUS, J. P. (1965). Mechanisms of morphogenetic movements. *In* "Organogenesis" (R. L. DeHaan and H. Ursprung, eds.), pp. 55–104. Holt, New York.

TUGE, H. (1937). The development of behavior in avian embryos. *J. Comp. Neurol.* **66**, 157–180.

ULETT, G., DOW, R. S., AND LARSELL, O. (1944). Inception of conduction in the corpus callosum and the corticoponto-cerebellar pathway in young rabbits with reference to myelinization. *J. Comp. Neurol.* **80**, 1–10.

VOELLER, K., PAPPAS, G. D., AND PURPURA, D. P. (1963). Electron microscope study of development of cat superficial neocortex. *Exptl. Neurol.* **7**, 107–130.

WATSON, J. D. (1965). "Molecular Biology of the Gene." Benjamin, New York.

WATSON, W. E. (1965). An autoradiographic study of the incorporation of nucleic acid precursors by neurones and glia during nerve stimulation. *J. Physiol. (London)* **180**, 754–765.

WEISS, P. A. (1936). Selectivity controlling the central-peripheral relations in the nervous system. *Biol. Rev.* **11**, 494–531.

WEISS, P. A. (1941). Self-differentiation of the basic patterns of coordination. *Comp. Psychol. Monograph* **17**, 1–96.

WEISS, P. A. (1952). Central versus peripheral factors in the development of coordination. *Res. Publ., Assoc. Res. Nervous Mental Disease* **30**, 3–23.

WEISS, P. A. (1965). Specificity in the neurosciences. Chairman's synthesis. *Neurosci. Res. Prog. Bull.* **3** (5), 5–35.

WEISS, P. A., AND ROSSETTI, F. (1951). Growth responses of opposite sign among different neuron types exposed to thyroid hormones. *Proc. Natl. Acad. Sci. U.S.* **37**, 540–556.

WHITING, H. P. (1955). Functional development in the nervous system. *In* "Biochemistry of the Developing Nervous System" (H. Waelsch, ed.), pp. 85–103. Academic Press, New York.

WIESEL, T. N., AND HUBEL, D. H. (1963a). Effects of visual deprivation on morphology and physiology of cells in the cat's lateral geniculate body. *J. Neurophysiol.* **26**, 978–993.

WIESEL, T. N., AND HUBEL, D. H. (1963b). Single cell responses in striate cortex of kittens deprived of vision in one eye. *J. Neurophysiol.* **26**, 1003–1017.

WIESEL, T. N., AND HUBEL, D. H. (1965a). Comparison of the effect of unilateral and bilateral eye closure on cortical unit responses in kittens. *J. Neurophysiol.* **28**, 1029–1040.

WIESEL, T. N., AND HUBEL, D. H. (1965b). Extent of recovery from the effects of visual deprivation in kittens. *J. Neurophysiol.* **28,** 1060–1072.

WINDLE, W. F. (1940). "Physiology of the Fetus. Origin and Effect of Function in Prenatal Life." Saunders, Philadelphia, Pennsylvania.

WINDLE, W. F. (1944). Genesis of somatic motor function in mammalian embryos: A synthesizing article. *Physiol. Zool.* **17,** 247–250.

WINDLE, W. F. (1950). Reflexes of mammalian embryos and fetuses. *In* "Genetic Neurology" (P. Weiss, ed.), pp. 214–222. Univ. of Chicago Press, Chicago, Illinois.

WINDLE, W. F., AND ORR, D. W. (1934). The development of behavior in chick embryos: Spinal cord structure correlated with early somatic mobility. *J. Comp. Neurol.* **60,** 287–308.

WINDLE, W. F., FISH, M. W., AND O'DONNELL, J. E. (1934). Myelogeny of the cat as related to development of fiber tracts and prenatal behavior patterns. *J. Comp. Neurol.* **59,** 139–165.

YOUNG, J. Z. (1963). The number and sizes of nerve cells in octopus. *Proc. Zool. Soc. London* **140,** 229–254.

YOUNGSTROM, K. A. (1938). Studies on the developing behavior of Anura. *J. Comp. Neurol.* **68,** 351–379.

ZAMENHOFF, S. (1942). Stimulation of cortical-cell proliferation by the growth hormone. III. Experiments on albino rats. *Physiol. Zool.* **15,** 281–292.

ZAMENHOFF, S., MOSLEY, J., AND SCHULLER, E. (1966). Stimulation of the proliferation of cortical neurons by prenatal treatment with growth hormone. *Science* **152,** 1396–1397.

AUTHOR INDEX

Numbers in italics indicate the pages on which the complete references are listed.

SUBJECT INDEX

398   SUBJECT INDEX

Avian myeloblastosis virus, 43
  conversion by, 43
  cytodifferentiation and oncogenesis by,
    43
Axial gradient, 119
Axodendritic synapses, 343
Axolotl, 34, 37
Axosomatic synapses, 343
Azure B, 290

B

Bacteria, 13
Bacterial flagella, 208, 210
Bacterial reproduction, 13
Bacteriophage, 11
Barley aleurone, 273
Barley endosperm
  effect of gibberellin on α-amylase, 273
Basal granules, 35
Basitarsus, 89
Behavior, ontogeny of, 339
  molecular mechanisms underlying, 349
Bence-Jones proteins, 61
Benzypyrene, 330
Biaxial gradient system, 360
Biological changes, amplification of, 246
Biological oscillator, 211
Bipolar myoblasts, 48
Bismarck brown, 290
Black Minorca strain, 181
Blastemas
  of leg, rate of transdetermination in, 96
  of wings
    transdetermination in, 96
    rate of, 96
Blastoderm, deep cell of, 165
Blastomere-periblast contact, 160
Blastopore, 114
Blastula cells, 152
Blood-forming regions of early chick em-
  bryo, 30
Bone marrow, 97
Bougainvillea spectabilis, 198
Brain and retina connections, 353
Brilliant cresyl blue, 290
Bristle apparatus, 200
Bristle differentiation, 188

Bristle pattern, 189
  in insects, 187
  marginal in Drosophila, 193
Bryan strain of RSV, 51
Bryophyllum daigremontianum, 263
Butterfly wings
  color patterns of, 200
  hinges of, 200
  scales of, 200

C

Cancer theories, 315
Carcinogenesis
  cell surface in, 315
  chemical, 330
Cardiac muscle, 46
Cartilage, 39
Cartilage cells, 46, 47
Cathepsin, 305
CCC (Cyclocel) , 260
Cecropia, 18
Cell
  cartilage, 46, 47
  chick germ, 126
  hybridization of, 70
  I, 87
  neural crest, 126
  retinal pigment, 46, 138
  scale stem, 201
  stoma stem, 197
  tissue culture growth of, 321
  translocation of, 139
Cell death
  competence for, 298, 299
  in morphogenesis, 289
  patterns stained with Nile blue, 297
  prospective fate, 298
  topographical distribution of, 292
Cell differentiation, 19
  in leaf epidermis, 281
Cell division
  effect of AMO-1618 on, 264
    of gibberellin on, 264
Cell dynamics, cell structure and differentiation, 217
  cell density and, 324
  critical density for, 325